SONGS OF FELLOWSHIP

VOLUME FIVE

MUSIC EDITION

KINGSWAY
EASTBOURNE

26-28 Lottbridge Drove, Eastbourne, East Sussex, BN23 6NT, UK.
First published 2011

ISBN 978-1-842914-51-9

Edited by Paul Hughes & Phil Johnson
Production by Freddie Strong
Cover Design by Andy Colthart
Music Setting by David Ball and Paul Hughes
CD-ROM compiliation and typesetting by Chris Tice
With thanks to: Richard Herkes, Alan Jackson and Rachel Ashley-Pain

Print production by Scantech Lithographic Ltd for
KINGSWAY COMMUNICATIONS LTD
Lottbridge Drove, Eastbourne, East Sussex, BN23 6NT, UK.
Printed in Europe

Contents

Important notes

Order of songs

The songs appear in alphabetical order by first line (letter by letter), not necessarily by author's title, for easy use in praise and worship meetings. An index of titles and first lines is included at the back, along with other useful indexes and chord charts (see Contents page).

To further facilitate the use of this book, most two-page songs and hymns appear on facing pages to avoid turning over, while maintaining the alphabetical order.

Numbering of songs

The songs are numbered from 2201 to 2710, continuing the numbering sequence from the companion Songs of Fellowship 4 Music Edition. This numbering and song order is also reflected in the enclosed computer disk (see below).

Scripture references

References – listed in biblical order – are to the key Bible passages quoted or echoed in the songs, and to some passing references. In many cases the whole Bible passage will repay further exploration, beyond the verses listed. A full index to the Scripture references is provided at the back of the book.

Computer Disk

The computer disk contains the words to all 510 hymns and songs in Songs of Fellowship 5. For instructions on how to use the disk on your computer, please refer to the 'Using The Computer Disk' pages at the back of this book.

2201. A frame so beautifully formed

(All my shame)

Gen 1:27; 2:7; Ps 139:14-15; Eccles 7:20; Jn 8:44; Rom 1:20; 3:10

Capo 3 (G)

Gently

Ben & Hannah Dunnett

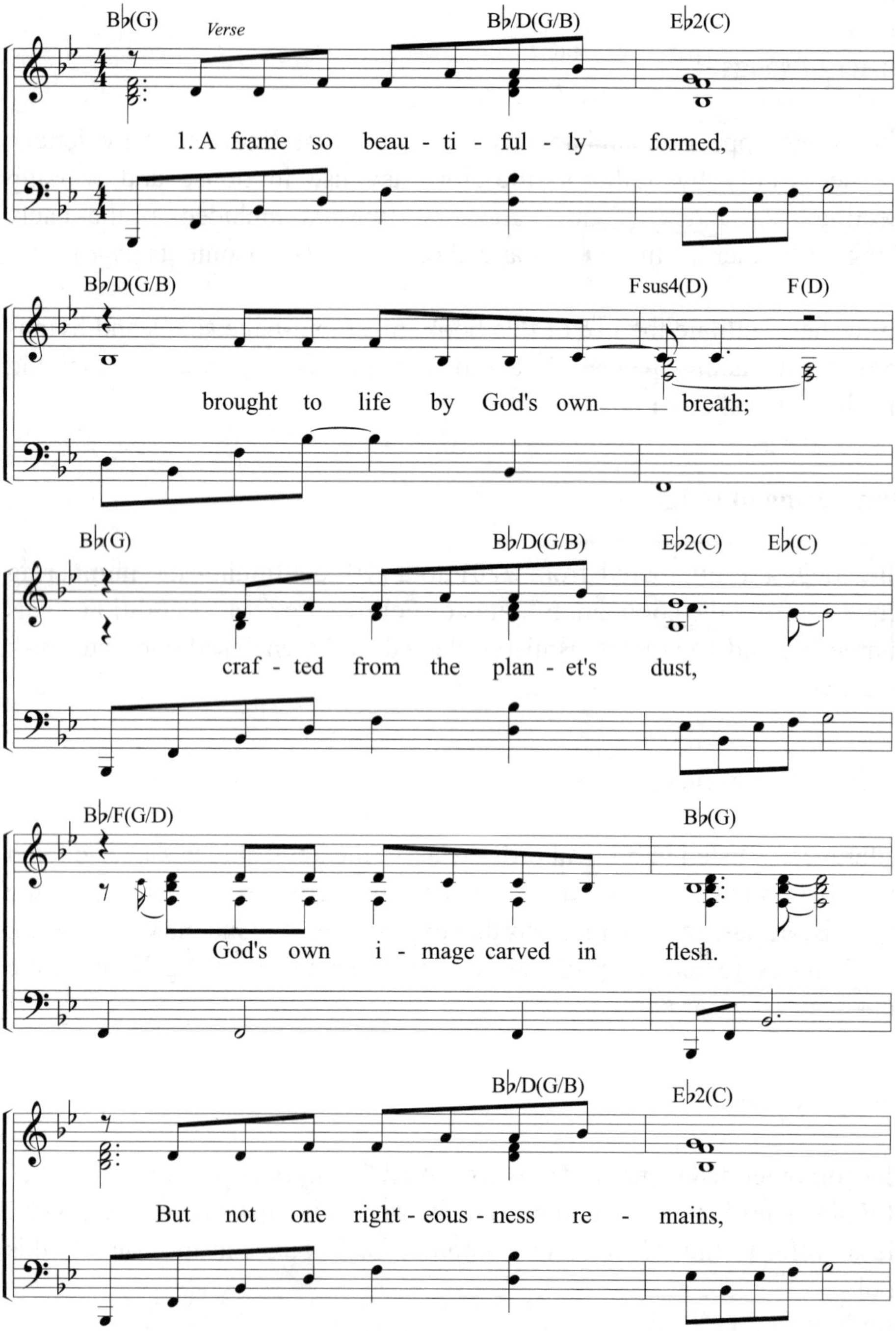

Bb(G) *Verse* Bb/D(G/B) Eb2(C)

1. A frame so beau - ti - ful - ly formed,

Bb/D(G/B) Fsus4(D) F(D)

brought to life by God's own breath;

Bb(G) Bb/D(G/B) Eb2(C) Eb(C)

craf - ted from the plan - et's dust,

Bb/F(G/D) Bb(G)

God's own i - mage carved in flesh.

Bb/D(G/B) Eb2(C)

But not one right - eous - ness re - mains,

B♭/D(G/B)
Fsus4(D)
F(D)
per - fec - tion lost and beau - ty stained.
B♭(G)
B♭/D(G/B)
E♭2(C)
E♭(C)
Far from the safe - ty of God's side,
B♭/F(G/D)
B♭(G)
Chorus
E♭(C)
F(D)
in - no-cence tra-ded for a lie. All my
B♭(G)
E♭(C)
F(D)
Gm(Em)
shame, all I've failed to be,
E♭/G(C/E)
F/A(D/F♯)
B♭(G)
B♭/F(G/D)
F(D)
nailed up-on a cross and left at Cal - va -

2. A world of fabulous design,
Yet scarred with misery and pain,
But underneath this brokenness
Our Maker's signature remains.
And only Your redeeming love
Can pay the debt we can't afford.
Salavation worked by Your own hand,
Your broken workmanship restored.

2202. All because of You

1 Jn 4:19

A
F♯m7
Gmaj7
I live be-cause You live,
I
D
A
1.
F♯m7
Gmaj7
love be-cause You loved me first.
D.C.
2.4.
D.S.
D
F♯m7
Gmaj7
I
3.,5.
F♯m7
Gmaj7
1st time only
D
D/F♯
Mid section
(After D.S.S.)
Bm7
A
F♯m7
G2
I'm a-live cos You're a-live,
I'm a-live cos You're a - live,

Bm7
A
F♯m7
G2
(Fine)
I'm a-live cos You're a-live in me.
G
A/G
Bm/G
A/G
D.S.S. al fine
Sing,

2203. All for Christ

Lk 9:62; Rom 12:1; 2 Cor 10:5; Eph 5:8; 1 Pet 2:9; I Jn 1:7

Nick J. Drake & Nick Herbert

Last time to Coda
Am
Fmaj7
C2
for Christ. I'm out of dark - ness:
1.,3.
1° D.C.(v.2)
2° D.S. al Coda
2.
G
Am
G/B
Am
G/B
all that I am is now all for Christ. for Christ.
Dm
Fmaj7
C
G
All for Christ.
Fmaj7
C
Em
Am
D.C.(v.1)
Coda
Em
Fmaj7
all that I am is now all for Christ.
2. Take these hands,
Take this heart
For Your praise;
Every thought,
Every word
Bless Your name.

2204. All I am

2204.
All I am
Mt 7:14; 12:20; Rom 1:20; 12:1; 2 Cor 9:7; Jas 1:17
Capo 2 (D)
Andy Flannagan
Worshipfully
Chorus
E(D) A2(G) C♯m7(Bm) B(A) E(D) A2(G)
All I am I of-fer to You, all I have
C♯m7(Bm) B(A) C♯m7(Bm) B/D♯(A/C♯) E(D) E/G♯(D/F♯) F♯m/A(Em/G)
is Yours. My all I give a-way;
3rd time to Bridge
E(D) B(A) A(G) B(A) E(D) B(A)
take this life I lay be-fore You.
A(G) B(A) E(D)
Verse
B(A) A(G) B(A)
1. Each per - fect gift has come from You,
(v.3)
E(D) B(A) A(G) B(A) E(D) B(A)
yet I cling tight - ly. And I pray, O Lord,

2. Your fingerprints reveal the plan
For this world's story.
We have no other purpose
Than to bring You glory.

3. Your footsteps mark the path of peace,
But this road is narrow;
It leads me only to a cross –
Lord, I will follow.

2205. All I have

Ps 27:4; Mt 25:21, 23; Rom 11:36 - 12:1; Phil 1:21; 3:13-14; 2 Tim 4:7

Matt Osgood

Capo 2 (G)

D(C)
Chorus
B7(A)
For Your glo - ry, for Your glo -
D(C)
A(G)
E(D)
- ry, let me live, let me live. For Your glo -
B7(A)
D(C)
(Fine)
A(G)
- ry, for Your glo - ry, let me live.
1.
D.C.(v.2)
2.
Mid section
F♯m(Em)
2. The things be - hind This I pray for,
E/G♯(D/F♯)
Bm7(Am)
D(C)
F♯m(Em)
this I long for, this I hope for,

2. The things behind, I will leave,
For I know I will receive
The final prize:
To see the glory of the Lord.
I long to hear my Father say,
'You have done well, you've kept the faith,
Now enter in
And see the glory of the Lord.'

2206. All I have and all I am
(All to You)

Rom 12:1-2

Capo 3 (D)

Eoghan Heaslip & Neil Bennetts

Worshipfully

Verse

F(D) B♭(G) C(A) F/A(D/F♯) B♭(G)

All I have and all I am I lay here at Your feet.

Csus4(A) C(A) F(D) B♭(G) C(A) Dm(Bm)

Lord, I bring my ev - 'ry part here as

B♭(G) C(A) B♭(G)

an of - fer - ing.

Bridge

Take my will, my

B♭(G) C(A) F/A(D/F♯) B♭(G) C(A) Dm(Bm)
- der all to You. As I live my life, be glo - ri - fied.
Gm7(Em) B♭(G) C(A) 1. F(D)
I sur - ren - der all to You.
Dm7(Bm) B♭6(G) F(D) Dm7(Bm) B♭6(G) D.C. 2. Mid section Dm(Bm)
Je - sus, all for You,
B♭(G) F/A(D/F♯) C(A)
Je - sus, all for You, I'll live now and for - ev - er.
(2º)
Gm(Em) B♭(G)
Now and for - ev - er. Take my will, my

C(A)
F/A(D/F♯)
B♭(G)
C(A)
F/A(D/F♯)
heart, my mind, my all; let my ev-'ry breath be for You.
B♭(G)
C(A)
F/A(D/F♯)
B♭(G)
Take my will, my heart, my mind, my all; let my ev-'ry
C(A)
F(D)
breath be for You.

2207. All of your questions

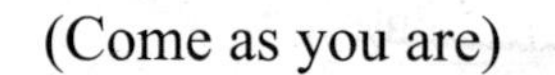

Mt 11:28

Trè & Tori Sheppard
& Kathryn Scott

Reflectively

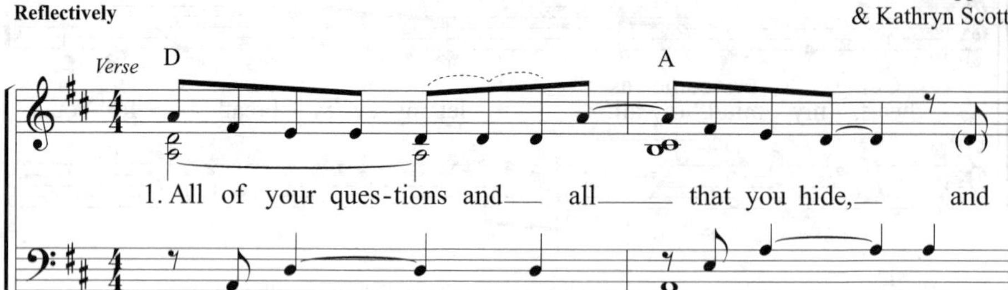

Chorus
D
A
Come, come as you are, with ev - 'ry - thing bro -
Bm
G
D
- ken, all that's not spo - ken. Come, come as you are.
Last time to Coda
A
Bm
Ev - en if it's all o - ver, I've got ev - 'ry - thing
G
D
G
cov - ered. Come as you are, come as you are.
1.
2.
D
G
G
You can come as you are.

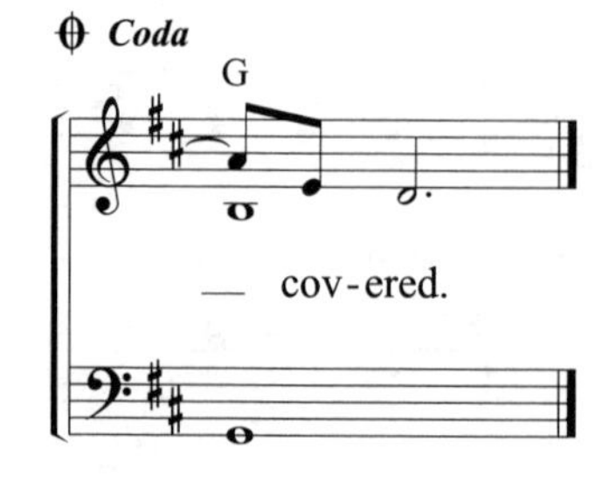

2. All of your heartache and all of your pain,
All of the wounds, the tears and the stains.
Come with your sorrows, your guilt and your shame.
Come when you've got only you left to blame.

Come to me, all you who are weary and burdened, and I will give you rest.

MATTHEW 11:28

2208. All that I am

Rom 12:1; 1 Pet 3:18; Rev 7:14

Prayerfully

Mike Burn

Verse

D Em7 D/F# G D/F# Em7 A D A G/A D Em7 D/F# G D/F# Em7 A D

1. All that I am, all that I'll be, all of my hopes, all of my dreams, Lord, I give to You my praise and all I am. All I've done wrong, washed by Your blood, all of the past, left at the cross, Lord, I give to You my praise and all that I am.

Chorus

D/F#

For I know

2. All that I say, all that I do,
Help me to be faithful to You.
Lord, I give to You my thoughts,
My words, my deeds.
Fill every hour, Lord, with Your power,
Keeping me clean, may Christ be seen.
Lord, I give to You my praise
And all that I am.

2209. All the earth cries, 'Holy, holy'

(Glory to Your name)

Deut 32:4; Ps 16:11; 102:15; Is 6:3; Rev 4:8; 5:12-13; 19:11

Robin Mark

2. Our cry shall be, 'Glory, glory,'
To Your name give glory, glory.
Glory to the Lamb of God who died for us.
We declare Your majesty, majesty,
All surpassing majesty, majesty
Riding out for justice, truth and righteousness.

2210. All the heavens praise

(Great and glorious)

Jer 10:6-7; Phil 2:10; Rev 4:8; 5:11, 13

Steady and rhythmic

Jo Petch

F♯m *Verse* D A E F♯m D A E F♯m D A

1. All the hea - vens praise Your won-der-ful ways, O God. Choirs of an - gels sing, sing of all You've done, O God. Ev - 'ry knee will bow to wor - ship at Your throne, O God.

(v.2)

E
F♯m
Ev - 'ry heart will cry:
D
A
'Ho-ly is Your name, ho-ly is Your name.'
Chorus
E
D
A
Great and glo - ri - ous, You reign,
C♯m
F♯m
D
You reign. All the hea - vens and the earth
Last time to Coda
1.
D.C.(v.2)
A
E
cry out in praise.

2.,4.
D.S.
3.
Mid section
E
There's no
D
E
D
one high - er, no one great - er; no one is more pow -
E
1.
D
E
- er - ful. There's no one wi - ser, no one stron - ger than You.
D/F#
E
2.
Bm
There's no one wi - ser, no
E
D
E
D.S. al Coda
one stron - ger than You, our God.

2. Over all the earth
Your glory fills the skies, O God.
High and lifted up,
And holy is Your name, O God.
Every knee will bow
To worship at Your throne, O God.
Every heart will cry:
'Holy is your name, holy is your name.'

2211. All the room was hushed and still

Jn 13:5,15, 34-35

Gm(Em)
F(D)
E♭2(C)
this is what I want the world to see, who it is you fol-low.'
E♭maj9(C)
E♭(C)
B♭(G)
Chorus
F6(D)
'Love each o - ther, one a-no - ther,
Gm7(Em)
E♭2(C)
love each o - ther in the way that I have loved you.
B♭(G)
F6/A(D/F♯)
Walk to-ge - ther, and what-e - ver comes,
Last time to Coda
2° D.S.
Gm7(Em)
E♭2(C)
E♭maj9(C)
love each o - ther in the way that I have loved you.'

2. Let the room be hushed and still,
Let us go to where He kneels
And join Him as he serves,
And learn His ways of love.

2212. All the way my Saviour leads me

(All that I am)

Mt 11:28; Mk 7:37; Lk 1:78; Jn 14:2, 27; 1 Cor 15:54; 2 Cor 1:3; 5:1-2, 7

Reflectively

Music & new chorus: Chris Bowater

Verse

G C2 D/F♯ G
1. All the way my Sa - viour leads me; what have

C2 D Em C2 D
I to ask be - side? Can I doubt His ten - der

Em Am9
mer - cy, who through life has been my guide?

Dsus4 D G C2 D/F♯ G
Heav-'nly peace, di - vi - nest com - fort, here by

C2 D Em C2 D
faith in Him to dwell! For I know, what-e'er be -

Chorus
Em
Am
C/D
D
C/D
fall me, Je-sus al-ways does all things well. All that I
G
Em7
Am7
am, all that I have, all that I'm going to be,
G/B
D
giver of life, giver of hope, I owe it all
C/E
D
C/D
G
to You. All that I am, and all that I have,
Em7
Am7
all that I'm going to be, giver of life,

2. All the way my Saviour leads me;
Oh, the fullness of His love!
Perfect rest to me is promised
In my Father's house above.
When my spirit, clothed immortal,
Wings its flight to realms of day,
This my song through endless ages:
Jesus always led me all the way.

Fanny J. Crosby (1820–1915)
Adpt. Chris Bowater

2213. All the way my Saviour leads me

Ps 23:2, 6; Jn 6:51; 1 Cor 15:53; 2 Pet 3:13; Jud 24; Rev 12:11

Gently

Words: Fanny J. Crosby (1820–1915)
Arrangement & additional lyrics: Chris Tomlin & Matt Redman

G C2/G

Verse

1. { All the way my Saviour leads me;
All the way my Saviour leads me;

(2°)

G C2/G

who have I to ask beside?
and cheers each winding path I tread,

Am7 C/G D2

How could I doubt His tender mercy,
and gives me grace for ev'ry trial,

Am7 C/G 1.,3. D2 2.,4. Dsus4

who through life has been my guide?
feeds me with the living bread.

(1st time only)

(You)

2nd time only
Chorus
C2
Dsus4
C2
G/B
Je-sus lead me all the way!
You lead me, and
Dsus4
C2
G/B
keep me from fall - ing.
You car - ry me
Dsus4
D
Am7
G
close to Your heart,
and sure - ly Your
1.
D.C.(v.2)
Dsus4
D
Am7
G
Dsus4 D
good - ness and mer - cy will fol - low me.
2.
D.S.
3.
Dsus4
D
Dsus4
D
Am7
G
Dsus4
me.
You me,
will fol - low me.

G C2/G G
All the way my Sav - iour
C2/G G C2/G
leads me;
Verse
G C2/G G C2/G
2. All the way my Sa-viour leads me; oh, the full - ness of His love!
Am7 C/G D2 Am7 C/G D2
Oh, the sure - ness of His pro - mise in the tri - umph of His blood.
G C2/G Em7 D2 C2
When my spi-rit, clothed, im - mor - tal, wings its flight to realms of day,
Am7 C/G D2 Am7 C/G D2
this my song through end-less a - ges: 'Je-sus led me all the way;
C2 Dsus4
Je - sus led me all the way.'

When the perishable has been clothed with the imperishable, and the mortal with immortality, then the saying that is written will come true: Death has been swallowed up in victory.

1 CORINTHIANS 15:54

2214. Almighty God, our hearts are open to You

Moderately

Ps 139:23; Jn 6:63; 2 Cor 3:18; Col 3:17

Paul Hughes

Chorus
D Bm7 Esus4 D
lift our hearts to praise. Lord of all cre-a-tion,
ceive Your peo-ple's praise.
E F♯m7 D
awe-some God, ho-ly One, Spi-rit, dwell a-mong us
E F♯m Bm7
in Your pow'r. Still our thoughts to hear You,
C♯m7 F♯m7 D Bm7
move our hearts that we would be, by
Esus4 D
grace, trans-formed by Your glo-ry,

1. D.C.(v.2)
E F♯m7 D Esus4
trans-formed by Your glo - ry.
2.,3.
E F♯m7 D
Last time to Coda
Trans-formed by Your glo - ry,
E F♯m7 D E
Mid section
trans-formed by Your glo - ry. Ri-sen
A D Bm Esus4 A D
Sa - viour, Re - deem - er, we are here to wor-ship You.
Bm Esus4 A D Bm Esus4
Let Your pre - sence em - pow'r us to

2. Almighty God,
Expectantly we seek You;
Meet us here in Your power.
Speak words of life
That comfort, heal, restore and
Satisfy our hunger.
We are trusting in Your name;
Lord, receive our hearts of praise.

2215. And can it be?

Is 61:10; Rom 8:1; Phil 2:7-8; 2 Tim 4:8; Heb 4:16

2. He left His Father's throne above,
   So free, so infinite His grace;
   Emptied Himself of all but love,
   And bled for Adam's helpless race;
   'Tis mercy all, immense and free;
   For, O my God, it found out me.
   'Tis mercy all, immense and free;
   For, O my God, it found out me.

3. Long my imprisoned spirit lay
   Fast bound in sin and nature's night;
   Thine eye diffused a quickening ray,
   I woke, the dungeon flamed with light;
   My chains fell off, my heart was free;
   I rose, went forth and followed Thee.
   My chains fell off, my heart was free;
   I rose, went forth and followed Thee.

4. No condemnation now I dread;
   Jesus, and all in Him, is mine!
   Alive in Him, my living Head,
   And clothed with righteousness divine,
   Bold I approach the eternal throne,
   And claim the crown, through Christ my own.
   Bold I approach the eternal throne,
   And claim the crown, through Christ my own.

Charles Wesley (1707–88)

2216. Anthems fill the skies with praise

(We cry out)

Ps 19:1-2; Mt 5:16; Lk 19:40; 2 Cor 4:6; Tit 3:4-5; Rev 15:4

Brenton Brown & Jeremy Camp

Moderately, with a strong beat

C
D
C
Chorus
that You've done and we can-not be still. We will cry
G
Em
out to You. Your lov-ing kind-ness and Your truth,
it has de-li-vered us, You have de-
D
C
G
li-vered us. Great is Your glo-ry, Lord.
Em
When na-tions learn of Your ways they will bow

2. We who called upon Your name
Cannot be silent – we will praise,
We will sing it out, we will sing it out.

3. Into all the world we take
The mystery of Your saving grace;
Shine the light into the darkness.

2217.
A rich young man
(Simple living)
Mk 8:36; 10:17-23; 12:41-44;
2 Cor 9:7; Phil 4:12
Capo 1 (D)
Stuart Townend
& Keith Getty
Folk feel
E♭(D) (Em) Fm (D/F♯) E♭/G A♭(G)
1. A rich young man came to ask of Christ: 'Good
B♭(A) E♭(D)
Tea - cher, will You tell me, what — must I do for e -
(Em) Fm (D/F♯) E♭/G A♭(G) B♭(A) E♭(D)
ter - nal life? I've kept Your laws com - plete - ly.' 'Sell
A♭(G) E♭/G(D/F♯) Fm7(Em) B♭(A) A♭(G) E♭/G(D/F♯)
all — you have, give to the poor, then hea - ven's trea - sure
Fm7(Em) B♭(A) (Bm) Cm/B♭ B♭7(A) E♭(D)
shall be yours.' How — hard for those who are

(Em) (D/F♯)
Fm E♭/G A♭(G)
1.
B♭(A) E♭(D)
rich on earth to gain the wealth of hea-ven.
(Em) (D/F♯)
Fm E♭/G A♭(G)
D.C.(v.2)
B♭(A) E♭(D)
2.
D.C. (inst)
B♭(A) E♭(D)
2. Now— count-ing.
3.,5.
1° D.C.(v.3)
2° D.S.
4.,6.
B♭(A) E♭(D)
B♭(A) E♭(D)
E♭(D)
A♭(G)
3. Oh,— hea-ven.
hea-ven. Yes, I'd
1.
B♭(A) E♭(D)
2.
B♭(A) Cm(Bm)
Fm(Em)
(F♯m)
Gm Cm(Bm)
D♭(C)

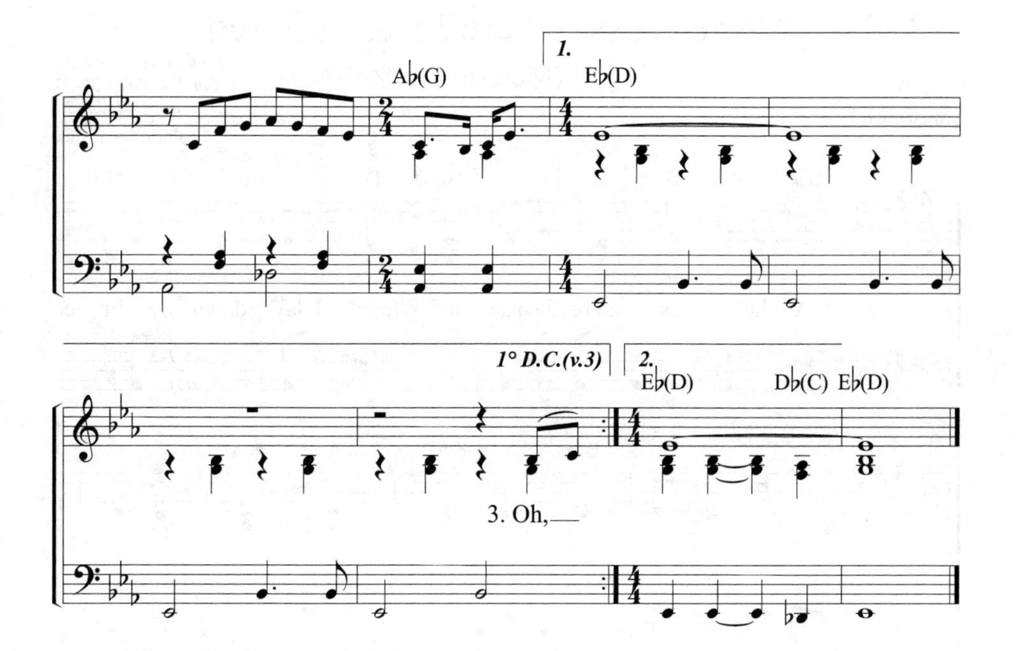

2. Now Jesus sat by the offering gate
   As people brought their money:
   The rich they filled the collection plate;
   The widow gave a penny.
   'Now she's outgiven all the rest –
   Her gift was all that she possessed.'
   Not what you give but what you keep
   Is what the King is counting.

3. Oh, teach me, Lord, to walk this road,
   The road of simple living;
   To be content with what I own
   And generous in giving.
   And when I cling to what I have
   Please wrest it quickly from my grasp;
   I'd rather lose all the things of earth
   To gain the things of heaven.

2218. At the cross, where Jesus suffered

(Merciful)

Mt 6:14; Lk 23:34; Rom 8:28; 2 Cor 1:4; Eph 4:29-30; Col 2:14; Jas 3:8

Graham Kendrick

Moderately

D
Chorus
D/F♯
G
F♯m
loss.
For my Father in heaven showed
R.H.
G
Bm
A
G
D/F♯
mer - cy to me.
How can I not be
G A Bm
Em
Em/A Bm7
mer-ci-ful when God's been mer-ci-ful to me, God's been
1.,3.
D.C.(v.2,3)
2.
D.S. (inst. ch.)
Em
Em/A
D
D
mer-ci-ful to me?
2. I'll not me.
4.
D/F♯
D.S.
5.
D
D
D/F♯
Bm
me?
For my
me?

2. I'll not use my words as weapons
Or the past to gain control;
On my tongue no trace of venom,
Only grace to comfort and make whole.
I am weak but God is with me,
Past and future in His hand;
Turns to good the ill we suffer,
Works all things into Love's plan.

3. Holy dove, return and rest here
As I think and speak the best;
Though it takes ten thousand choices,
I'll press on to honour and to bless.
For the love of Christ my Saviour,
By the strength He daily gives,
This will be the thanks I offer:
I will totally forgive.

2219. At the name of Jesus

Mt 24:30-31; Jn 1:1-2; 1 Cor 10:13; Phil 2:8-11

A
E/G♯
F♯m7
E/G♯
This is your God, this is your, this is your God, this is your,
D9
E
A
E
this is your God, this is your God! Say — it to the go-vern-ment:
A
E/G♯
F♯m7
E/G♯
This is your God, this is your, this is your God, this is your,
(Fine)
D.C.(v.3/5)
D9
E
A
E
this is your God, this is your God!

3. Humbled for a season,
To receive a name
From the lips of sinners
Unto whom He came,
Faithfully He bore it,
Spotless to the last,
Brought it back victorious
When from death He passed:

4. Bore it up triumphant,
With its human light,
Through all ranks of creatures
To the central height,
To the throne of Godhead,
To the Father's breast;
Filled it with the glory
Of that perfect rest.

5. In your hearts enthrone Him,
There let Him subdue
All that is not holy,
All that is not true;
Crown Him as your captain;
In temptation's hour;
Let His will enfold you
In its light and power.

6. Brothers, this Lord Jesus
Shall return again,
With His Father's glory,
With his angel train,
For all wreaths of empire
Meet upon His brow,
And our hearts confess Him
King of glory now.

Caroline Maria Noel (1817–77)
Adpt. Godfrey Birtill

2220. At Your name

Chorus
A
Lord of all the earth, we'll shout Your name, shout Your name,
F♯m7
fill-ing up the skies with end-less praise, end-less praise.
E
D
Yah-weh, Yah-weh, we love to shout Your name, O Lord.
1.,4.
Last time to Coda
D.C.(v.2)
A Bm F♯m A Bm F♯m E
2. At Your name,
3.
D.S. al Coda
2.
Mid section
A Bm F♯m A Bm F♯m
There is

2. At Your name, the morning breaks in glory.
At Your name, creation sings Your story.
At Your name, angels will bow,
The earth will rejoice,
Your people cry out.

2221. Awaken us to see

(Suddenly)

1 Cor 13:12; 15:52; 1 Pet 4:7; 2 Pet 3:10-12; Rev 1:7; 22:17

Vicky Beeching

Brightly

Verse

E F♯m7

1. A - wa-ken us to see the re - a - li - ty

D A E

of e-ter-ni-ty and feel it near. A - wa-ken us to pray

F♯m7 D

as we watch and wait and an - ti - ci - pate with ho -

A Bm7

- ly fear; for the day You'll re - turn a - gain

(v.2)

A/C♯ D Dsus2 *Chorus*

is clo-ser now than it's ev - er been. Sud - den -

A
F♯m7
E
-ly, ev'-ry eye will see as You re-turn in
D
A
F♯m7
glo-ry. Sud-den-ly, ev'-ry knee will fall
Last time to Coda
E
D
A
be-fore heav-en's com-ing King.
1. D.C.(v.2)
2.
F♯m7
Esus4
Dsus2
Dsus2
Mid section
The
F
G
Spi-rit and the bride say, 'Come soon, Lord.' The

2. Jesus, here we stand, lifting up our hands,
Asking You to purify our lives.
So on that glorious day
When we stand face to face,
Unashamed, we'll dance in heaven's light.
For the moment is drawing near
When our radiant King will appear.

2222.

Beauty unspoken

Gen 1:16; Ps 8:3; 33:6; Is 53:4-5; Mt 11:28; Jn 1:1,5; 10:30; Rom 5:9; Phil 2:7-8; Rev 21:6; 22:13

Paul Oakley

2. Light in the darkness,
One with the Father,
The beginning and the end.
Lifter of burdens,
Bruised and forsaken,
Jesus Christ – the sinner's friend.

2223. Before the first

Gen 1:16; Ex 33:20; Ps 90:2; 104:5; Is 6:2-3; Lk 15:24; 2 Cor 4:6; 12:10; Rev 1:8

1.
D.C.(v.2)
2.
Mid section
E♭2(C)
F(D)
Who can meet
Gm7(Em)
E♭(C)
Your gaze,
bear to see Your face,
C7(A7)
stand be-fore You in the ho - li-est place, the
ho - li-est place?
D.C.(v.3) al Coda
Coda
Mak-er of hea - ven and earth,
trea-sure of in - fi-nite worth,

2. You hung the stars,
Rolled out the skies
And set the earth in place.
All the works
Your hand has made
Reflect Your glory,
Sing Your praise, O Lord.

So glorious,
You are so glorious.
Maker of heaven and earth,
You are so glorious.

3. Yet here we stand,
Amazed by grace,
For by the light of Your Son
Lost are found,
The weak made strong,
And broken hearts
Rejoice as one and sing.

So glorious,
You are so glorious.
Living, eternal One,
Maker of heaven and earth,
Treasure of infinite worth
You are so glorious,
You are so glorious,
You are so glorious,
You are.

2224. Before the world was made
(Glory to God forever)

Is 40:22; Jn 1:1; Rom 12:1; 1 Tim 6:15

Steve Fee
& Vicky Beeching

Moderately

Chorus
Dsus2 A E F♯m7
Glo-ry to God, glo-ry to God,
Dsus2 A E Dsus2 A
glo-ry to God for-ev-er. Glo-ry to God,
Last time to Coda
1.
Esus4 F♯m7 Dsus2 A E
glo-ry to God, glo-ry to God for-ev-er.
Dsus2 A E F♯m7
D.C.(v.2)
2.
Dsus2 A Esus4 E Esus2 E E

2. Creator God, You gave me breath so I could praise
Your great and matchless name
All my days, all my days.
So let my whole life be a blazing offering:
A life that shouts and sings
The greatness of our King.

2225.
Behold the Lamb of God
Is 53:5; Jn 1:29; 1 Cor 7:23; Phil 2:8-9; Rev 1:16; 5:9, 11-12
Capo 2 (D)
Relaxed feel
Chris Orange
Verse
E(D) B(A) E(D)
1. Be - hold the Lamb of God, who takes a -
A(G) E(D) B(A)
way all the sin of the world. He con-quered
A(G) E(D) B(A)
through pre-cious blood, pur-chased us with His
C♯m7(Bm7) A(G) B(A)
love; now He has pow - er to save.
1. D.C.(v.2) 2.,3.
Chorus
A(G) E(D)
For You are wor - thy, You are

2. Behold the champion of grace;
He bore our sin on the cross, took our place.
Our humble God gave His life,
One complete sacrifice;
Now He is seated on high.

3. Behold our King is alive,
He's crowned in glory and power, clothed with light.
All heaven sings out His name
With an anthem of praise,
Jesus, the glory of God.

2226. Be still, there is a healer

(I lift my hands)

Ps 51:1; 59:16; Jn 7:37; Eph 3:18; Rev 21:6; 22:2

Chris Tomlin, Matt Maher & Louie Giglio

Steadily, with strength

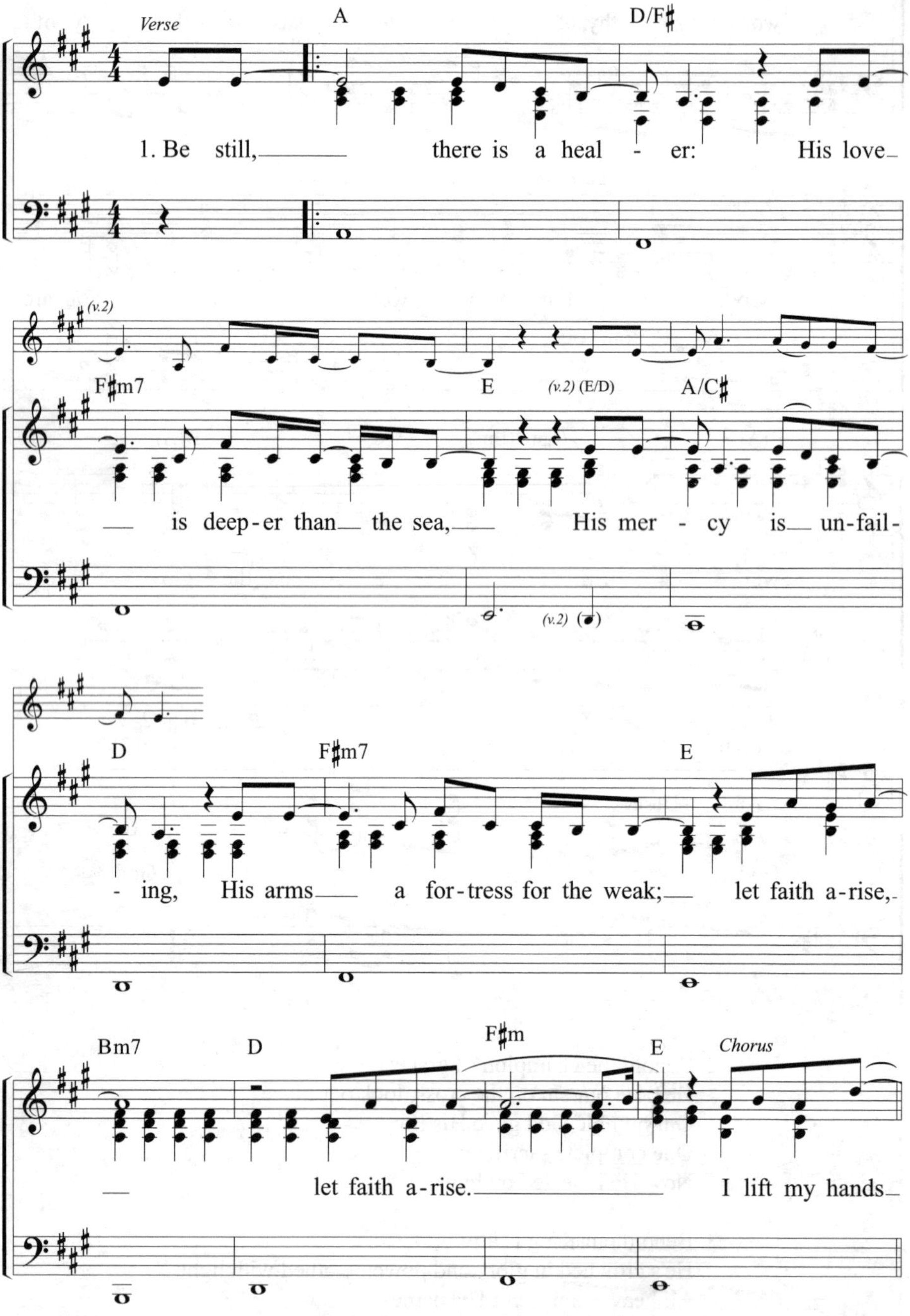

Verse

A D/F♯

1. Be still, there is a heal - er: His love

F♯m7 E (v.2) (E/D) A/C♯

is deep-er than the sea, His mer - cy is un-fail-

D F♯m7 E

- ing, His arms a for-tress for the weak; let faith a-rise,

Bm7 D F♯m E *Chorus*

let faith a-rise. I lift my hands

A
F♯m
to be-lieve a-gain; You are my re - fuge, You are my strength.
Last time to Coda
(D.S. 1° A/E)
A/C♯
D
As I pour out my heart, these things I re-mem -
(D.S. 1° small notes)
1.
Em7
D
- ber: You are faith - ful, God, for-e - ver.
A(no3rd)
D6sus2
F♯m7
E(no3rd)
2.,4.
G/B
2. Be still - ful, God, for- e-
D.S. (2° al Coda)
3.
D
G
D
Mid section
- ver. I lift my hands - ful, God, for-e - ver. Let faith a-eyes,

A
F♯m
let faith a-rise;
o-pen my eyes,
o-pen my eyes.
D
A/C♯
I lift my eyes,
let faith a-rise;
G6
o-pen my eyes,
o-pen my eyes.
D
D.S.
I lift my eyes
Coda
A/E
these things
I re-mem - ber:
You are faith-

2. Be still, there is a river
That flows from Calvary's tree;
A fountain for the thirsty:
Your grace that washes over me.
Let faith arise, let faith arise.

2227. Be the reason we are here

(To make Your name great)

Ps 34:3; Is 61:1; Mt 5:16; Jn 12:32

John Hartley, Kelly Minter & Gary Sadler

E D A D
— to the ed-ges of — the earth, — to sing Your high - est praise
E D A D
— for the glo-ry You — de-serve. — Let our wor-ship start
F♯m E D
— with the pas - sion of — our hearts — to make Your
Last time to Coda
1.
D.C.
E A D F♯m7 E
name — great. —
2.
Bm
Mid section
A E Bm
— Je - sus, make Your name great. — We want

2. Let us tell the truth You've shown,
Raise Your cross and make You known,
Take You to the weak and the poor.
Lay Your justice on our hearts,
Be the light that we impart,
Till the world can see You are Lord.

2228. Blessèd assurance

Ps 130:5; Mt 24:42; Eph 1:14; Heb 10:22; Rev 7:14

New music & words adaptation: Chris McClarney, John Hartley & Chris Eaton

Chorus
F G C F G
This is my sto - ry, this is my song:
C F G Am
prais-ing my Sa - viour, oh,
1.
D.C.(v.2)
Dm7 G F
all the day long, all the day long.
2.,3.
G C/E F G Am
This is my sto - ry,
C F G C/E F
this is my song: prais-ing my Sa -

2. Perfect submission, perfect delight,
Visions of rapture now burst on my sight.
Angels descending bring from above
Echoes of mercy, whispers of love.

3. Perfect submission, all is at rest,
I in my Saviour am happy and blessed.
Watching and waiting, looking above,
I'm filled with His goodness, I'm lost in His love!

Fanny J. Crosby (1820–1915)

2229. Blessèd is the King

Lk 2:14; 19:38, 40

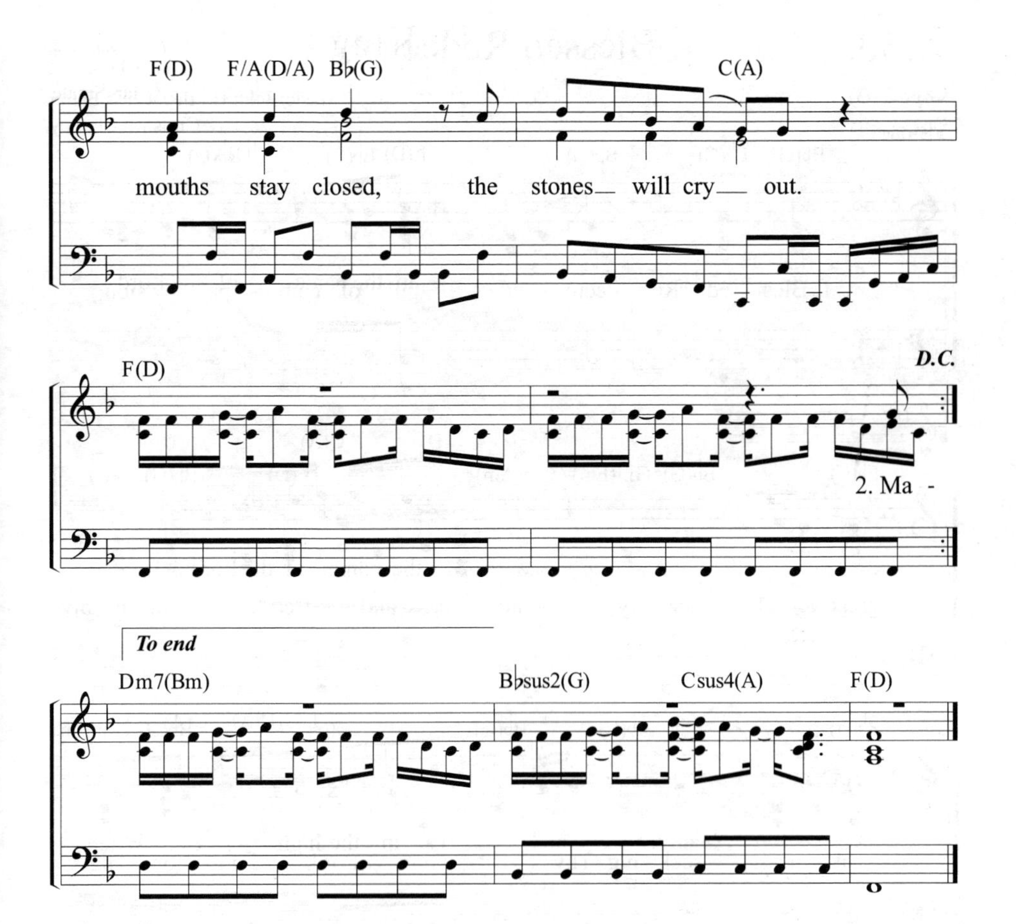

2. Majestic is the King who comes
   In the name of the Lord...

3. Triumphant is the King who comes
   In the name of the Lord...

2230. Blessèd Redeemer

Ps 18:2; Dan 7:13; Mt 9:36; Jas 4:8

Capo 3 (G)

Music: John Hartley, Chris Eaton & Chris McClarney

Flowing

2. Blessèd Redeemer, Thou art my refuge,
Under Thy watch-care, safe I shall be.
Gladly adoring, joyfully trusting,
Still I am coming closer to Thee.

3. Blessèd Redeemer, gracious and tender,
New and forever dwell Thou in me.
Thou, my protector, shield and defender,
Draw me and keep me closer to Thee.

Fanny J. Crosby (1820–1915)

2231. Bless the Lord, O my soul

(10,000 reasons)

Ps 103:1, 8

Jonas Myrin
& Matt Redman

2. You're rich in love and You're slow to anger,
Your name is great and Your heart is kind.
For all Your goodness, I will keep on singing;
Ten thousand reasons for my heart to find.

3. And on that day when my strength is failing,
The end draws near and my time has come,
Still my soul will sing Your praise unending:
Ten thousand years and then forever more!

2232. Blow, mighty breath of God

Jn 19:34; Acts 2:2-3; 1 Jn 5:6

Anthony Skinner, Ross Huskinson,
Tom Lane & Scott MacLeod

Prayerfully

G A D2
come in pow'r and grace.
C2 Verse G A D
1. Streams of mer - cy flow - ing down,
C2 G A
light of hea - ven all a-
D Em
round, fall - ing
C G Asus4 A D.C.
to the ground.

2. Wind of wisdom, light the way.
Revelation for today,
Chasing fear away.

3. Spirit fire, fan the flame,
Passion for Your holy name,
Burning everything.

4. Blood and water washing all;
From the cross, see it fall.
Jesus, Lord of all.

This is the one who came by water and blood— Jesus Christ. He did not come by water only, but by water and blood. And it is the Spirit who testifies, because the Spirit is the truth.

1 JOHN 5:6

2233. Breathe on me, breath of God

Ps 34:1; Jn 20:22

Capo 1 (C)

Claire Hamilton

G♭(F)
D♭(C)
A♭(G)
a praise that's Yours a - lone. Your praise
B♭m7(Am)
G♭(F)
D♭(C)
will fall from my lips at all times,
A♭(G)
B♭m(Am) G♭(F)
A♭(G)
for I know, I know the love of God.
D♭(C)
G♭/D♭(F/C)
D♭(C)
G♭/D♭(F/C)
D.C.
D♭(C)

2234.
Bring heaven to earth, Lord
(We are blessed)
Gen 1:26; Mt 6:10; Lk 4:18; Jn 1:14; 20:22; Rom 5:20; Gal 5:22-23; 2 Pet 3:18
Capo 3 (D)
Moderate 4
Andy Flannagan
Verse
F(D) C(A) Bb(G)
1. Bring hea - ven to earth, Lord, bring peace where there's fear;
bring life where there's death, Lord, bring joy in these tears.
Bring love where there's lust, Lord, bring
hope where there's pain; bring rest where there's cha -
- os, bring faith where there's fame.

Gm(Em) Bridge F/A(D/F♯) B♭(G) C(A) (Em) (Bm) Gm Dm
(v.2)
You in-vite us to part - ner with You, to see Your
C(A) B♭(G) Chorus F(D)
king - dom come. We are blessed, to bless
C(A) Gm(Em) B♭(G)
a world in pie - ces. We are loved,
F(D) C(A) Gm(Em) F/A(D/F♯)
to love where love is not.
B♭(G) F(D) C(A)
We are changed, to be the change You pro-
Gm(Em) B♭(G) F(D)
- mised. We are freed to be

2. Bring home to the homeless,
Bring keys to the chained;
Bring worth to the purchased,
And touch to the shamed.
Bring flesh from Your word, Lord,
Bring truth where there's spin;
Bring risk where there's safety,
And grace where there's sin.
In the broken we shall see restored
The image of our King.

3. Bring justice to profit,
Bring patience to growth;
Bring wisdom to progress,
Like food for the soul.
Bring freedom from debt, Lord,
An end to excess;
Bring closer Your kingdom
By quiet success.
May we grow in the knowledge of You
Through every heart and face.

'Our Father in heaven, hallowed be your name, your kingdom come, your will be done on earth as it is in heaven.'

MATTHEW 6:9b-10

2235. Bring to the Lord a glad new song

1 Chron 15:16; Ps 96:1; 149:1, 3, 7; 150

JERUSALEM

Words: Michael Perry (1942–96)
Music: C.H.H. Parry (1848–1918)

Slow but with animation

long – to in-stru-ments of mu - sic, sing! Let those be
Bm F♯m Bm7 E7 A Em B7
warned who spurn His name; na-tions and kings, at-tend His
Em Am Em G/D D7
poco cresc.
word – God's jus-tice shall bring ty-rants shame; let ev-'ry
G Em A A7 D G
f ff poco rit.
crea-ture praise the Lord!
D Gmaj7 A7 D Bm B7 Em
f a tempo

Praise Him with - in these hal-lowed
Bm G D G/D G
ff mf
8vb 8vb
walls, praise Him be - neath the dome of heav'n; by cym-bals'
D G D Bm G D
sounds and trum-pets' calls let prais-es fit for God be
Bm F♯m Bm F♯m Bm7 E7
giv'n. With strings and brass and wind re - joice – then join His
A Em B7 Em Am Em

praise with full ac - cord, all liv-ing things with breath and
G/D D7 G Em A A7
allargando
ff
voice; let ev-'ry crea-ture praise the Lord!
D G D Gmaj7 A7 D
rit.
G/D G D
ff
8vb

2236. Brokenness has brought me to my knees

Chorus
A♭(F) E♭/G(C/E) A♭(F) B♭sus4(G) B♭(G)
Give me an un - di-vi - ded heart; I want to love
E♭/G(C/E) A♭(F) B♭(G) E♭/G(C/E) A♭(F)
You with ev - 'ry part. Give me an un - di-vi - ded soul;
Last time to Coda
1.
B♭sus4(G) B♭(G) Fm7(Dm) E♭/G(C/E) A♭(F) B♭(G)
I want to be Yours a-lone, Yours a-lone.
Cm(Am) E♭/G(C/E) A♭(F) Fm7(Dm)
D.C.(v.2)
2.
Mid section
A♭(F) B♭(G) A♭(F) B♭(G) E♭/G(C/E)
a-lone. You make all things new, so take my

A♭(F)
B♭(G)
Cm(Am)
ash - es and make them some - thing beau - ti - ful.
A♭(F)
B♭(G)
E♭/G(C/E)
Do what on - ly You can do: take my
A♭(F)
B♭(G)
Cm(Am)
ash - es and make them some - thing beau - ti - ful.
A♭2(F)
Fm7(Dm)
D.S. al Coda
Give me an un -
Coda
A♭(F)
B♭(G)
Fm7(Dm)
E♭/G(C/E)
a - lone. I want to be Yours a - lone, Yours

2. At the cross I find Your open arms,
Reminding me there's grace for all I've done.
With Your blood You wipe away my past,
Taking on Yourself my sin and scars.
By Your power, help me change;
Break off every single chain.

2237. Broken people, call His name
(Lift high)

Ps 123:1; Lk 4:18; 11:2; Rev 5:9-10

Steadily

Steve Fee
& Eddie Kirkland

Last time to Coda
G D A Bm F♯m
alt the Son. Je-sus Christ, the ho-ly One,
G D A
1.
D Em7 D/F♯
we lift our eyes to You.
G D Em7 D/F♯ G D
D.C.(v.2)
2.
D
Mid section
A G D/F♯
Lift up your heads. Oh, lift up your heads, look on Him.
A
1.,2.
G D
Lift up your heads, oh, lift up your heads, look on Him.

2. Sinners, all exalt the Son,
Your ransom paid and freedom won.
We will see His kingdom come
When sinners all exalt the Son.

I lift up my eyes to you, to you whose throne is in heaven.

PSALM 123:1

2238. Brothers, let us come together

(By our love)

Jn 13:35; 2 Cor 4:6; Gal 5:25; Col 3:1

Christy Nockels

Gently

Verse

G D D/F♯ G D D/F♯
1. Bro - thers, let us come to - ge - ther, walk-ing in the

Em D G D/F♯
Spi - rit; there's much to be___ done. We will come

Em Bm/D C G/B **1.** Am
reach-ing out___ from our com - forts and they will know us by our

D/F♯ ***D.C.(v.2)*** **2.,3.** Am D/F♯ 𝄋 G
love. and they will know us by___ our love.

Chorus
The time is___

D/F♯ C/E G
___ now,_______ come, church, a - rise. Love with His___

2. Sisters, we were made for kindness,
We can pierce the darkness
As He shines through us.
We will come reaching,
With a song of healing,
And they will know us by our love.

3. Children, you are hope for justice,
Stand firm in the truth now,
Set your hearts above.
You will be reaching
Long after we're gone,
And they will know you by your love.

2239. By every nation, race and tongue

Ps 148:3; 1 Cor 15:54; 2 Cor 5:7; Col 1:14; Rev 5:9, 13; 14:12

EASTER SONG

Geistliche Kirchengesang, Cologne 1623
Arr. Paul Hughes

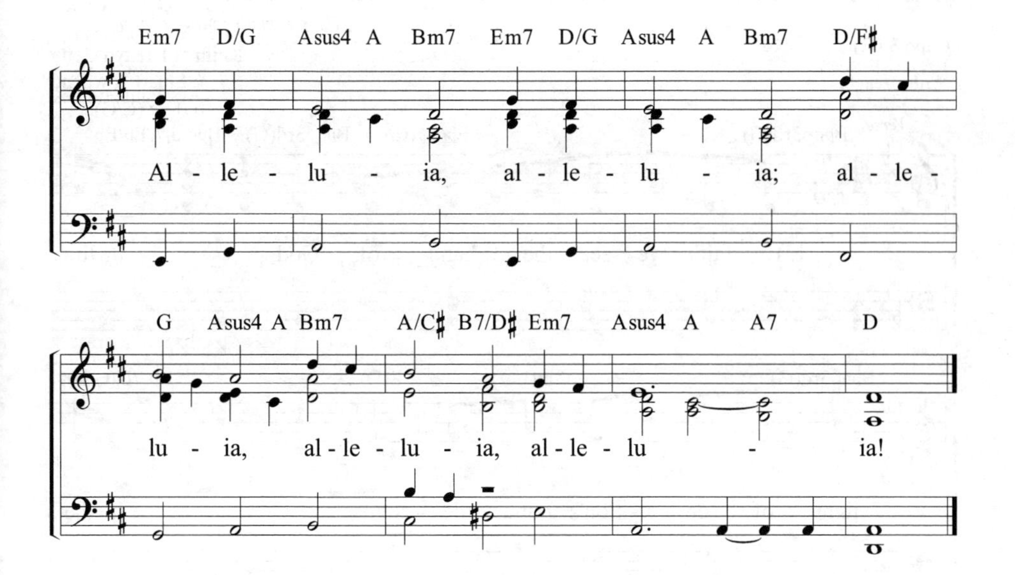

2. Saints who on earth have suffered long,
   For Jesus' sake enduring wrong,
   Ever faithful: Alleluia!
   Where faith is lost in sight, rejoice
   And sing with never-wearied voice:
   Alleluia, alleluia;
   Alleluia, alleluia, alleluia!

3. Let earth and air and sea unite
   To celebrate His glorious might,
   Their Creator: Alleluia!
   Sun, moon and stars in endless space
   Echo the song of every race:
   Alleluia, alleluia;
   Alleluia, alleluia, alleluia!

H. B. George (1838–1910)

2240. By faith we see the hand of God

Mt 17:20; 28:19; Lk 4:18; Acts 1:8; 2 Cor 5:7; Phil 4:13; Heb 11:3, 10, 13; 12:2

B♭(G)
Gm(Em)
E♭2(C)
pro - mise, we will fix our eyes on Him, our
B♭(G)
F(D)
B♭(G)
Gm(Em)
E♭2(C)
soul's re - ward. 'Till the race is fin - ished and the
(G/B)
B♭(G) B♭2/D E♭2(C)
Cm7(Am)
E♭(C)
F(D)
Last time to Coda
work is done, we'll walk by faith and not by
1.,2.
D.C.(v.3/v.5)
3.
D.S. al Coda
B♭sus2(G)
(C/G)
E♭/B♭
B♭sus2(G)
(C/G)
E♭/B♭
B♭(G)
sight.
sight. We will
Coda
Gm(Em)
Cm7(Am)
E♭(C)
F(D)
sight. we'll walk by faith and not by

2. By faith our fathers roamed the earth
With the power of His promise in their hearts:
Of a holy city built by God's own hand –
A place where peace and justice reign.

3. By faith the prophets saw a day
When the longed-for Messiah would appear
With the power to break the chains of sin and death,
And rise triumphant from the grave.

4. By faith the church was called to go
In the power of the Spirit to the lost,
To deliver captives and to preach good news
In every corner of the earth.

5. By faith this mountain shall be moved
And the power of the gospel shall prevail,
For we know in Christ all things are possible
For those who call upon His name.

2241. By the grace of God alone

Lk 7:22; 15:18; Jn 1:29; Rom 1:4; 10:13; Eph 2:8; Col 1:14, 20; Rev 5:12; 12:11

With a celtic lilt

Johnny Vogt

Last time to Coda
G A Bm Em7 (2° onwards) A
blood of Christ the Son, we have re - ceived e - ter - nal
1.
D.C.(v.3)
D Dsus4 D G D D/F♯ Em7 A7sus4 D
life. 3. Hear the
2.,4. D.S. (al Coda)
3.
D D/F♯ D
Mid section
D G
life. By the life. Hal - le - lu - jah, He is
D G D
wor - thy, hal - le - lu - jah, Christ the Son. Hal - le -
G D Em7 A
lu - jah, He is ho - ly, so lift your voice to the ho - ly

2. Sing for joy and celebrate,
   Dance with those who once were lame;
   Deaf ears hear them as they sing,
   'I have been healed in Jesus' name.'

3. Hear the Saviour calling home
   Every soul that's lost their way.
   See them turn away from sin,
   As they call out the Saviour's name.

2242. Called and named before Your birth

(Servant of God Most High)

Is 53:2-11; Lk 1:31; 4:18, 42; Jn 3:34; 12:46

Simon Pedley

Brightly

Verse

A D A/C♯ Bm7 A/C♯

1. Called and named before Your birth, chosen One,

D E A D A/C♯

Jesus Christ, given now to all the earth;

Bm7 A/C♯ E A

Spirit-filled, perfect light. Bringing peace and

D A/C♯ Bm7 A/C♯ D E

righteousness, freeing slaves, ending night;

F♯m D A/C♯ Bm7 A/C♯

honoured in the sight of God, You're His joy,

Chorus
D Esus4 E A
His de-light. Ser-vant of God Most High,
F♯m7 D2 Bm7 A/C♯
Sa-viour of all the earth, we can-not rea-son why You
D2 Esus4 E A
came to die for us. Shout prai-ses to our King,
F♯m7 D2 Bm7 A/C♯
burst forth with songs of joy: Je-sus has set us free to
D2 Esus4 A F♯m7
serve Him e - ver more.

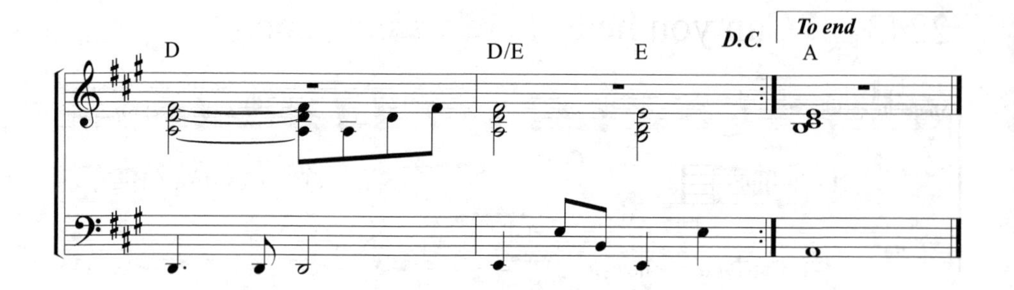

2. Your appearance was so marred;
So despised, so reviled,
Like a lamb led to its death,
Silently, You faced the cross.
For our sin and for our guilt,
You were crushed, You were killed;
All of this for God's own will,
That by Your death we might live.

3. Buried like a sinful man;
Innocent, holy One,
God's will prospered in Your hand,
Servant King, obedient Son.
Raised as our victorious Lord,
Glorified, forgiving sin;
Sharing with Your children now
Righteousness and life in heaven.

2243. Can you hear there's a new song?

Rev 5:9

C♯m
A-live,
come a-live;
A
E(no3rd)
let the song a-rise.
Last time to Coda
1.
D.C.(v.3)
2.
A/E E
E(no3rd)
A/E E
A/E E
3. All the
Mid section
D
F♯m
E
Oh,
(oh,)
yeah.
(yeah.)
D
F♯m
Let the song a-rise,
(let the song a-rise,)
yeah.

2. Let us sing love to the nations,
Bringing hope of the grace that has freed us.
Make it known and make Him famous;
Sing it out, sing a new hallelujah.

3. All the world sings a new song,
Reaching out with a new hallelujah.
Every son and every daughter,
Everyone, sing a new hallelujah.

2244. Christ be in my waking

Mt 14:24; Jn 10:14, 27; Rom 12:1-2; Col 3:9; 1 Jn 1:7

Stuart Townend
& Simon Brading

Chorus
Am E7/G♯ C7/G D7/F♯ G/F C/E
Je - sus, this is my de - vo - tion, all my life to know You, ev - 'ry day to
F C/E G Am E7/G♯ C7/G D7/F♯
walk with You. Sa-viour, You're my deep-est long - ing, You're the One I
G/F C/E
1.,2.,4.
F C/E G
live for. Teach me, Lord, to walk with You.
D.C.(v.3.,4.,1. al Coda)
C/E
3.
F C/E G
D.S.
Coda
Am2
3. Christ be in my walk with You.
end-ing,
Am E7/G♯ C7/G C7/F♯ Fm F/E♭

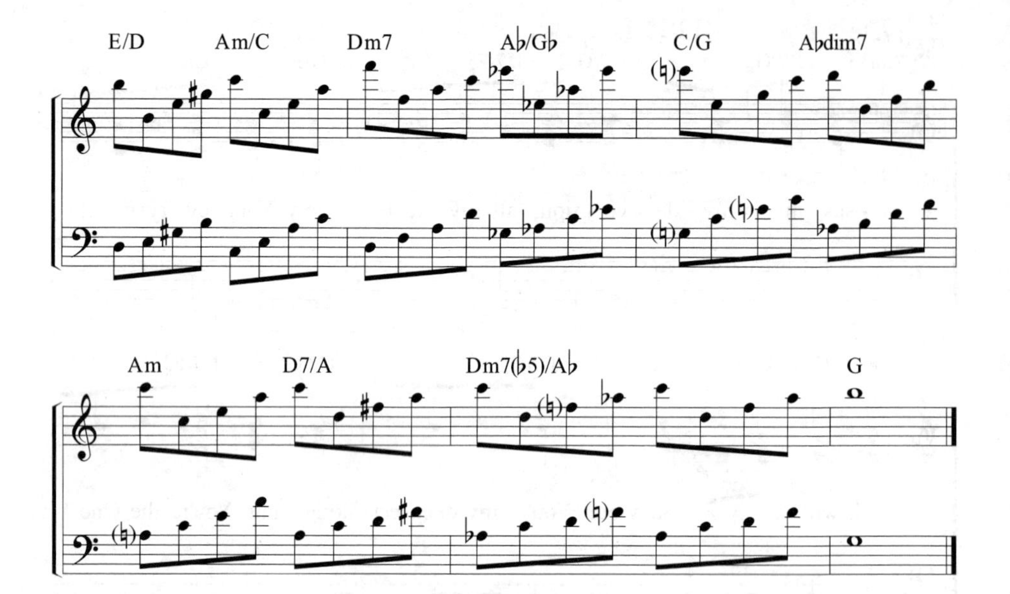

2. Christ be in my thinking
And my understanding,
Guarding me from evil,
Walking in the light.
Christ be in my speaking,
Every word a blessing,
Pure and not deceiving,
Grace to all who hear.

3. Christ be in my gladness
For the joy of living,
Thankful for the goodness
Of the Father's hand.
Christ be in my sorrow,
In my day of darkness,
Knowing that I follow
In the steps He trod.

4. Christ when hope has faded,
Nothing left to cling to,
Every pleasure jaded,
Every well is dry.
Christ the loving Shepherd
Draws me with His kindness,
Leads me from the desert
To the streams of life.

2245. Christ for me! a love so deep

(Christ for me!)

Rom 8:31; 1 Cor 13:12; 15:56-57; Gal 2:20; 1 Thess 4:16

Edwin Brown

1st time only
D
Chorus
G
me!
(me.)
Oh, bleed-ing
Lamb
of Cal - va-
D/F♯
G
A
ry,
who gave His
life
un - self - ish -
Bm
G
D/F♯
A7
ly;
for no one else
could set me
3rd time D.S.S.
Last time to Coda
1.
Bm
G
D/A
A7
D
free:
Christ for me!
Christ for
me!
D.S.
2.
Dsus4
D
3. When dark - ness
me!

3. When darkness comes and thunders roll,
When guilt and fear hold fast my soul,
I'll stand upon His word and know:
Christ for me! Christ for me!

4. And when I take my final breath,
I'll take the hand that conquered death
And rise to meet Him face to face:
Christ for me! Christ for me!

2246. Christ is the world's true light

Is 2:4; 9:6; Heb 2:10; Rev 7:9; 22:16

2. In Christ all races meet,
Their ancient feuds forgetting,
The whole round world complete
From sunrise to its setting:
When Christ is known as Lord
All shall forsake their fear,
To ploughshare beat the sword,
To pruning-hook the spear.

3. One Lord, in one great name
Unite all who have known You,
Cast out our pride and shame
That hinder to enthrone You:
The world has waited long,
Has laboured long in pain,
To heal its ancient wrong;
Come, Prince of peace, and reign!

G. W. Briggs (1875–1959)

2247. Come, let us enter in now

Ex 3:14; 15:26; Ps 92:2; 100:4; 146:9-10; Mt 11:28; Jn 10:3; Acts 2:21; Rom 10:13; Heb 4:16; 1 Pet 5:6

Rhythmically

Nathan & Lou Fellingham & busbee

Chorus
3rd time D.C.(v.3)
G
C
You're the Lord e - ter - nal, great
will rise in thanks
I Am, and You're reign - ing with Your migh -
and praise, for Your awe - some pow'r, out - ra -
G
- ty hand; watch - ing o - ver all, sus - tain -
- geous grace; our pro - vi - der, mas - ter, heal -
F
C
1.,3.,5.
G
F
- ing all so gen - 'rous - ly.
So our song
- er, Lord of ev - 'ry - thing.
2.
D.C.
4.
D.S.
6.
G
F
G
F
G
F

2. We will declare You're faithful,
We will rejoice that we are saved and known by name.
We will believe Your promise,
With full assurance we draw near, no guilt or shame.

3. Come and find rest and shelter,
There is protection for the one who trusts in Him.
Bow down in sweet surrender,
Call on His name, declare Him Lord and you'll be saved.

2248. Come, let us return to the Lord

(Gloria)

2 Sam 19:28; 1 Chron 29:14; Hos 6:1; Jn 10:3

Brenton Brown & Matt Maher

Punchy

Em
C
G
-on You. Glo-ri-a, glo-ri-a, turn our
Last time to Coda
1.
D.C.(v.2)
D
G
hearts to You a-gain.
3.
D.S. al Coda
2.
Mid section
G
G
Glo-ri-a Look what You've done,
Am
Em
D
look what You've done. All that we have is Yours a-
G
Am
Em
-lone. What can we give? What of-fer-ing? You de-serve

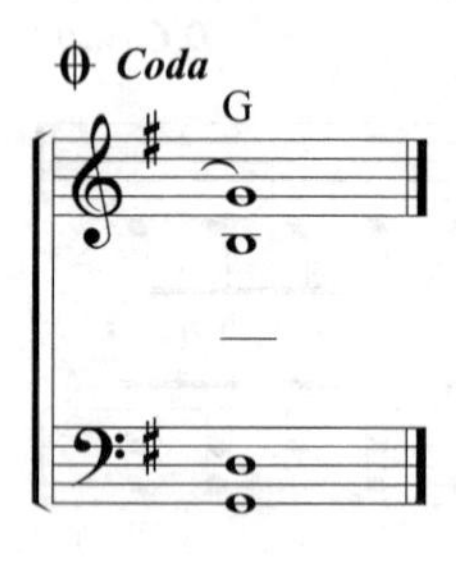

2. Welcomed to the table of the King.
Welcomed to the table of the King.
Homeless and ashamed,
The Saviour called our names.
We've been welcomed to the table of the King.

3. So let mercy rise like praise to Your throne.
Let mercy rise like praise to Your throne.
Father, touch Your church
Till justice fills the earth.
Let mercy rise like praise to Your throne.

The watchman opens the gate for him, and the sheep listen to his voice. He calls his own sheep by name and leads them out.

JOHN 10:3

2249. Come, people of the risen King

Ps 23:6; 30:5; 123:1; Lam 3:22; Rom 5:2, 5; Eph 1:7; Phil 4:4; Col 1:17; Heb 12:4; 2 Pet 1:19; 1 Jn 4:18; Rev 22:16

Moderately

Keith & Kristyn Getty & Stuart Townend

2. Come, those whose joy is morning sun,
And those weeping through the night.
Come, those who tell of battles won,
And those struggling in the fight.
For His perfect love will never change
And His mercies never cease,
But follow us through all our days
With the certain hope of peace.

3. Come, young and old from every land,
Men and women of the faith.
Come, those with full or empty hands,
Find the riches of His grace.
Over all the world His people sing –
Shore to shore we hear them call
The truth that cries through every age:
'Our God is all in all!'

2250. Come, satisfy us

Ezek 37:4, 10; Jn 7:38; Rev 7:17

Capo 1 (D)

Claire Hamilton

Prayerfully

Verse

Eb(D) Ab2(G) Eb(D)

1. Come, sa - tis - fy us, come, sa - tis -

Bb(A) Eb(D) Ab(G)

fy us, Lord. Come, sa - tis - fy us, and

Eb(D) Bbsus4(A) Eb(D) Eb(D) Ab(G)

1. ***D.C.(v.1)*** ***2.,3.*** ***1st time only*** *(not 2°)*

breathe on these dry bones. bones.

Eb(D) Bbsus4(A) Eb(D)

Chorus

Eb(D) Ab(G)

O liv-ing wa - ter, come,

Eb(D) Bb(A) Eb(D) Ab(G)

fall a-fresh on us. Fill our bar-ren pla-ces with

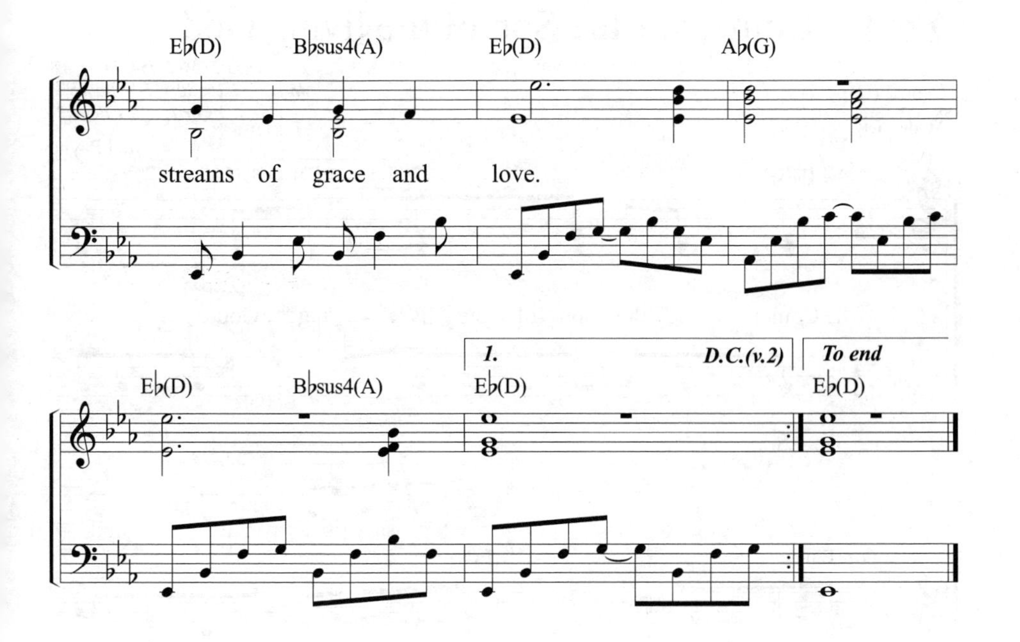

2. Come, sanctify us,
Come, sanctify us, Lord.
Come, sanctify us,
And breathe on these dry bones.

2251. Come, see the Son of the living God

Is 53:5; Mt 27:54; Lk 23:47; Jn 1:14; 3:16; 20:1, 5-7; Rom 5:9; 1 Cor 15:57; 1 Pet 2:24

Capo 3 (G)

Moderately

Joel Payne

F(D)
B♭(G)
Chorus
a-go-ny a-cross His face.
1. This is love
E♭(C)
B♭/D(G/B)
dis-played,
this is mer - cy per - fect-ly
Gm(Em)
E♭sus4(C)
F(D)
por-trayed in Christ,
the cross of Christ.
1.,2.
1° D.C.(v.2., ch1.)
2° D.C.(v.3., ch2.)
B♭(G)
Gm7(Em)
F/A(D/F♯)B♭(G)
Gm7(Em)
F/A(D/F♯) B♭(G)
3.
D.S.(ch.2)
4.
B♭(G)
B♭(G)
Yeah, this is vic -

2. Come, see the innocent Son of God
Punished there for us,
Rescuing us with His blood.
Come, see the healer of wounded souls
Crucified for us,
Broken there to make us whole.

3. Come, see the tomb where they laid Him down;
The stone is rolled away,
Nothing but the grave clothes now.
Come, see the King is alive again,
Risen from the dead,
Ushering a new age in.

(Chorus 2)
This is victory,
This is life for everyone who will believe
In Jesus Christ.

He was pierced for our transgressions, he was crushed for our iniquities; the punishment that brought us peace was upon him, and by his wounds we are healed.

ISAIAH 53:5

2252. Come to Me all you who are weary

Mt 11:28-30

Doug Horley

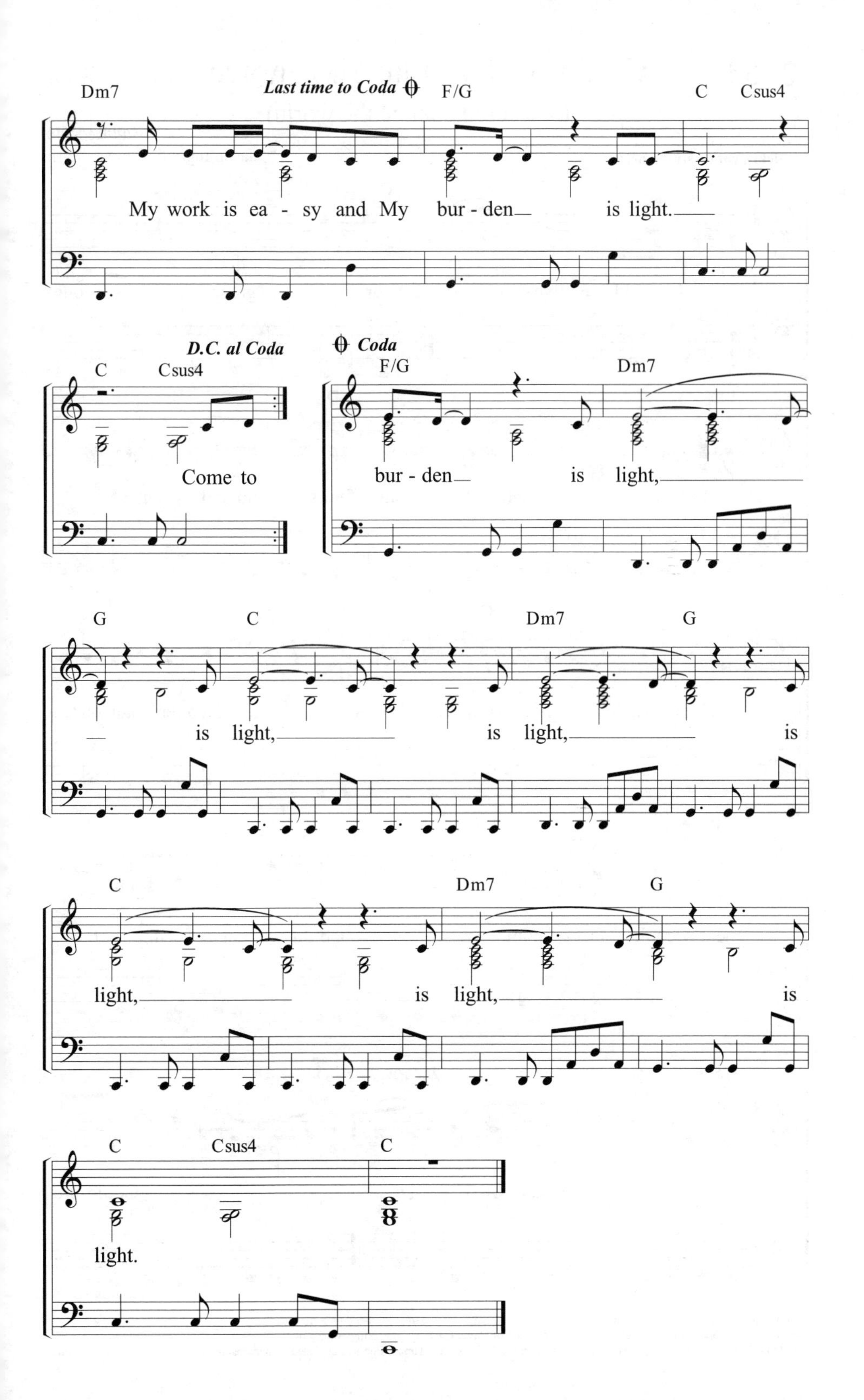
Dm7
Last time to Coda
F/G
C
Csus4
My work is ea - sy and My bur - den is light.
D.C. al Coda
C
Csus4
Come to
Coda
F/G
Dm7
bur - den is light,
G
C
Dm7
G
is light, is light, is
C
Dm7
G
light, is light, is
C
Csus4
C
light.

2253. Could we live like Your grace?

(We could change the world)

Mt 5:16; Rom 6:14; Eph 3:18-19

Matt Redman, Jason Ingram & Jonas Myrin

Chorus
Em D G
live like this? Yes, our God
D/F♯ Em D C
is all He says, all He says He is. Je - sus, in Your name
Em D G
we could change the world. We stand in Your
D/F♯ Em D
love, in Your pow'r, and all You say we are.
C Em D
Last time to Coda
Je - sus, in Your name we could change the world.
1. D.C.(v.3) 2. C
3. We be-lieve Your Je - sus, in Your name

Em
D
Mid section
we could change the world.
We're say-ing
Am G Bm Em
yes, Lord, yes, Lord!
Am Em G
What else could we say, what else could we say?
D/F♯ Am G Bm
We're say-ing yes, Lord, yes,
Em Am Em
Lord! We're go-ing all the way, we're
G D
go-ing all the way. We're going to live like this.

2. Could we live like Your name is higher
Than every other power?
Could we live like Your ways
Are wiser than our understanding?
Could we live like this?
Could we live like this?

3. We believe that Your grace is stronger
Than all our faults and failures.
We believe that Your love
Is deeper than our hearts could fathom.
So could we live like this
And shine in all the world?
Could we live like this?

2254. Creation brings an offering

(On the third day)

Is 55:12; Hos 6:2-3; Lk 24:46; Jn 17:22; Rom 8:22-25; 1 Cor 15:4, 55; Eph 2:8; Col 1:22; 2:13

With expectancy

Marc Byrd & Matt Maher

A/C♯ E/B Bsus4 B
— for ev - 'ry-thing — must die — to rise — a-gain. -
1.
2.-4.
Chorus
E E
— 2. The win - ter's — — On the
A E B A
third day, — be-hold — the King, on the third day, — death has -
C♯m7 B A
— no sting, on the third day, — we're for -
Last time to Coda
1.,2.
D.C.(v.3/4)
F♯m7 B E
gi-ven and re - con-ciled. — 3. The earth, it

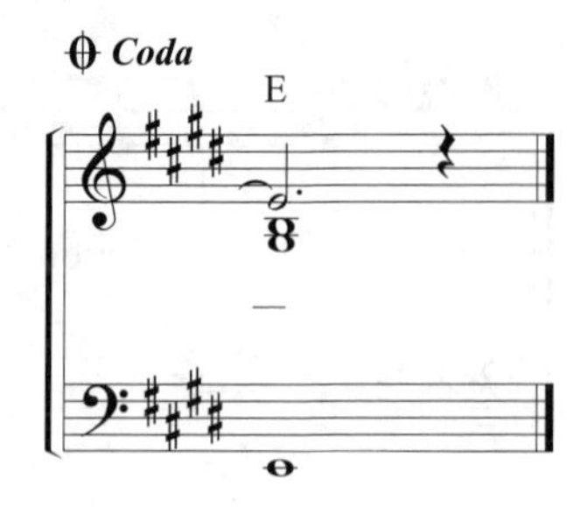

2. The winter's chill, a bitter cold,
As sin and shame leave us to fall.
The clouds, now full of newborn snow,
For grace to come and save us all.
Within the darkest night of man
Was found Your saving hand;
For everything must die to rise again.

3. The earth, it groans in labour pains
As flowers stretch to heaven above.
Your creatures sing the prophet's song,
To be a gift of selfless love.
The sun is rising in the east
And Your spirit is unleashed;
For everything must die to rise again.

4. And so we wait in joyful hope
For You to come and take us home;
And so we join beneath the cross,
In suffering from whence we go.
The greatest act of sovereign grace
In the universe displayed;
For everything must die to rise again.

(Chorus 2)
On the third day, the saints rejoice,
On the third day, we lift our voice,
On the third day, united and glorified.

After two days he will revive us; on the third day he will restore us, that we may live in his presence. Let us acknowledge the LORD; let us press on to acknowledge him. As surely as the sun rises, he will appear; he will come to us like the winter rains, like the spring rains that water the earth.

HOSEA 6:2-3

2255. Creation sings the Father's song

Mk 13:7-8; Rom 8:19, 22; 1 Cor 15:22, 45; 2 Cor 5:19; Gal 3:13; Rev 21:1

Capo 3 (G)

Keith & Kristyn Getty & Stuart Townend

With a celtic lilt

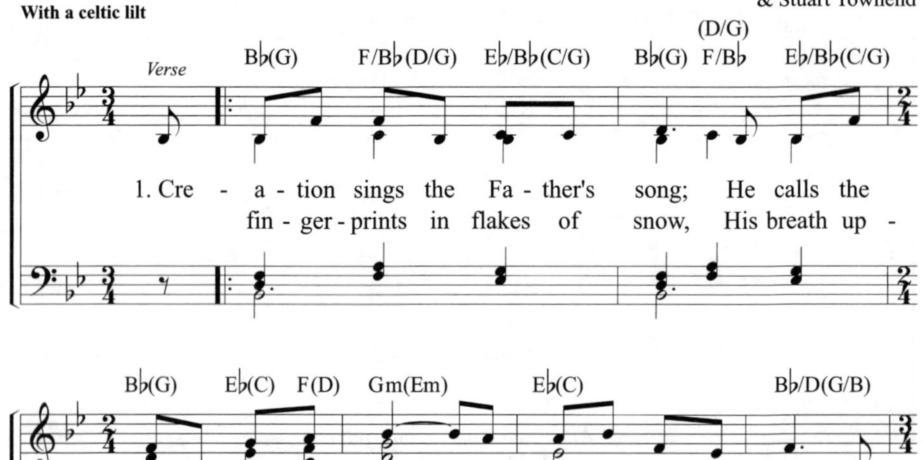

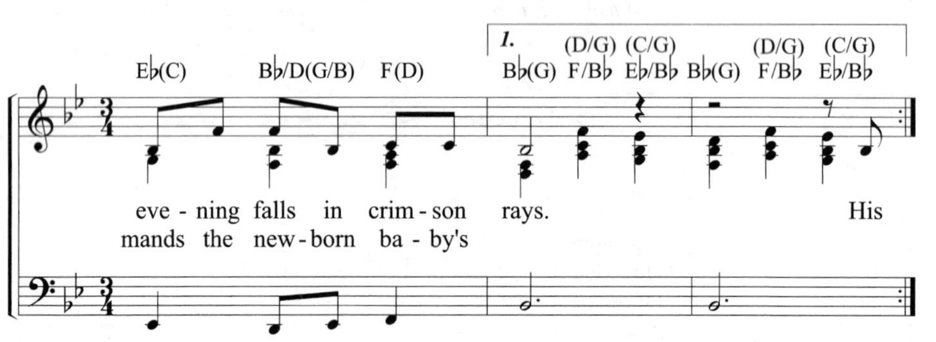

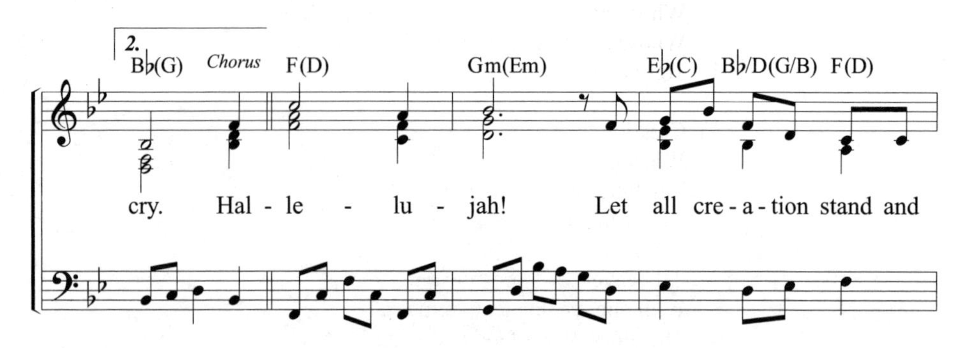

2. Creation gazed upon His face;
   The ageless One in time's embrace,
   Unveiled the Father's plan
   Of reconciling God and man.
   A second Adam walked the earth,
   Whose blameless life would break the curse,
   Whose death would set us free
   To live with Him eternally.

3. Creation longs for His return,
   When Christ shall reign upon the earth;
   The bitter wars that rage
   Are birth pains of a coming age.
   When He renews the land and sky,
   All heaven will sing and earth reply
   With one resplendent theme:
   The glory of our God and King!

2256.
Creator, sustainer
(Wonderful)
Ps 23:1; 27:4-5; 65:4; Jer 31:3; Lk 15:20; Jn 15:15; Gal 4:6; Col 1:16-17
Capo 4 (G)
With increasing intensity
Brenton Brown & Doug Bacon
B(G) Verse
F♯(D)
G♯m(Em)
1. Cre-at - or, sus-tain - er, our hearts were made
E(C)
B(G)
F♯(D)
for You. Our Ab - ba, our Fa - ther,
(v.2)
G♯m(Em)
E(C)
Bridge
F♯/A♯(D/F♯)
the home we're run - ning to. Drawn by Your
E(C)
F♯/A♯(D/F♯)
E(C)
F♯/A♯(D/F♯)
kind-ness, held by Your grace, Your ge-ne-rous
E(C)
G♯m(Em)
F♯(D)
(Fine)
E(C)
mer - cy in - spires songs of praise, yeah.

Chorus
B(G)
F♯(D)
Wonder-ful, wonder-ful, You're the one
beau-ti-ful, more than a -
G♯m(Em)
E(C)
(2°)
thing that we need. How we long
ny o - ther thing. We were born
B(G)
F♯(D)
G♯m(Em)
for Your house, for the heal - ing that it brings.
for Your courts, for the pre - sence of the King,
1.
D.C.(v.2)
2.
D.S.
3.
Esus2(C)
E(C)
E(C)
Beau-ti - ful yeah.
Mid section
B(G)
F♯(D)
1.-3.
G♯m(Em)
1.,3. You're all we need, Lord; Je - sus, our
2.,4,. You're all we need, Lord; Je - sus, no

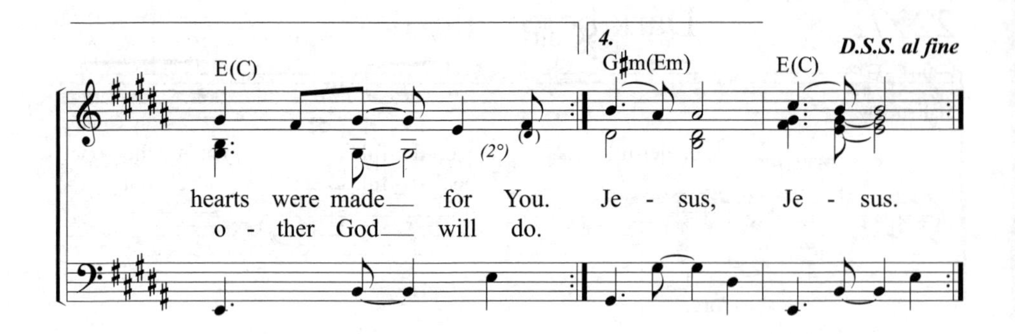

2. Protector, provider,
The God who calls us friend.
Our shepherd, our shelter,
We turn to You again.

2257.
Dark before the dawn
(His love)
Lam 3:23; Lk 22:42; Jn 18:11; 19:3, 30; Rom 8:21; 1 Cor 7:23; Gal 2:20; Col 1:14
Capo 3 (G)
Phil Barlow, Steve Barlow & Ray Goudie
Majestically
Verse
B♭(G) E♭/B♭(C/G) F/A(D/F♯) (C/G) E♭/B♭ B♭(G)
1. Dark be-fore the dawn, the Fa-ther's heart is bro - ken:
Gm7(Em) B♭/D(G/B) E♭(C) B♭/F(G/D) F(D)
watch - ing while His on - ly Son is beat-en shame-ful-ly.
B♭(G) E♭/B♭(C/G) F/A(D/F♯) E♭/B♭(C/G) B♭(G)
Here I stand a - mazed: He drank the cup of suf - fer-ing,
Gm7(Em) E♭(C) B♭/F(G/D) F(D)
lay - ing down His own life to die in a - go-ny.
B♭/D(G/B) E♭(C) B♭/F(G/D) Gm(Em)
What a great sur - ren - der, what a great sur - ren - der,

Chorus
B♭/D(G/B)
E♭(C)
Cm7(Am)
Fsus4(D)
F(D)
what a great_ sur-ren-der: He gave His life_ for me! His
B♭(G)
E♭(C)
B♭/D(G/B)
E♭(C)
love has more than con-quered, His love has paid for_
Fsus4(D)
F(D)
(B/D♯)
D/F♯
Gm(Em)
Gm/F(Em/D)
C/E(A/C♯)
_ me. The price that was de-mand-ed: oh, my_
1.,2.,4.
B♭/F(G/D)
Fsus4(D)
F(D)
B♭sus4(G)
B♭(G)
_ Sa-viour, why so_ much for me?
D.C.
Last time to Coda
3.
D.S. al Coda
E♭2(C)
E♭maj7(C)
B♭/F(G/D)
F(D)
B♭(G)
_ Sa-viour, why so much for me?_ His

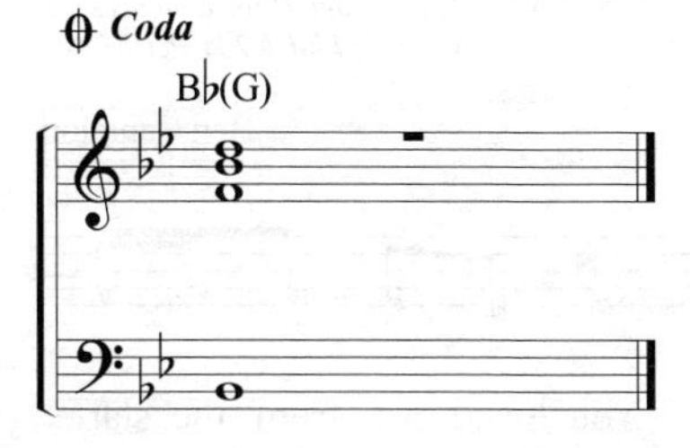

2. There upon the cross,
I see the plan unfolded.
Why the One so lovely
Was crucified for me.
Even through the pain,
He offered such forgiveness.
All He did was love us,
And how did we repay?
We are now forgiven,
We are now forgiven,
We are now forgiven,
And this is now our claim:

2258. Defender of this heart

(Remain)

Is 63:1; Jer 10:6; Lam 3:22-23; Mt 1:23; Phil 4:7; 1 Pet 1:24-25

Ben Cantelon

2.
A
Chorus
G
D/G
You are God with us, You're vic - tor -
A
D/G
G
D/G
- i - ous, You are strong and migh - ty to save.
A
G
D/G
For Your word stands true, there is none
A
D/G
G
D/G
like You, and when all else fades You re-main.
1.
2.
A
A
Em
You are God
G
D
A
D
2. When troubles come my way,
You guide and You sustain;
Lead me, I pray.
Forever You will be
The great eternal King,
Now and always.

2259. Deliverer, come set me free

Mt 21:21; Lk 4:18; 1 Cor 13:12; 15:52; 2 Cor 3:17; Rev 1:5

Vicky Beeching
& Sarah MacIntosh

D.C.(v.2)
2. A/C♯
(Fine)
2. You say the word there is heal - ing. Where the
Em7
Bm7
A
Spi - rit of the Lord is, there is free - dom. Where the
Em7
Bm7
A
Spi - rit of the Lord is, there is hope. Where the
Em7
Bm7
A
Spi - rit of the Lord is, there is heal - ing.
G
Mid section
And Your blood

2. You say the word and mountains are moved;
Oceans and stars stand in awe of You.
Just say the word, I will be changed.
We'll see Your face and we will not be the same.

2260. Desperate to see Your glory

(We see Your glory)

Ex 13:22; 2 Chron 7:1, 14; Hab 2:14; Mt 6:10

Capo 2 (D)

Ian Yates

Rock

Verse

Bm7 G

1. Des-p'rate to see Your glo - ry, we're
(2.) liv - ing for Your glo - ry, we're

(Guitar riff)

D Bm7

des-p'rate to see You move.
liv - ing to see You move.

(v.3)

Come and change this bro-

G D

3rd time to Coda 1 𝄌 **1.** **D.C.(v.2)**

- ken land, O God.

2. We're

2. D *Chorus* 𝄋 Bm7

We're des-p'rate to see Your glo -

G
D
- ry, we're des-p'rate to see You move, we're
Bm7
Last time to Coda 2
G
des-p'rate to see Your king - dom on the earth.
1.
2.
D.C.(v.3)
D
D
We're
3. We're
Coda 1
D
Bm7
Ne-ver to be the same, we long for the cloud,
G
D
we long for the fire, we're

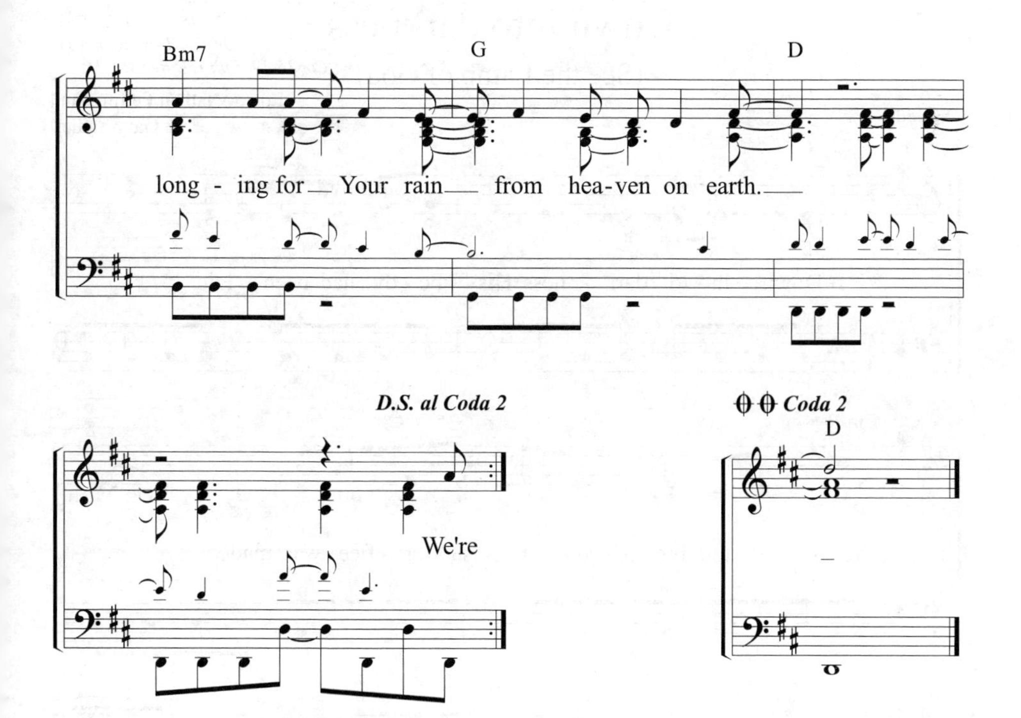

3. We're waiting for Your glory,
We know that day will come,
When the glory of
Our God will fall on us.

2261. Down into darkness
(See the Lamb of God)

Mt 27:46, 51, 60; Lk 1:33; Jn 1:3; 14:6; Rom 8:11; 1 Cor 15:19; Eph 1:7; Rev 4:8, 11; 5:6

Lou & Nathan Fellingham & Gary Sadler

G
Am
His reign will ne - ver end.
Hail Him King of love,
Em
C
Je - sus Christ the Lord,
the cham - pi - on of hearts
G
1.
Am
G/B
who lives for - e - ver more
where ev - 'ry - thing cries,
C
Em
G/B
'Ho - ly,
ho - ly,
ho - ly
is our God.'
Am
D.C.(v.3)
2.
Am
D.S.
See the Lamb of God

2. He who had come, as the truth, the life, the way,
Nailed to a cross, God-forsaken and betrayed;
But His blood spilled for all to redeem the world He made,
Jesus saves us now.

3. God shook the earth as His power was displayed,
Death put to death as Jesus Christ was raised.
God is alive and His Spirit lives in us,
Hallelujah!

If the Spirit of him who raised Jesus from the dead is living in you, he who raised Christ from the dead will also give life to your mortal bodies through his Spirit, who lives in you.

ROMANS 8:11

2262. Each morning when I rise

(Great is Your faithfulness)

Lam 3:22-23; Eph 5:20

Marc James

Strong 4

Verse

C D Em7 Gmaj7/B

1. Each morn-ing when I rise, through the dark-est night,

C D Em

great is Your faith-ful-ness. New

C D Em7 Gmaj7/B

mer-cy ev-'ry dawn, grace to the tired and worn,

C D Em *Chorus* C D

great is Your faith-ful-ness. Bring You glo-ry,

Em7 Gmaj7/B C D Em

glo-ry, great is Your faith-ful-ness. Bring You

Last time to Coda
C D Em7 Gmaj7/B C D
glo - ry, glo - ry, great is Your faith - ful - ness.
G
1.
C D Em7 Bm7 C D
G Em7
D.C.(v.2)
2.
Em
Mid section
C
In ev-'ry cir - cum - stance Your love
G D/F♯ Em
re-mains. So I will give
C
1.
G Bm7
You thanks and bring You praise.

2.
G
Bm7
C
D
You praise. I'll bring You praise.
Em7
Chorus 2
C
Glo - ry, glo - ry,
G
Dsus4 D
Em7
great is Your faith - ful - ness. Glo - ry,
D.S. al Coda
C
G
D/F♯
glo - ry, great is Your faith - ful - ness. Bring You
Coda
C
D
G
great is Your faith - ful - ness.

Verse
C
D
Em7
Gmaj7/B
C
D
2. As I lift my eyes, I come to re - a-lise You de - serve faith-ful - ness.
Em
C
D
Em7
Gmaj7/B
I of-fer You my praise, I'll live for You each day.
C
D
Em
You de - serve faith - ful - ness.

2263. Elohim, Creator God

(Blessing and honour)

Gen 1:1; 14:18-20; 16:13; 17:1; 21:33; 22:14; Judg 6:24; 1 Sam 1:3; 17:45; 2 Sam 6:2; Ps 9:2; 23:1; 24:10; 91:1; 93:2; Ezek 48:35; Mt 1:21, 23; Phil 2:9; Rev 7:12

With quiet devotion

2. Jehovah Jireh, God provides,
   Sabaoth, the Lord of Hosts on high.
   Shepherd God, Jehovah Raah,
   Ever near, the Lord Shammah.

3. Adonai, my Master leads,
   El Roi, who watches over me.
   Lord Shalom, the God of peace,
   Immanuel, here with me.

2264. Empires fall, but You're still standing

(Higher)

Ps 62:5-6; 90:2; Mt 6:33; 13:44; Jn 1:2; 10:28; Acts 26:13; Rom 8:38; Phil 2:10; Rev 22:13

Brenton Brown

1.
A
B
E
that re-mains.
D.C.(v.2)
2.,3.
A
E
A
2. You're the
The be-gin-
C♯m
A
E
ning and the end - ing, e-ver-last - ing, ne-ver end-
B
C♯m
A
B
- ing, Je-sus, we're held in Your hands.
Last time to Coda
Mid section
E/G♯
A
E/B
You are the for - tress that will not be
You are our rock, You're the hope of this

1.
A
E/G♯
B
sha - ken. You are the strength of our hearts.
na - tion,
2.
D.S. al Coda
and we will trust in You, God. You are high -
Coda
C♯m
E
Je - sus, we're held in Your hands, (we're)
held in Your hands, (we're) held in Your hands.
(2° Fine)

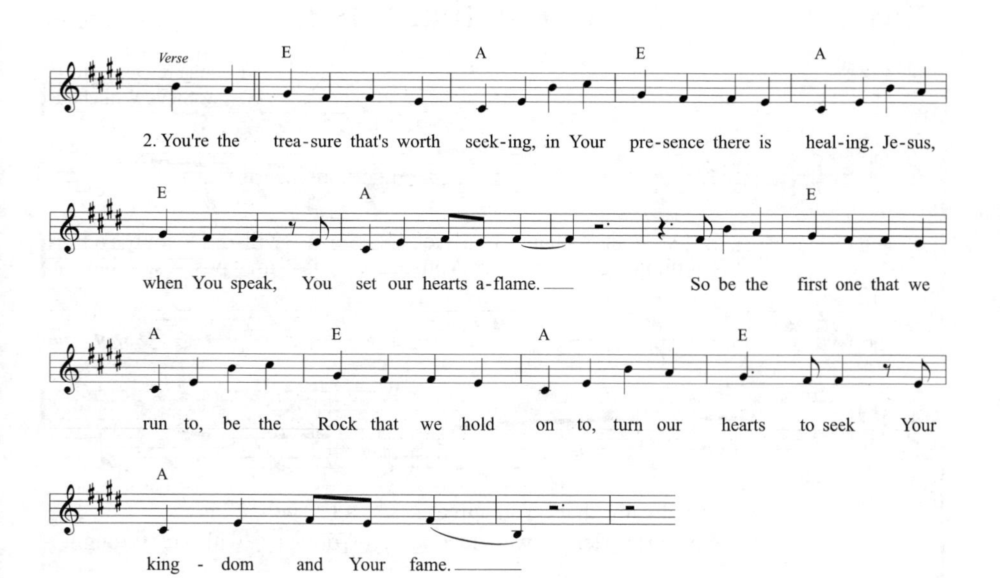
Verse
E A E A
2. You're the trea-sure that's worth seek-ing, in Your pre-sence there is heal-ing. Je-sus,
E A E
when You speak, You set our hearts a-flame. So be the first one that we
A E A E
run to, be the Rock that we hold on to, turn our hearts to seek Your
A
king - dom and Your fame.

2265. Every day that I live

Ps 118:14; Lk 1:37

Light pop feel

Belinda & Doug Horley
& Steve Whitehouse

Verse

E B C♯m7 A E B A A A B C♯m7 F♯m

1. E - v'ry day that I live I will ho - nour You,
e - v'ry dream that You give I will cling to;
e - v'ry day I will try to make You smile.

Nothing e - ver for You is im - pos - si - ble:
all the prob - lems we face You are with us through;
not one ounce of Your love will You hold back.

Chorus

You are my God; how I love You. You are my friend; how I need You.
King; how I trust You. You are my life, lost with - out You.
You are my

2. Every hurt, every pain,
I will give to You,
In my sunshine and rain,
I will worship You;
I will hold nothing back from You, my King.
All my doubts and my fears
Are much smaller now;
I don't face them alone –
I won't be that proud.
In the light of Your smile
My spirit soars.

2266.
Every joy, every smile
1 Cor 1:9; Tit 3:4; Jas 1:17
Capo 2 (D)
(Thankful)
David Lyon
Rhythmically
Verse
E(D)
B/D♯(A/C♯)
Asus2(G)
1. Ev'-ry joy, ev-'ry smile, ev-'ry dream, ev-'ry
see, all we know, all we have, all we
C♯m7(Bm7)
E(D)
B(A)
Asus2(G)
child;
hold;
ev-'ry-thing is a gift from You.
1.
2.
Chorus
C♯m(Bm)
A(G) E(D)
All we
We are thank-ful, we are
B(A)
C♯m(Bm)
A(G) E(D)
thank-ful to You, our Fa-ther: You are faith-ful in
1.,3.,5.
B(A)
E(D)
B/D♯(A/C♯)
A(G)
E(D)
all that You do.

2. Every star, every sky,
Every breath, every life;
Everything is a gift from You.
All we see, all we know,
All we have, all we hold;
Everything is a gift from You.

2267. Everything I am

(Lay it down)

Mt 13:46; 16:25

Brenton Brown
& Matt Maher

Gradually building

(melody on rpt)
4.
Mid section
Am7
G
Fmaj7
F6
Fmaj7
F6
O pearl of great - est price,
no act of sa-
C2/E
C/E
C2/E
C/E
Dm9
Dm
- cri - fice
could match the gift of life
G/D
C
C6
Cmaj7
I find with-in Your gaze.
Oh, what a sweet
Fmaj7
F6
Fmaj7
F6
C2/E
C/E
ex - change,
I die to rise a - gain:

C2/E C/E Dm9 Dm G/D
lift-ed up from the grave in-to Your hands of grace.
1. C C6 Cmaj7
2. Am7 C2/E Fsus2
O pearl of great -
Chorus
C F
I lay it down, I lay it down, I lay it down
Am7 G C
at Your feet. I lay it down, I lay it down,

F
Am7
G
C
I lay it down at Your feet. I lay it down,
C/E
F
Am7
G
I lay it down, I lay it down at Your feet.
C
I lay it down, lay it down, lay it down

Am7
G
C
at Your feet.

2268. Exalted, He is exalted

(Yahweh)

Phil 2:9; Rev 5:12; 7:12

Capo 1 (A)

Chris Tomlin
& Jesse Reeves

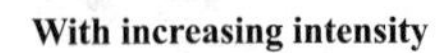

With increasing intensity

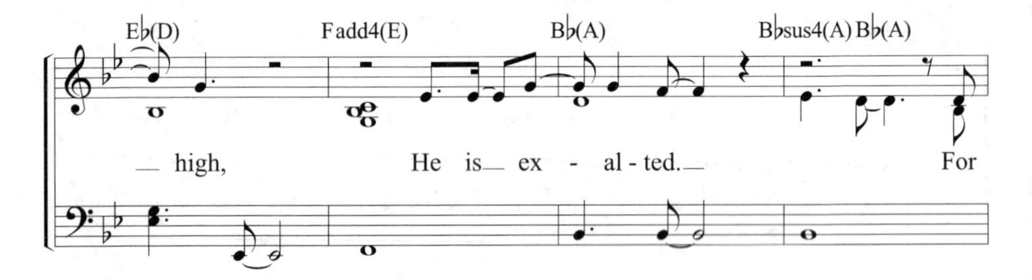

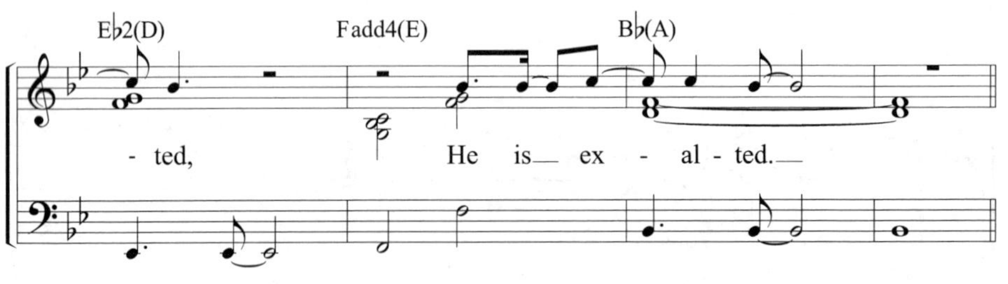

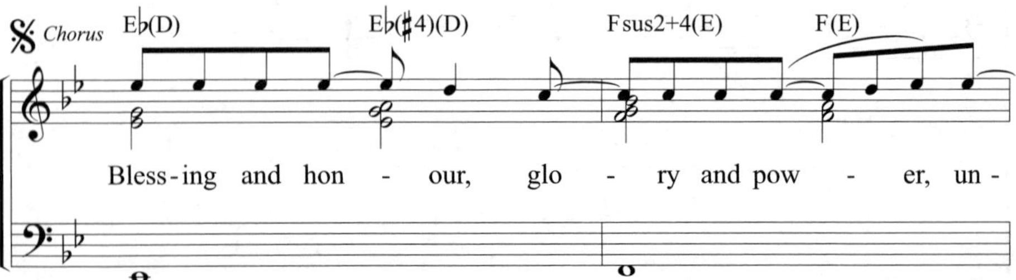

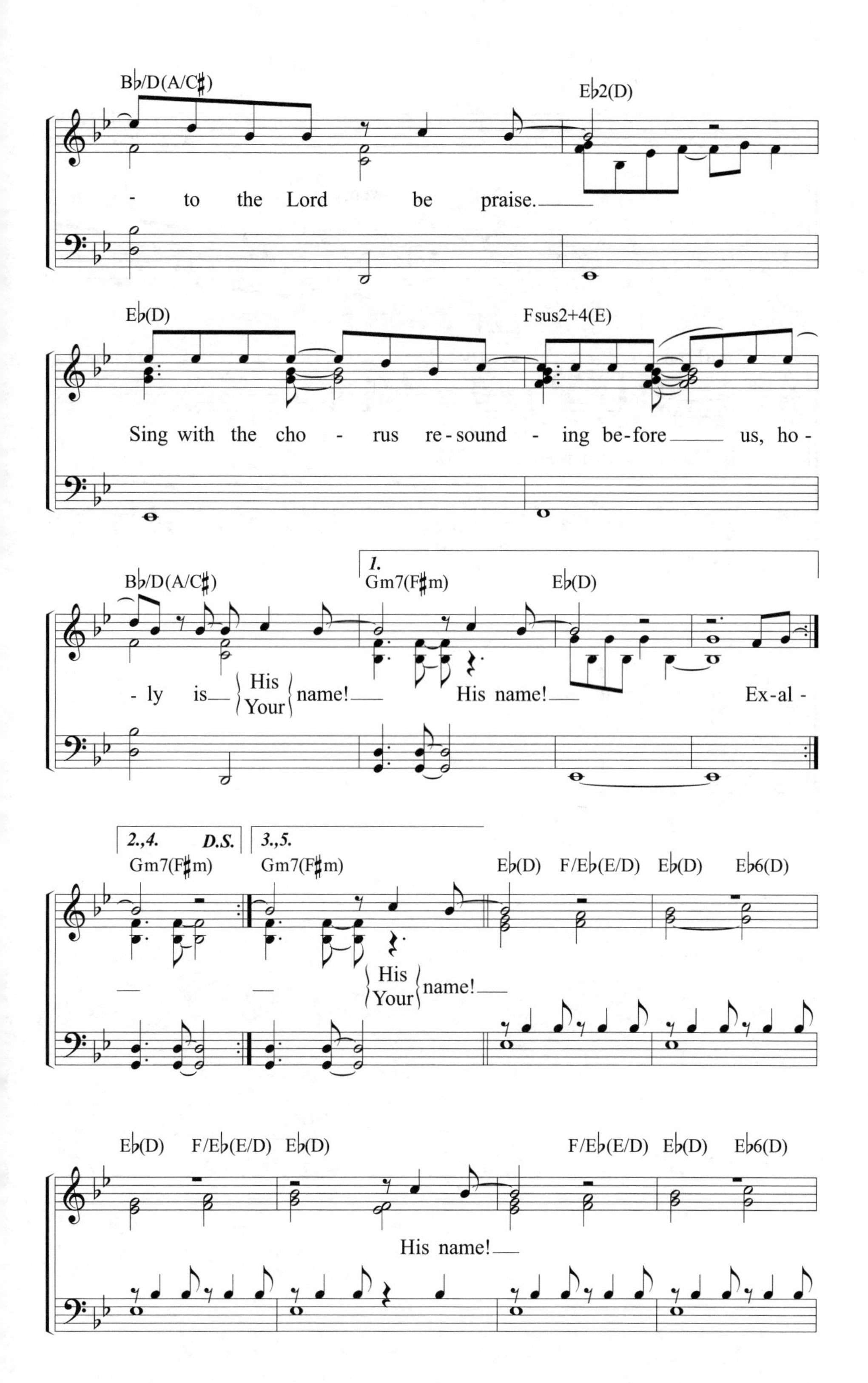

B♭/D(A/C♯)
E♭2(D)
- to the Lord be praise.
E♭(D)
Fsus2+4(E)
Sing with the cho - rus re-sound - ing be-fore us, ho -
B♭/D(A/C♯)
1.
Gm7(F♯m)
E♭(D)
- ly is His Your name!
His name!
Ex-al -
2.,4.
D.S.
3.,5.
Gm7(F♯m)
Gm7(F♯m)
E♭(D)
F/E♭(E/D)
E♭(D)
E♭6(D)
His Your name!
E♭(D)
F/E♭(E/D)
E♭(D)
F/E♭(E/D)
E♭(D)
E♭6(D)
His name!

E♭(D)
F/E♭(E/D)
E♭(D)
Mid section
B♭(A)
Fadd4(E)
Yah - weh, holy
Gm7(F♯m)
1.,2.,3.
E♭2(D)
4.
E♭2(D)
1st time D.S.
is Your name! Yah -
To end
E♭2(D)

Therefore God exalted him to the highest place and gave him the name that is above every name, that at the name of Jesus every knee should bow, in heaven and on earth and under the earth, and every tongue confess that Jesus Christ is Lord, to the glory of God the Father.

PHILIPPIANS 2:9-11

2269. Fairest Lord Jesus

Lk 22:69; Jn 20:31; Heb 1:3-4; Rev 15:3

SCHÖNSTER HERR JESU

Music: Silesian folk song
Arr. Paul Hughes

Gradually building

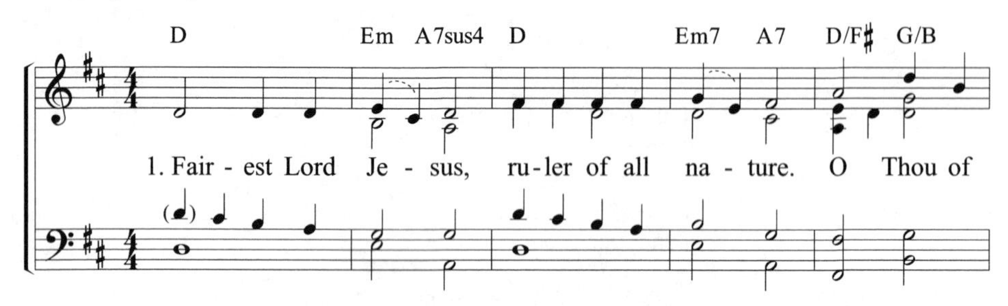

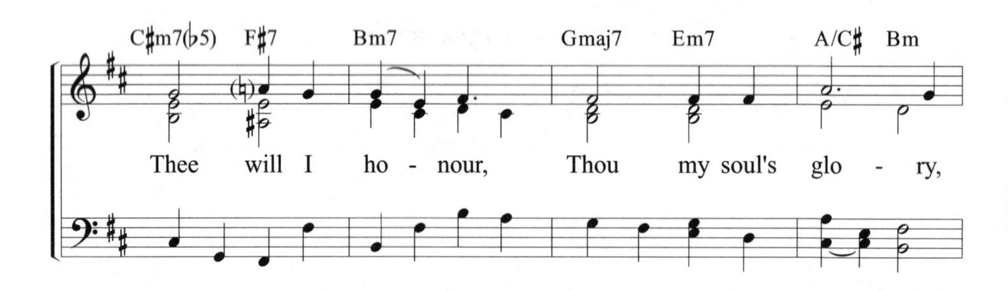

2. Fair are the meadows,
Fairer still the woodlands,
Robed in the blooming garb of spring;
Jesus is fairer,
Jesus is purer,
Who makes the woeful heart to sing.

3. Fair is the sunshine,
Fairer still the moonlight,
And all the twinkling starry host;
Jesus shines brighter,
Jesus shines purer,
Than all the angels heaven can boast.

4. All fairest beauty,
Heavenly and earthly,
Wondrously, Jesus, is found in Thee;
None can be nearer,
Fairer or dearer,
Than Thou, my Saviour, art to me.

5. Beautiful Saviour!
Lord of all the nations!
Son of God and Son of man!
Glory and honour,
Praise, adoration,
Now and forever more be Thine.

From the German (17th century)
Lilian Stevenson (1870-1960)

2270. Faith as small as a mustard seed

Mt 17:20

Doug Horley

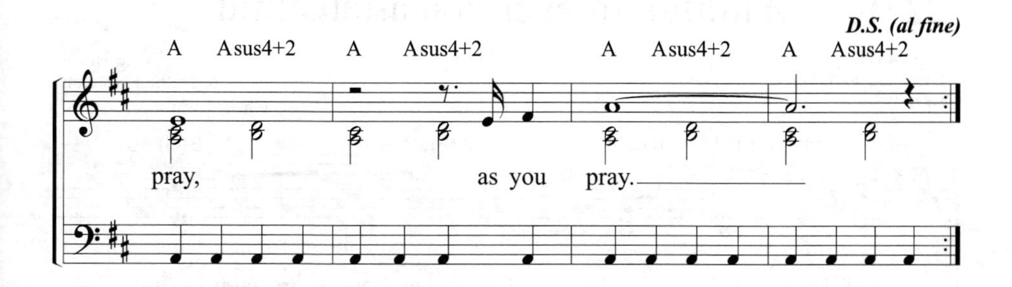
D.S. (al fine)
A Asus4+2 A Asus4+2 A Asus4+2 A Asus4+2
pray, as you pray.

2271. Faithful, forever You are faithful

Ps 23:4; 68:5; 72:4; 1 Cor 1:9; Col 1:17; Rev 7:15; 19:11

A(F)
B(G)
E(C)
sing to the Ma-ker of hea-ven and earth, God, You
A(F)
B(G)
E(C)
reign for-e-ver and Your love will en-dure.
A(F)
C♯m(Am) C♯m/B(Am/G) A(F)
Faith-ful and true is the name of the Lord;
Last time to Coda
1.
F♯m7+4(Dm)
B(G)
C♯m(Am) C♯m/B(Am/G) A(F)
You are faith-ful, God.
D.C.(v.3)
2.
F♯m7+4(Dm)
E(C)
Esus4(C)

Descant
You are there in ev - 'ry
E(C)
Mid section
B(G)
E(C)
You are there
sea - son of my soul. You are there,
E/G♯(C/E)
A(F)
E/G♯(C/E)
B(G)
in ev - 'ry sea - son. You are
You're the an-chor that will hold. You are there
E(C)
E/G♯(C/E)
A(F)
E/G♯(C/E)
B(G)
there, You're the an - chor. You are
1.
in the val - ley of the sha - dows; You are
C♯m(Am)
B(G)
A(F)
F♯m7+4(Dm)
there in the val - ley of the sha - dows; You are

2. Faithful, forever You are faithful,
   Lover of the wounded heart,
   You defend the poor and the forgotten;
   You are faithful, God.

3. Faithful, forever You are faithful,
   Shelter for the fragile soul,
   You lift us up, You hold us all together;
   You are faithful, God.

2272.
Father above
1 Chron 29:11; Mt 6:9-13
Capo 4 (G)
Marc James
& Nick Herbert
Steadily
Verse
B(G) G♯m7(Em)
1. Fa-ther a-bove, to You we pray,
B/D♯(G/B) E(C) B(G)
ho-ly is Your al-migh-ty name. Give us to-day
G♯m7(Em) B/D♯(G/B)
all that we need, and may our lives
(v.2)
E(C) F♯(D)
re-flect Your grace.
Bridge
Lord, let Your king-
G♯m7(Em) B/D♯(G/B) E(C) F♯(D)
-dom come on earth as

Chorus
E/G♯(C/E)
F♯/A♯(D/F♯)
B(G)
in heaven.
Yours is the kingdom,
F♯(D)
G♯m(Em)
B/F♯(G/D)
the pow'r and the glory
forever and ever.
E(C)
B/D♯(G/B)
B(G)
We lift You higher.
Yours is the kingdom,
F♯(D)
G♯m(Em)
B/F♯(G/D)
the pow'r and the glory
forever and ever.
1.,5.
Last time to Coda
D.C.(v.2)
E(C)
B/D♯(G/B)
C♯(A)
E(C)
We lift You higher,
Father above.

2.,4.
D.S. (al Coda)
3.
E(C)
B/D♯(G/B)
We lift You high-er.
We lift You high-er,
C♯(A)
E(C)
Fa-ther a-bove.
Mid section
(1° & 2° 8vb, opt.)
F♯(D)
Lord, let Your will
G♯m(Em)
B/D♯(G/B)
1.-3.
E(C)
be done.
4.
E(C)
F♯(D)
on
E/G♯(C/E)
F♯/A♯(D/F♯)
B(G)
E(C)
earth. Hal-lo-wed be Your name, hal-lo-wed be
B/D♯(G/B)
E(C)
B(G)
Your name, hal-lo-wed be Your name,

2. Father above, forgive us our wrongs,
As we forgive those who wrong us.
Lead us today in the path that is straight,
And from all evil deliver us.

2273. Father of everlasting grace

(My soul is complete)

Ps 134:2; Mal 3:6; Mt 11:28; Jn 1:14; 8:36; 2 Cor 1:3; Heb 10:20

Gradually building

Phil Shaw

Chorus
D
A
E/G♯
A/C♯
My soul is com-plete in Je - sus, in
D
E
F♯m
E/G♯
Je - sus. Your grace and Your truth have
Last time to Coda
1.
D
A
made a way, and now I'm free in You.
D.C.(v.3)
2.
Dsus2
A
Dsus2
D
now I'm free in You,
A
F♯m
Mid section
I'm free in You.
With hands held high,

2. Faithful Lord, You never change;
When all is lost, You remain.
Saviour, all my hope is found in You,
In You.

3. King of glory, be lifted high;
I'll worship You with my whole life.
Fill my heart with a joy that's found in You,
In You.

Lift up your hands in the sanctuary and praise the LORD.

PSALM 134:2

2274. Father of life

(We cry out)

Ex 6:3; Rom 10:13

Steadily

Walker Beach

2. Father of love, never failing to forgive,
Each moment is a gift from You to live.
We're only here to tell the world about Your grace
Until the day You take us all away.

2.
Chorus
Esus4 E A E/G♯
We will cry out Your name, El Shad-
ly on Your grace, A - do -
Bm F♯m D
dai, God of grace, Lord Most
nai, crowned in praise, Lord Most
1.,3.
A/C♯ Esus4 E
High, Je-sus Christ. We re -
2.,4.
Esus4 E A A/D
High, Je - sus Christ.
1° D.C.(v.2)
F♯m Esus4 E A

2275. Father of the strong embrace

(Back to You)

Is 54:10; Lk 15:20; Jn 9:25; 2 Tim 2:13

Kees Kraayenoord,
Arend Jansen & Henk Pool

Moderately, with a strong beat

(2°)
D
A
G
blind, now I see; once in pri - son, now I'm free.
light, shine on me, let Your mer - cy co - ver me.
D/F♯
Your love takes me, Your love makes
G
A
1.
me run back to You.
God of
2.
(Small notes 2°)
D
A
Back to You,
(Your arms are o - pen, I'm gon-na
G
D
make me run back to You.
run back to You.)
(Your arms are

2. Father of this wandering heart,
I cannot understand
The greatness of this love,
'Cause every time I fall away
Your faithfulness remains.
So how can I walk off
And keep on running from Your heart?

Though the mountains be shaken and the hills be removed, yet my unfailing love for you will not be shaken nor my covenant of peace be removed, says the LORD, who has compassion on you.

ISAIAH 54:10

2276. Father, You are holy

Is 45:18; Mk 10:45; Jn 1:14; 14:17

Geraldine Latty
& Mike Pears

2. Jesus, You are perfect,
   Absolutely perfect;
   Nothing in this world compares with You:
   How You came and lived here with us,
   Gave Yourself to serve us,
   And I know that You forgive me too.

3. Spirit, You are with us,
   Absolutely with us;
   Nothing in this world compares with You.
   How You breathe Your life into us.
   Challenge us, yet hold us,
   And I know Your power makes me new.

4. Father, Spirit, Jesus,
   Beautiful in holiness,
   Nothing in this world compares with You.
   So we bend our will towards You,
   Open our hearts to You,
   As You send us out to live for You.

2277. Find me in the river

Martin Smith

D
D/F♯
G2
and bought our pre-tty crowns,
A
D
Dsus4
D
Dsus2
Chorus
but ne-ver paid the price.
Find
G2
G
D2/F♯
me in the ri-ver, find me there, find
G2
G
D
Asus4
me on my knees with my soul laid bare. E-
G2
G
D/F♯
Asus4
ven though You're gone and I'm cracked and dry, find

2. Find me in the river,
Find me on my knees.
I've walked against the water,
Now I'm waiting, if You please.
We didn't count on suffering,
We didn't count on pain,
But if the blessing's in the valley,
Then in the river I will wait.

2278.
Fire by night
(We will not go)
Ex 3:14; 13:22; Num 9:22; Ps 46:10
Capo 1 (D)
John Hartley, Kelly Minter,
Stephen Leiweke & Henk Pool
With a strong beat
Verse
E♭(D) B♭(A) Cm(Bm)
1. Fire by night, cloud by day, our God will
De - sert sand or pro - mised land, our God will
A♭(G)
lead the way.
lead the way.
Bridge
Fm7(Em)
For - e - ver we
B♭(A) Fm7(Em) E♭/G(D/F♯)
will fol - low, no mat - ter what to - mor - row holds.
A♭(G)
Chorus
E♭(D)
We will not go, we will not move,
B♭/D(A/C♯) Cm(Bm)
we will not walk with - out Your pre -

A♭(G) E♭/G(D/F♯) Fm7(Em) B♭(A) E♭(D)
- sence, we will wait for You. The great I Am,
B♭/D(A/C♯)
Al - migh - ty God, we are des -
Cm(Bm) A♭(G) E♭/G(D/F♯)
- p'rate for Your pre - sence; with - out You
Last time to Coda
1.
Fm(Em) B♭(A) E♭/G(D/F♯) A♭(G)
we will not go.
Cm(Bm) B♭(A)
2.
E♭(D)

2. Troubled soul, when darkness comes
Our God will lead the way.
Joyful heart, when blessings flow
Our God will lead the way.

2279. For every song

(You are)

Ex 3:14; Jn 8:58; Heb 10:12; Jas 1:17

Capo 3 (G)

Ben Cantelon, Nick Herbert & Tim Hughes

Cm7(Am) Gm7(Em) E♭(C)
- 'ry-thing, You are the e-ter - nal King. Je - sus,
B♭(G) Cm7(Am) Gm7(Em)
Last time to Coda
You're the song we sing; You are, You are, You are.
E♭(C)
1. D.C.(v.2)
2. Mid section
E♭(C)
2. For Your You will al - ways be, You will
F(D) Gm7(Em)
al - ways be, You will al - ways be the great I Am.
1. Fadd4(D)
2. Fadd4(D)
D.S. al Coda
You will You are
Coda
B♭(G)
2. For Your word, full of grace,
For all the steadfast promises You make.
For the cross, for new life,
For the beauty of Your sacrifice.

2280.
Forgiveness comes to me
(All I want)
Jn 10:15; 1 Pet 2:24; 1 Jn 3:1
Capo 1 (G)
Brenton Brown
Moderately
A♭(G) Verse
A♭2/C(G/B)
1. For-give-ness comes to me, though I do not de-serve
Fm7(Em)
D♭2(C)
it; I bare-ly speak the words and You draw near a-gain.
A♭(G)
A♭2/C(G/B)
It's so hard to be-lieve that I am real-ly worth
Fm7(Em)
D♭2(C)
it, that You laid down Your life to car-ry all my sin.
E♭(D) Bridge
What kind of love is this? What kind of love is this,

D♭2(C)
Chorus
that we are called the child-ren of God? All I've got,
A♭(G)
A♭2/C(G/B)
all I want is in You, it's in You. Like the air
Fm7(Em)
D♭(C)
in my lungs, I will breathe You in. All I want,
A♭(G)
A♭2/C(G/B)
all I need is Your grace and Your truth. Fill me up,
Fm7(Em)
1.,4.
D♭(C)
A♭(G)
fill me up, let me sing a - gain, yeah.

2. Father, without Your flame
My life is lived in darkness;
I know I need You now,
I'm reaching for Your hand.
Without Your mercy, Lord,
There'd be no second chances,
But You reach for Your child
And lift me up again.

2281.
For God loved the world so much
(Good news)
Capo 5 (G)
Rock feel
Is 53:5; Lk 2:10, 14; Jn 3:16-17; 1 Cor 15:58; 2 Cor 5:21
Brenton Brown
Verse
C(G)
B♭(F)
F(C)
Csus4(G)
C(G)
B♭(♯4)(F)
G(D)
Dm7(Am)
Chorus
(v.2, 1°)
(v.2, 2°)
1.
2.
1. For God loved the world so much that He gave His only Son, that whoever would believe in Him
would not perish but be saved. Oh, how surprising is His grace; the invitation is for ev'ry-one.
For ev'ry-one, for ev'ry-one, yeah.
This is the good news, it's

Am7(Em)
G(D)
a hope that is true. Lord, we sing 'cause we've found peace
F(C)
1° D.C. (v.2)
C(G)
on earth. And death can - not shake us,
Am7(Em)
G(D)
our sins have been tak - en. A-live, we're a-live, and we'll sing
F(C)
Last time to Coda
Mid section
C(G)
Your worth. Take these words and
Am7(Em)
make them loud - er, take these words and make them loud - er,

2. Jesus did not come to condemn
But that we might live again;
His holy mission was to rescue us.
For long before we cried for help,
He took our sins upon Himself;
He took our shame and gave us righteousness.
His righteousness, we are His righteousness.

2282. Forth in Your name, O Lord

(Be glorified in me)

Ps 16:8; 139:16; Mt 11:30; 13:22; 25:13; 26:41; 28:19; Rom 12:2; 1 Cor 2:2; 2 Cor 4:18; Col 3:3, 17; 2 Tim 4:7; 2 Pet 3:12

Capo 4 (C)

Words: Charles Wesley (1707–88)
Adpt. Graham Kendrick
Music: Graham Kendrick

Moderately

E/B(C/G) B(G)
2.
A(F)
E/B(C/G) B(G)
Lord. will. In Your name I go.
Chorus
A2/C♯(F/A)
B/D♯(G/B) E(C) F♯m7(Dm7)
Be glo-ri-fied in me, be glo-ri-fied in me.
1. D.C.(v.2)
2.,3.
Bsus4(G) B(G) Bsus4(G) B(G)
A2/C♯(F/A)
B/D♯(G/B) E(C)
Je-sus, be glo-ri-fied in me,
F♯m7(Dm7)
1. D.C.(v.3)
2.
Mid section
Bsus4(G) B(G) Bsus4 (G) B(G)
be glo-ri-fied in me. In all I do,
1.-3.
A2/C♯(F/A)
B/D♯(G/B) E(C) F♯m7(Dm7)
in all I say, Je-sus, be glo - ri-fied in me.

2. Preserve me from my calling's snare,
   And hide my simple heart above;
   Above the thorns of choking care,
   The gilded baits of worldly love.
   In Your name I go, Lord.
   You may I set at my right hand,
   Whose eyes my inmost being know,
   And labour on at Your command,
   And offer all my works to You.
   In Your name I go.

3. Give me to bear Your burden light,
   And every moment watch and pray,
   And things eternal keep in sight,
   And hasten to Your glorious day.
   In Your name I go, Lord.
   For You delightfully employ
   Whatever bounteous grace has given;
   And run my course with steady joy,
   And closely walk with You to heaven.
   In Your name I go.

Whatever you do, whether in word or deed, do it all in the name of the Lord Jesus, giving thanks to God the Father through him.

COLOSSIANS 3:17

2283. Freedom is coming

(Freedom)

Mt 6:34; Jn 8:36; Rom 6:14; 8:2; 1 Cor 7:23; 2 Cor 1:3; 1 Pet 5:7

Johnny Parks
& Claire Hamilton

Joyfully

Verse G

1. Free - dom is com - ing, free - dom is here;
Join in the an - them, join in the song;

D

shake off your wor - ries, lay down your fears.
dance in the free - dom of vic - to - ry won.

C

No more sad - ness, there is joy.
Bring your bur - dens, bring your fears,

1. Em

No more an - guish, there is peace.

2. D Em/D D Em/D D G/D D

bring them in - to glo - rious free - dom!

2. Once we were captive, now we are free,
Shame cannot grip us, we've been redeemed.
Hope is His message, hope in our hearts:
The King of our freedom has paid the great cost.
No more sorrow – there is comfort.
No more heartache – there is healing.
Bring your burdens, bring your fears,
Bring them into glorious freedom!

2284. From the rising of the sun

Ps 113:3; Is 53:4-5; Joel 2:23; Jn 3:16; 12:32; 14:6; Acts 2:47; 4:12; Phil 2:9-10; 1 Pet 2:9

Steady rock style

Nathan Fellingham

2. There's a people You have called
And You're drawing them to come.
This Your church is growing day by day.
Only one way You have made,
It's through Jesus, God the Son,
Sent to carry all our sin and shame.
Heaven, rain down;
Shower righteousness and grace.

2285. From the thankful heart

(We still believe)

Mk 9:24

Capo 1 (G)

Kathryn Scott

Steadily

D♭2(C)
A♭(G)
we still be-lieve, we're still sur-ren-
E♭(D)
der-ing our hearts; Your faith-ful-ness
Fm7(Em)
D♭2(C)
is our re-ward. We still be-lieve, we still be-lieve,
A♭(G)
E♭(D)
and though the jour-ney has been hard, we will con-fess
Last time to Coda
1.
Fm7(Em)
D♭2(C)
A♭(G) A♭/C D♭maj7(C)
(G/B)
Your good-ness, God. We still be-lieve.

2. From the reborn hope to the weary soul,
From the quest for truth to those who see,
From the soaring wings to the shattered dream,
From the broken to those who have been healed,
We cry out as one:

2286. Give Him all the praise

(Praise Him)

Ps 48:1; 149:1, 3, 6; 150:6

Capo 3 (G)

Miriam & Simeon Webster

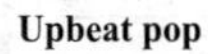

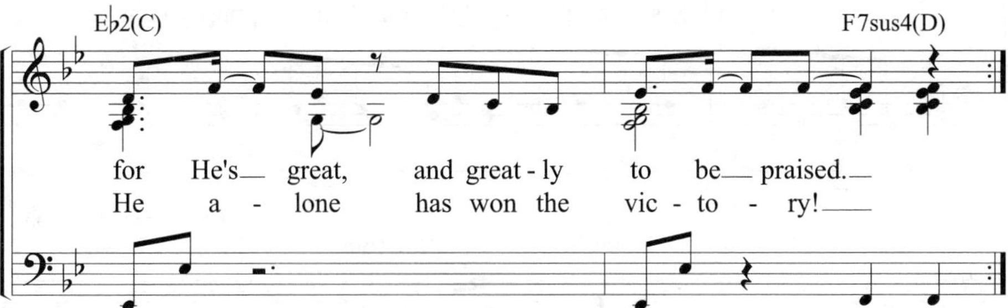

B♭(G)
E♭2(C)
praise Him for His lov - ing kind - ness, for His ten - der mer -
Gm7(Em)
E♭(C)
F7sus4(D)
1.,3.
B♭(G)
Dm7(Bm)
- cies, for all His migh - ty won - ders, praise Him,
D.C.
Last time to Coda
E♭2(C)
F7sus4(D)
B♭(G)
Dm7(Bm)
E♭2(C)
F7sus4(D)
praise Him.
2.
Gm7(Em)
E♭2(C)
B♭(G)
F(D)
(Praise Him.)
Mid section
E♭(C)
Shout to God with a voice of tri - umph,

B♭(G)
Fsus4(D)
F(D)
shout to God, let His praise be in our mouth.
Cm(Am)
Shout to God with a voice of tri - umph,
B♭(G)
Fsus4(D)
F(D)
D.S. al Coda (inc. rpt)
shout to God, let His praise be in our mouth.
Coda
B♭(G)
Praise Him.

2287.

Give me a heart of love

(Lend me Your heart)

Ezek 36:26; Mt 9:36; Lk 4:18

Claire Hamilton

Medium pace

2. Give me a heart of love
That reaches past appearance;
Lend me the heart of Christ
That serves the least with justice.

3. Give me a heart of love
That's emptied of its hardness;
Lend me the heart of Christ
That stirs compassion in the proud.

4. Give me a heart of love
That longs to aid the humble;
Lend me the heart of Christ
That yearns to free the captive soul.

2288. Give me eyes to see
(The greatness of our God)

1 Kings 8:27; Ps 8:1; Rom 8:38-39

Jason Ingram, Stuart Garrard & Reuben Morgan

Capo 2 (D)

Quite slow, worshipfully

Verse

A(G) E(D) B(A)

1. Give me eyes to see more of who You are, may what I

A(G) E(D) B(A)

be-hold still my anx - ious heart. Take what I

A(G) E(D) B(A)

have known and break it all a-part; You, my God,

A(G) B(A) *Chorus* A(G) E(D)

are great-er still. And no sky con-tains, no

Bsus4(A) B(A) A(G) E(D)
God. I spend my life to know, and I'm
B/D♯(A/C♯) C♯m(Bm) A(G)
Last time to Coda
far from close to all You are; the great-ness of our
1.
Bsus4(A) B(A) A(G) B(A) A(G) B(A)
God. 2. Give me grace
2.,4. D.S. (Chorus 1)
3.
Bsus4(A) B(A) B(A) A(G) B(A) A(G)
God. And no God.
B(A) Mid section A(G) E(D)
And there is no - thing that could e-ver se - pa-rate

B(A)
A(G)
E(D)
— us, — there is no - thing that could e - ver se - pa - rate —
B(A)
C♯m(Bm)
A(G)
E(D)
— us from Your — love. No life, no death, of
B/D♯(A/C♯)
C♯m(Bm)
A(G)
this I am — con - vinced: — You — my God, — are great - er — still. —
1.
2.
D.S. (Chorus 2)
B(A)
B(A)
And there is no - —
And no
Coda
Bsus4(A)
B(A)
A(G)
— God. To all — You are; — the great - ness of our

(Chorus 2)

And no words could say.
Or song convey all You are;
The greatness of our God.
I spend my life to know,
And I'm far from close to all You are;
The greatness of our God.

2289. Glorious, incredible

(You are great)

1 Kings 8:27; Ps 145:3

Ken Riley
& Andrew Neve

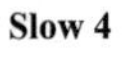

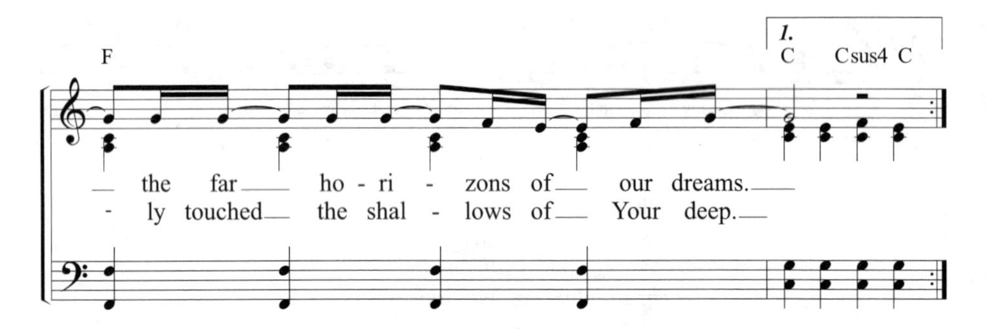

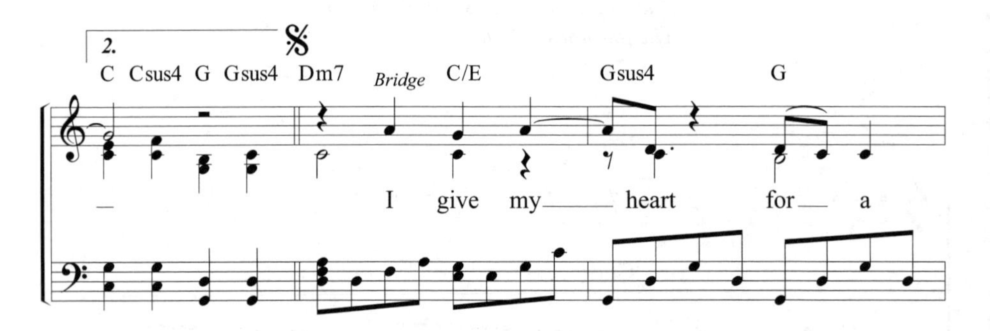

Chorus
Dm7 C/E Gsus4 G C
mo - ment with my God. You are great, You are
G F
great; all - suf - fi - cient, pow - er - ful,
Dm7 Gsus4 G C
Fa - ther, Son and Spi - rit, You are great, so
G/B Dm7
great! God who needs no o - ther, yet You

(3°)
gave Your Son to save us. You are
3rd time D.S.S. al Coda
Last time to Coda
1.
F Gsus4 G C Csus4 G Gsus4
long to share e - ter - ni - ty with us.
D.C.
2.
F C G F Am G Gsus4
us.
F Am G Gsus4 F6 Dm7 C/E
I give my
D.S.
Coda
Gsus4 G Dm7 C/E Gsus4 G C
heart for a mo - ment with my God.
us.

Great is the LORD and most worthy of praise; his greatness no-one can fathom.

PSALM 145:3

2290. Glory and honour and thanks to You

Rev 4:9-11

(Forever worthy)

Aaron Keyes
& Andy Lehman

Moderate pace

2. Seated on Your throne You reign;
   You live forever and ever.
   We cast crowns in ceaseless praise;
   You live forever and ever.

2291.
God, be in my head
(God, be in everything)
Rom 12:1-2; Col 3:17
Capo 3 (D)
Prayerfully
Kees Kraayenoord,
Chris Eaton & Henk Pool
Verse
F(D) Dm(Bm) (A/G) (G) C/B♭ B♭ F/A(D/F♯) C(A)
1. God, be in my head and in my un-der - stand -
F(D) (A/C♯) C/E Dm(Bm) (A/G) (G) C/B♭ B♭ F/A(D/F♯)
ing; God, be in my eyes and in my
Csus4(A) C(A) 1. F(D) D.C.(v.2) 2.,3. F(D)
look - ing. ing.
Chorus B♭(G) (F♯m) (Bm) Am Dm C(A) Gm(Em) Dm(Bm) (A/C♯) C/E F(D)
God, be in ev - 'ry-thing, ev - 'ry-thing,

2. God, be in my mouth and in my speaking;
God, be in my heart and in my thinking.

3. God, be in my voice and in my confessing;
God, be in my hands and in my embracing.

2292. God, be in my head

Rom 12:1-2; Col 3:17; Rev 22:13

New words & music:
Jared Anderson & Sidney Lytlington
Original words taken from the *Book of Hours*, 1514,
In English in the *Sarem Primer*, 1558

Chorus
C
Am7
God, be in my head,
God, be in my eyes,
F2
Dm7
G
God, be in my heart,
God, be in my life.
C
Am7
God, be in my mouth,
God, be in my hands,
1.
D.C.(v.2)
F2
G
C
God, be all I want, be - gin-ning and the end.
2.,3.
Fmaj7
Mid section
G
Fmaj7
end. Oh, oh, oh,

G
Fmaj7
oh.
Be - gin - ning and the
Last time to Coda
G
Fmaj7
end, be - gin - ning and the end, be - gin - ning and the
G
F
end.
God, be in my step,
G
F
God, be in my breath.
God, be all a - round,
G
D.S. al Coda (after rpt)
Coda
G
F2
God, be in my breath.
end.

Therefore, I urge you, brothers, in view of God's mercy, to offer your bodies as living sacrifices, holy and pleasing to God – this is your spiritual act of worship. Do not conform any longer to the pattern of this world, but be transformed by the renewing of your mind. Then you will be able to test and approve what God's will is – his good, pleasing and perfect will.

ROMANS 12:1-2

2293. God immortal

Ex 33:20; Ps 47:2; 96:9; 103:15-17; 104:2; 144:4; Jn 1:3, 14; 1 Cor 13:12; 1 Tim 6:16

Lou & Nathan Fellingham & busbee

2. Giving life to both great and small,
He's the source and the life of all:
Needing nothing to make Him whole.
Man does flourish then fade to nought,
Like a breath that is quickly gone;
But our God's the eternal One.

3. God of splendour, we see in part,
But through Christ He has come to us:
Wondrous glory has won our hearts.

Inspired by the hymn 'Immortal, invisible, God only wise'
by W. Chalmers Smith (1824–1908)

2294. God is able

Acts 2:24; Rom 8:31, 37; Eph 3:20

E(C)
B/D♯(G/B)
F♯(D)
- ble. In His name we o-ver-come, for the Lord
Last time to Coda
1.
G♯m(Em)
F♯(D)
E(C)
B(G)
our God is a - ble.
F♯(D)
G♯m(Em)
E(C)
D.C.(v.2)
2. God is
3.
D.S. al Coda
2.
E(C)
E(C)
B/D♯(G/B)
F♯(D)
- ble Lift-ed up - - able.
G♯m(Em) F♯(D)
E(C)
Mid section
B/D♯(G/B)
God is with us, He will

2. God is with us,
God is on our side,
He will make a way.
Far above all we know,
Far above all we hope,
He has done great things.

God raised him from the dead, freeing him from the agony of death, because it was impossible for death to keep its hold on him.

ACTS 2:24

2295. God is here, God is present

Ian Smale

D Em G A
lov - ing You; You mean more to me than
Bsus4 B Em Cmaj7
a - ny - thing else. Lord, I won't stop
1.,3.
Last time to Coda
D Em G A B
lov - ing You; You mean more to me than life it-self.
Em Bsus4 Cmaj7 G Em Bsus4 Cmaj7 G
D.C.
God is
2.
D.S. al Coda
G A Bsus4 B
more to me than life it-self. Lord,
Coda
Em

2296. God is our strength and refuge

Ps 46:1-11

DAM BUSTERS MARCH

Music: E. Coates
Arr. David Ball

March

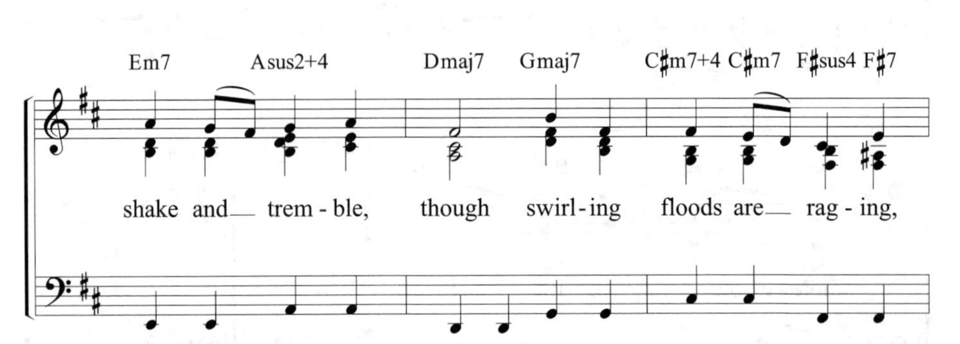

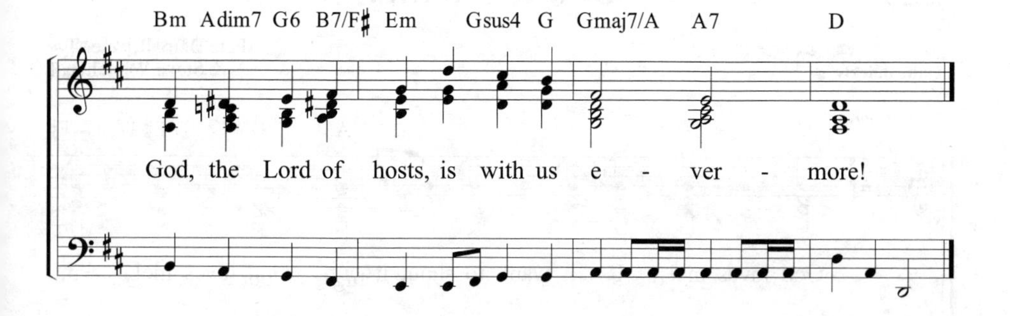

2. There is a flowing river
Within God's holy city;
God is in the midst of her –
She shall not be moved!
God's help is swiftly given,
Thrones vanish at His presence –
God, the Lord of hosts, is with us evermore!

3. Come, see the works of our Maker,
Learn of His deeds all-powerful:
Wars will cease across the world
When He shatters the spear!
Be still and know your Creator,
Uplift Him in the nations –
God, the Lord of hosts, is with us evermore!

Richard Bewes

2297. God loves me!

Pete Bignall, Peter Tye
& Steve Whitehouse

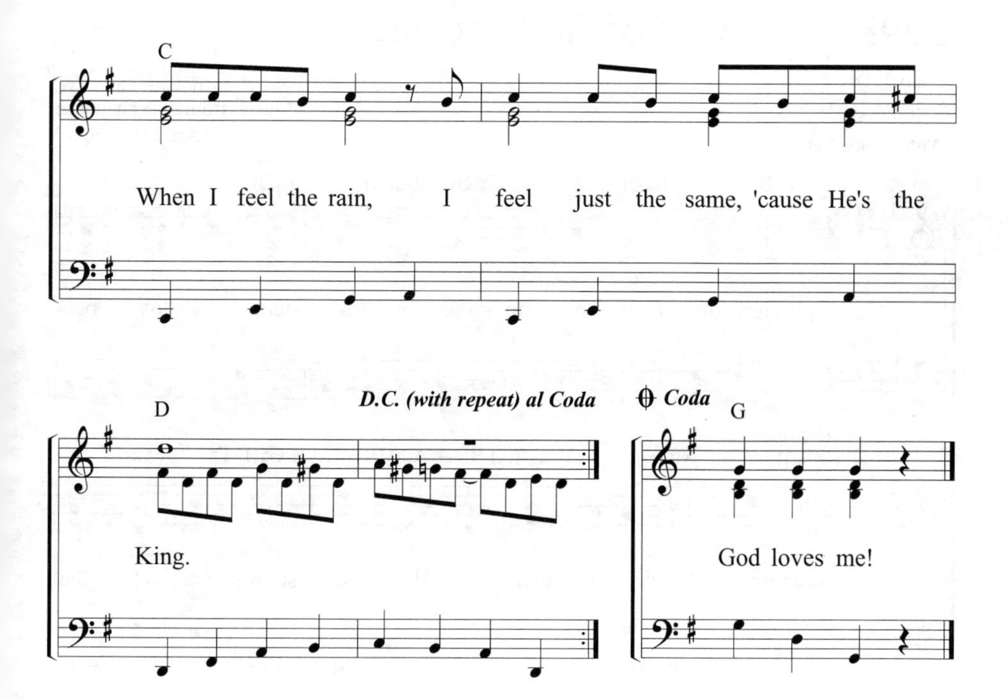
C
When I feel the rain, I feel just the same, 'cause He's the
D
D.C. (with repeat) al Coda
King.
Coda
G
God loves me!

2298. God of God, the uncreated

Lk 1:34; 2:7; Jn 1:3, 49, 51; Eph 1:4-5; Col 1:15; 1 Pet 1:10

Capo 2 (D)
CORDE NATUS

Music: from Piae Cantiones
Arr. Paul Hughes

With a Celtic feel

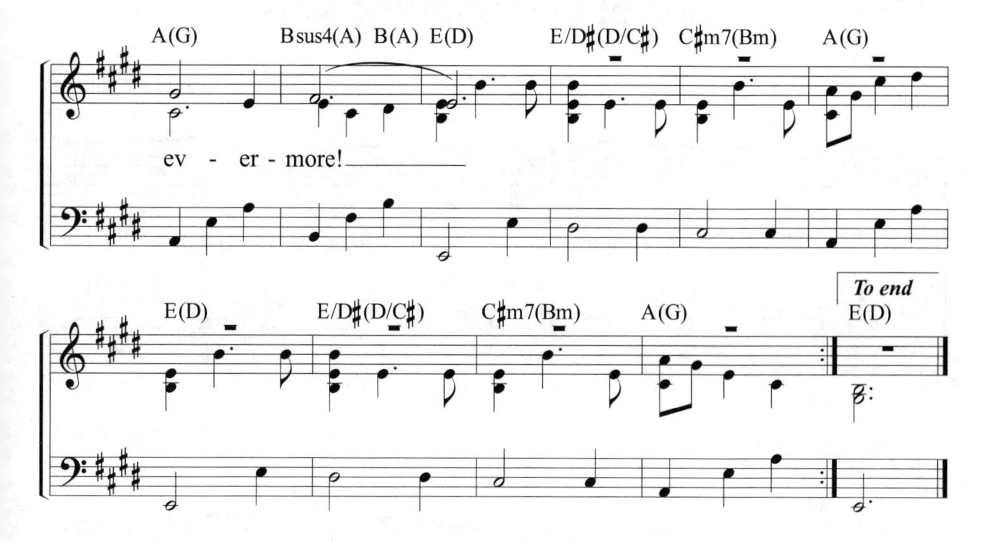

2. He is here, whom generations
   Sought throughout the ages long;
   Promised by the ancient prophets,
   Justice for a world of wrong,
   God's salvation for the faithful:
   Him we praise in endless song
   Evermore and evermore!

3. Happy is that day forever
   When, by God the Spirit's grace,
   Lowly Mary, virgin mother,
   Bore the Saviour of our race.
   Man and child, the world's Redeemer
   Now displays His sacred face
   Evermore and evermore!

4. Praise Him, heaven of the heavens,
   Praise Him, angels in the height;
   Priests and prophets, bow before Him,
   Saints who longed to see this sight.
   Let no human voice be silent,
   In His glory hearts unite
   Evermore and evermore!

5. Christ be praised with God the Father,
   And the Holy Spirit, praised!
   Hymns of worship, high thanksgiving
   Echo through a world amazed:
   Honour, majesty, dominion!
   Songs of victory be raised
   Evermore and evermore!

After Prudentius, J. M. Neale & H. W. Baker

2299. God of the moon and stars

(v.2)
(last time)
A2 E/G♯ F♯m7 Bsus4 B7
what will You make of me? I come to You.
Chorus
E F♯m7/E E E/G♯ A
(Fine)
God of the meek and mild,
B G♯m7 C♯m7
God of the reck - less and the wild, God of the un-
(ch.2&3)
A2 Bsus4 B/D♯ E F♯m7/E
- re-con-ciled, I come to You.
E G♯m7 A B/A
God of our life and death, God of our se-

2. God of the rich and poor,
God of the princess and the whore,
God of the ever-open door,
I come to You.
God of the unborn child,
God of the pure and undefiled,
God of the pimp and paedophile,
I come to You.

(Chorus 2)
God of the war and peace,
God of the junkie and the priest,
God of the greatest and the least,
I come to You.
God of the refugee,
God of the prisoner and the free,
God of our doubt and certainty,
I come to You.

(Chorus 3)
God of our joy and grief,
God of the lawyer and the thief,
God of our faith and unbelief,
I come to You.
God of the wounds we bear,
God of the deepest dreams we share,
God of our unspoken prayer,
I come to You.

3. God of a world that's lost,
God of a lonely cross,
God who has come to us,
We come to You.

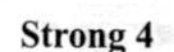

God only wise

1 Chron 29:14; Ps 123:1; Rom 16:27

Brenton Brown, Nick Herbert
& Eoghan Heaslip

Strong 4

G
Chorus
C
F
Take ev-'ry hope and long - ing, God, take all our
Am
G
C
joy and pain. Use us to bless this bro - ken world,
F
Am
G
use us to bring You praise. All that we
C
F
Am
have, we give You now; all that we are is Yours a-lone.
G
F
G
Teach us to trust You with our lives, God on-ly wise.

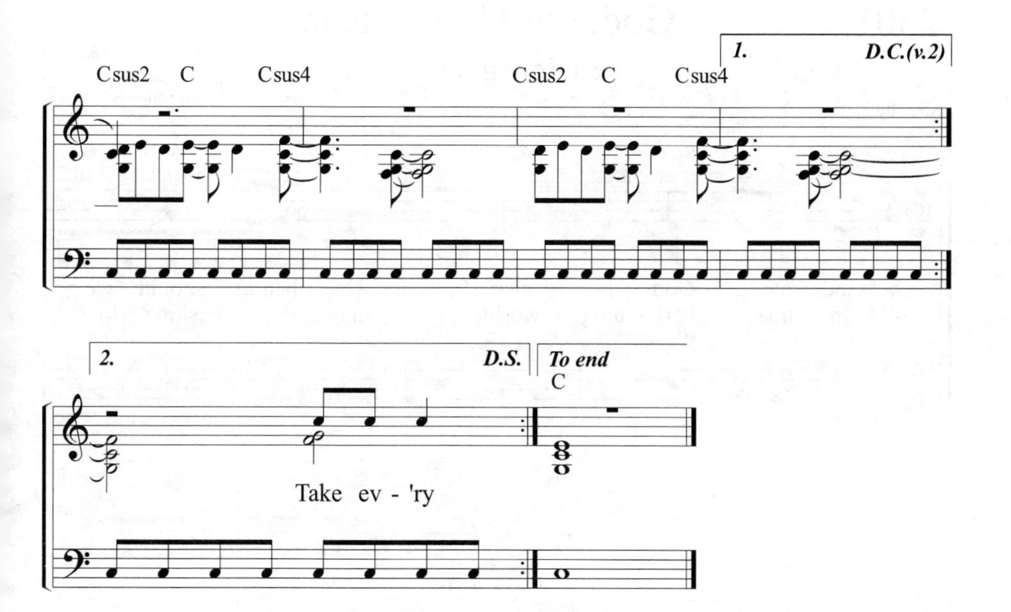

2. God only wise,
Who else can guide so faithfully?
Sovereign and kind,
You see beyond what we can see.

2301. God, our God is near

(Holy ground)

Josh 3:4, 10; Ps 29:3; 93:4; 1 Cor 10:4; Phil 2:15

Graham Kendrick

Steadily

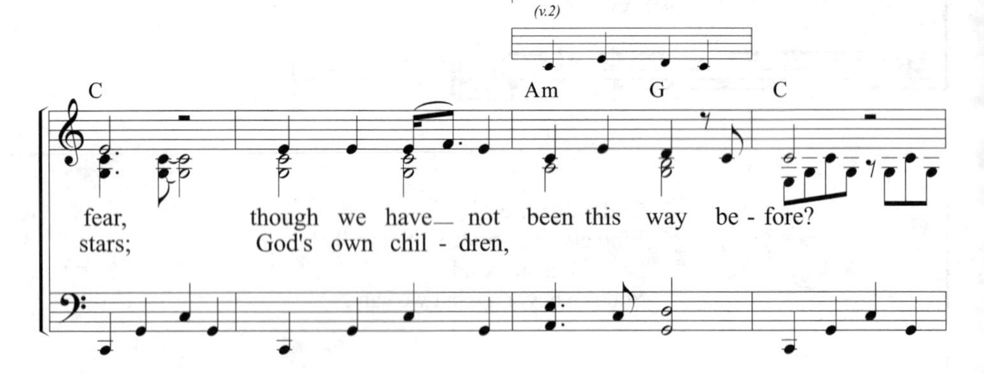

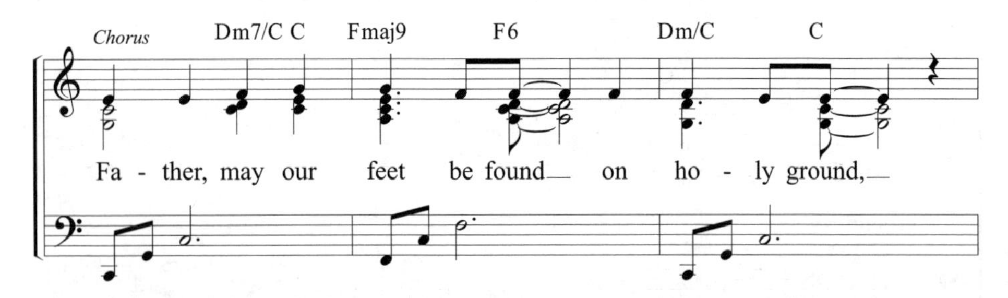

C/G G C Dm7/C C Fmaj9 Dm7
holy ground; purify Your church to stand on
Last time to Coda
1.
D.C.(v.2)
C/G G C Dm7/C C F/C
holy, holy ground.
2.
C F/A G F C/E G C F/A
ground.
D.C.(v.3)
G F C/E G C/E F6 G7sus4
Coda
Am C/G G C
ground, holy, holy ground.

2. Make us ready, Lord;
Beautify Your bride
With Your words, Your works, Your wonders.
Christ has won the day,
What can bar the way
When the God of glory thunders?

3. Though the earth may shake,
Storms upon us break,
Built on Christ the rock we stand.

The voice of the LORD is over the waters; the God of glory thunders, the LORD thunders over the mighty waters.

PSALM 29:3

2302. God so loved, that He gave His Son

(Saviour of the world)

Is 53:4; Jn 3:16; 10:15; 19:30; 1 Cor 15:55; Heb 2:9; 10:20; 1 Jn 4:14; Rev 22:20

Capo 4 (Em)

Ben Cantelon

Rock feel

Verse

G♯m(Em) F♯(D)
1. God so loved, that He gave His Son to lay

E(C) G♯m(Em) F♯(D) (v.2) G♯m(Em)
down His life for the sake of us. He bore the weight of our

F♯(D) E(C)
sin and shame; with a cry He said, 'It is

G♯m(Em) F♯(D) 𝄋 C♯m(Am)
fi - nished.' Christ the Lord o - ver - came the
(D.S.) reigns, ru - ler of the

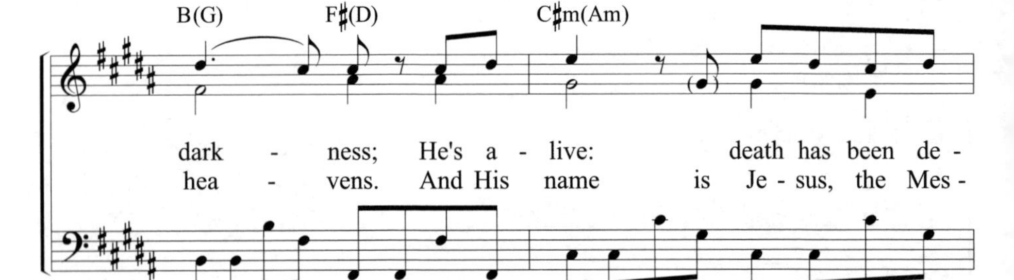

B(G) F♯(D) Chorus E(C)
fea - ted.
si - ah.
For He made us a way by which
G♯m(Em) B(G)
we have been saved. He's the Sa - viour of the world.
F♯(D) E(C)
So we lift up a shout for His
G♯m(Em) B(G) Last time to Coda
fame and re-nown. Praise the Lord, praise the Lord: Je - sus,
1.
F♯(D) G♯m(Em)
Sa - viour of the world.

D.C.(v.2)
F♯(D)
E(C)
F♯(D)
2. We must
2.
F♯(D)
C♯m(Am)
Sa - viour of the world. Oh,
B(G)
F♯(D)
C♯m(Am)
B(G)
F♯(D)
Christ the
C♯m(Am)
B(G)
F♯(D)
Lord o - ver-came the dark - ness, He's a -
C♯m(Am)
B(G)
F♯(D)
D.S. al Coda
live: death has been de - fea - ted. And He

2. We must spread the word of His soon return
   To reclaim the world for His glory.
   Let the church now sing of this coming King,
   Crowned with majesty: our Redeemer.
   And He reigns, ruler of the heavens.
   And His name is Jesus, the Messiah.

2303. God, You are my God

Capo 1 (D)

Ps 40:2; 63:1; Rom 5:2; Eph 1:4

Matthew Macaulay

Fm7(Em)
B♭sus4(A)
B♭(A)
Chorus
I de-clare Your praise, I will stand.
Be-cause Your
E♭(D)
Fm7(Em)
grace is wi - der and Your love, yes, it is high-
D♭(C)
- er; Your hope is stron - ger, You're the rock
A♭(G)
B♭(A)
E♭(D)
on which I stand. And Your word is e-nough
Fm7(Em)
for me, I'm saved for all e - ter - ni - ty; You came

Db(C)
Ab(G)
to earth and re - scued me, I'm cho - sen and I live
Bbsus4(A)
Eb(D)
Last time to Coda
to sing Your praise.
1.
D.C.(v.2)
2.
Abmaj7(G)
In
Mid section
(on repeat)
prai - ses rise high - er and high-er, our prai - ses rise high - er and
Eb(D)
Fm7(Em)
prai-ses rise high-er, our prai-ses rise high-er,

2. God, You are our hope;
Reveal to us Your glory.
God, You are our hope;
We'll live to tell Your story.
God, You are our hope,
God, You are our hope.

2304. Good news!

Ezek 36:26; Mt 1:21; Lk 2:10-11; Jn 3:16; Acts 1:11; 2:23-24; Rev 22:20

Capo 2 (D)

Cindy Rethmeier

Rock 'n' roll

Chorus

E(D) B(A) E(D) A(G) B(A)

Good news! Jesus was born. Good news! He died on the cross. Good news! He rose again. Good news! He's coming back soon.

Last time to Coda 1. E(D) Good

2. E(D)

-ing back soon.

Verse

A(G) E(D) A(G) E(D)

God sent Jesus, His only Son, to save me from my sin; He's the only One who can

A(G)
E(D)
change my heart and make me His own. He
F♯(E)
B(A)
D.C.
saved me, He loves me, my heart is His home. Good
Coda
E(D)
B(A)
- ing back soon. Good news! He's com -
E(D)
B(A)
- ing back soon. Good news! He's com -
E(D) A(G) E(D)
B(A)
E(D) A(G) E(D)
- ing back soon. Good news! He's com - ing back soon.

2305. Good news of great joy

(My soul magnifies the Lord)

Is 9:6-7; Lk 1:46, 49; 2:10-14; Rev 7:9

Bm7
mag - ni - fies the Lord. He has done great things
Last time to Coda
1.
G2
D
for me, great things for me.
D.C.(v.3)
2.,4.
D.S. (al Coda)
3.
Mid section
G
A
for me. My
for me. Of His go -
D
Em7
- vern-ment there will be no end; He'll e-stab - lish it with His right-
D/F♯
- eous-ness. And He shall reign on Da - vid's throne, and His name

G
D/A
shall be from this day on: Won - der-ful
G
D/F♯
Coun-sel-lor,
E-ver-last - ing Fa-
G
D/A
- ther.
Won-der-ful
Em7
Coun-sel-lor,
and His name shall be:
D/F♯
G
E-ver-last - ing Fa - ther.
Oh, yeah!

2. A company of angels,
'Glory in the highest!
And on the earth, peace among
Those on whom His favour rests.'
Come and worship,
Do not be afraid.

3. Unto you a child is born,
Unto us a Son is given;
Let every heart prepare His throne;
And let every nation under heaven
Come and worship;
Do not be afraid.

2306.
Go peaceful
Gal 5:22-23; Eph 4:15, 25; 1 Tim 6:11
Paul Field
Tenderly
Verse
D A/C♯ G/B D/A G D/F♯
1. Go peace-ful in gen-tle-ness through the vi-o-lence
Em7 Asus4 A D A/C♯ G/B D
of these days. Give free - ly, show ten-der-ness
G A7sus4
in all your ways.
1. D D.C.(v.2)
2.,3. D D/F♯
flame.
Chorus
C2 G/B Gm/B♭
God speed you, God lead you and keep you
D A/C♯ G/B Em7 D/F♯
wrapped a-round His heart. May you be

2. Through darkness, in troubled times,
Let holiness be your aim.
Seek wisdom, live faithfulness,
Burn light of flame.

3. Be righteous, speak truthfully
In a world of greed and lies.
Show kindness, see everyone
Through heaven's eyes.

(Chorus 2)
God hold you, enfold you
And keep you wrapped around His heart.
May you be known by love.
May you be known by love.

2307. Grace is not earned

(Grace)

Ps 121:7; Is 43:25; Jer 2:22; Lk 1:78; Jn 10:29; 19:17; Rom 3:22; 5:19; Eph 1:4; 2:8, 18; Col 2:14-15; 1 Pet 1:3

Kate Simmonds

2. You know how often I fail
 And all that I can't undo,
 Stains I've no means to erase,
 How can I stand before You?
 Christ takes the cross on His shoulders,
 Steadfast to Calvary's hill,
 Leaving my sin in the grave
 He rises, the conquering Son.
 Such amazing love!

3. Raised by Your life, now in Christ,
 Chosen and dearly loved,
 I am now seen through Your eyes:
 Righteous through Jesus' blood!
 Ransomed, restored and forgiven,
 My sins are remembered no more!
 Though still I'll stumble, You'll keep me.
 By grace I'll continue on
 In unending love!

2308. Great is our God

(One church, one voice)

Ps 95:1-3; Mt 6:10; 2 Cor 12:10; Eph 2:5; 4:7

Paul Robertson

2. We come to worship You
As different people joined as one.
One church, one voice, one song,
All saved by grace in Christ alone.

3. We come to worship You
In times of trouble, times of doubt.
One church, one voice, one song,
And in our weakness You are strong.

4. We come to worship You,
To celebrate when life is good.
One church, one voice, one song
To honour You, our faithful One.

5. We come to worship You
With all the gifts You give to us.
One church, one voice, one song
To see Your will on earth be done.

2309. Great is the Lord

Ps 19:1; 48:1

Capo 4 (G)

Chris Sayburn

Powerfully

Verse B(G) B/D♯(G/B) E(C) F♯/A♯(D/F♯)

1. Great is the Lord and most wor-thy of praise;

B(G) B/D♯(G/B) (v.2) E(C)

who can com - pare to His great-ness? Cre-

G♯m7(Em) F♯/A♯(D/F♯) D♯m(Bm) E(C)

a - tion dis - plays in mag - ni - fi-cent ways His

Chorus B(G) F♯/A♯(D/F♯) G♯m7(Em)

Great is the Fa - ther, great is the Son, great is the Spi - rit,

E(C)
G♯m7(Em)
great is the Three in One; sing-ing, 'Great is the
F♯/A♯(D/F♯)
B(G)
F♯/A♯(D/F♯)
Lord.' Great in His mer - cy, great in His love,
G♯m7(Em)
E(C)
great in His pow - er, great in His full-ness a - bove;
Last time to Coda
1.
G♯m7(Em)
F♯/A♯(D/F♯)
B(G)
sing-ing, 'Great is the Lord.'
D.C.(v.2)
2.
B/D♯(G/B)
E(C)
F♯/A♯(D/F♯)
Lord. How

2. Great is the Lord and most worthy of praise;
Who can determine His greatness?
The heavens display in extravagant ways
Your glory, Your majesty, Your splendour.

2310. Great is the love
(The light that shines)

Lk 1:78-79; Jn 1:5; 2 Cor 4:6; Eph 2:4

Noel Richards
& David Clifton

With a strong beat

Chorus
G
C2
Am7
The light that shines for ev - 'ry-one, the hope of all
Dsus4
G
C2
cre-a - tion, burn in our hearts the bright - est flame,
Last time D.S. al Coda
1.,3.
Am7
Dsus4
Em7
that all may see sal - va - tion.
Last time to Coda
2. Mid section
Em
Dark -
Bm7
Cmaj7
Dsus4
Em
ness fad - ing, day - light

Bm7
Cmaj7
Dsus4
D.S. al Coda
break - ing.

Coda
Em7

2311. Hail the day that sees Him rise

Ps 24:7, 9; Jn 1:29; Acts 1:9; 1 Cor 15:20, 56-57; 1 Thess 4:17; Heb 7:25; 9:24; Rev 7:10; 22:5

LLANFAIR

Music: R. Williams (1781–1821)
Arr. David Ball

Briskly

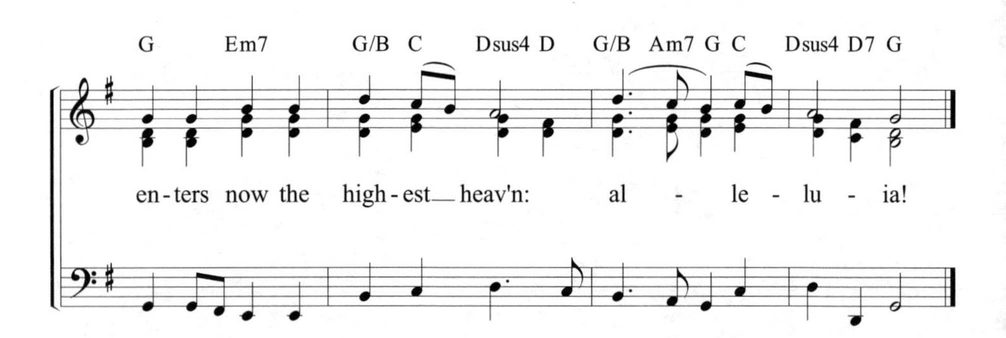

2. There for Him high triumph waits: alleluia,
Lift your heads, eternal gates, alleluia,
He has conquered death and sin, alleluia,
Take the King of glory in: alleluia!

3. See! the heaven its Lord receives, alleluia,
Yet He loves the earth He leaves; alleluia,
Though returning to His throne, alleluia,
Still He calls mankind His own: alleluia!

4. Still for us He intercedes, alleluia,
His prevailing death He pleads, alleluia,
Near Himself prepares our place, alleluia,
He the first-fruits of our race: alleluia!

5. Lord, though parted from our sight, alleluia,
Far beyond the starry height, alleluia,
Lift our hearts that we may rise, alleluia,
One with You beyond the skies: alleluia!

6. There with You we shall remain, alleluia,
Share the glory of Your reign, alleluia,
There Your face unclouded view, alleluia,
Find our heaven of heavens in You: alleluia!

C. Wesley (1707–88) & T. Cotterill (1779–1823)

2312. Hallelujah, hallelujah

Ps 48:1; 2 Thess 1:12; Rev 5:12

Capo 2 (G)

Ben Cantelon

With increasing intensity

2.
E/G♯(D/F♯)
F♯m(Em)
D(C)
A(G)
Hal-le - lu - jah,
hal - le - lu - jah,
E/G♯(D/F♯)
F♯m(Em)
D(C)
1.
A(G)
You are wor - thy of our praise.
E/G♯(D/F♯)
2.
A(G)
Hal - le - praise.

2313.
Have mercy on me
Ps 51:1-2, 10, 12, 17; 132:9; 2 Cor 3:18; 4:7; Phil 1:6
Capo 2 (G)
Nick J. Drake
Steadily
F♯m(Em) Verse E/G♯(D/F♯) A(G)
1. Have mer - cy on me, O my Lord,
(v.2)
Dmaj7(C) Esus4(D) E(D)
mer-cy on this bro - ken heart;
F♯m(Em) E/G♯(D/F♯) A(G)
Sa - viour, wash a - way all my sin,
Bm(Am) Esus4(D) E(D) Bridge Dmaj7(C) F♯m(Em)
take a-way these dir - ty clothes. Pick me up,

E(D)
F♯m(Em)
Dmaj7(C)
F♯m(Em)
E(D)
— turn me a-round; — I come to You now. —
Chorus
Bm(Am)
Esus4(D)
E(D)
Je - sus, You live — in me, — I'm
Asus4(G)
A(G)
walk - ing in — my Sa - viour's com - pa - ny; — like
Last time to Coda
Bm(Am)
Esus4(D)
E(D)
Asus4(G)
gold in a jar — of clay, — that's Your life — in — me. –
1.
D.C.(v.2)
A(G)
F♯m(Em)
E/G♯(D/F♯)
A(G)
Dmaj7(C)
Bm7(Am)

2. Have mercy on me, O my Lord,
Look upon this penitent heart.
Restore me again in Your love,
Clothe me with Your righteousness.

2314. Have you heard?

Is 40:28; Mk 1:15; Lk 4:18; Jn 1:3, 14; Acts 2:21, 23-24; Rom 8:21; Heb 7:25; 1 Jn 4:9

Capo 3 (G)

Moderately

Simon Brading, Graham Kendrick & Nathan Fellingham

Last time to Coda
Gm(Em)
F/A(D/F♯)
E♭/B♭(C/G) B♭(G)
oh, the joy of for - give - ness.
E♭/G(C/E)
F/A(D/F♯)
B♭(G)
E♭maj7(C)
Come, oh come, let us kneel be-fore the cross;
F(D)
1.
E♭maj7(C)
this is love, this is love.
Gm(Em) E♭(C) F(D) Gm(Em) E♭(C) B♭(G) F(D)
D.C.(v.3)
Gm(Em) E♭(C) F(D) Gm(Em) E♭(C) B♭(G) F(D)

2. Have you heard He was one of us,
   Shared our joy and tears?
   Did you know He restored the broken,
   Healed the lame, made the blind to see;
   Brought His kingdom near?

3. Have you heard He was crucified
   On a Roman cross?
   Did you know that He chose to suffer
   To restore a creation lost;
   Bearing all the cost?

4. Have you heard He was raised to life,
   Bursting from the grave?
   Did you know that He saves forever
   All who call on His mighty name,
   On Jesus' name?

(Last chorus)
Oh, the love, the love that God has shown;
Oh, the joy of forgiveness.
Sing, oh sing, of the God who came to us:
This is love, this is love.

2315. Heaven sings Your symphony

(Sing alleluia)

Ps 19:1-2; 96:11; Rev 1:7; 19:6; 21:4

Capo 3 (G)

Building in intensity

Al Gordon, Luke Hellebronth & Tom Smith

Verse B♭(G) E♭/B♭(C/G)

1. Hea - ven sings Your sym - pho - ny,

B♭(G) E♭/B♭(C/G)

we re - spond in har - mo - ny.

Gm(Em) E♭(C) *(Chorus)*

All a - round praise re - sounds: Al-le-lu-

1. B♭(G) E♭/B♭(C/G) ***D.C.(v.2)*** **2.,3.** B♭(G)

-ia. -ia,

Cm(Am) Gm(Em) E♭(C) B♭(G)

al-le-lu - lia, we will sing. Al-le-lu - ia,

Cm(Am)
Gm(Em)
E♭(C)
1.
B♭(G)
we give glo - ry to the King.
E♭(C)
B♭(G)
E♭(C)
D.C.(v.3)
2.
F(D)
Gm(Em)
B♭/D(G/B)
E♭(C)
Mid section
F(D)
Gm(Em)
One day You will come a-gain, ev - 'ry eye will
B♭/D(G/B)
E♭(C)
see the King. We will join the great 'al-le-lu - ia'!

2. Come, you stars, you blazing lights,
Lift your voice, burn the night.
Mountains bow, oceans roar:

3. Every heart, everyone,
Lift your hands, join the song.
All adore Christ the Lord:

2316.
Heaven's light breaking through
(You rescued us)
Ps 139:12; Lam 3:23; Mk 11:23; Jn 8:32; 10:28; Rom 8:38-39; 2 Cor 4:6, 8; 1 Pet 2:9; Rev 5:5
Capo 2 (G)
Confidently
Stuart Townend & Matt Redman
Verse
A(G) D2/A(C/G)
1. Hea - ven's light break - ing through,
Love has come, hope has dawned,
F♯m7(Em) E(D) D(C) E(D)
1.,3.,5.
2. D.C.(v.1)
turn - ing night to day; it's a new be - gin - ning.
driv - ing fears a - way;
4.,6.
E(D) D(C)
it's a new be - gin - ning.
Bridge
F♯m(Em) E/G♯(D/F♯)
Your mer - cy reached in - to the
A(G) (Gsus4) Asus4 A(G) F♯m(Em) E/G♯(D/F♯)
dark - est night to find us, Your blood has freed us from the
A(G) (Gsus4) Asus4 A(G) F♯m(Em) E/G♯(D/F♯)
curse of sin that bound us, Your truth de - li - vered us from

(Gsus4)
A(G) Asus4 A(G) B7(A)
all the lies that held us down
Dm(Cm)
Chorus
A(G)
when we were o - ver-whelmed. Oh,
D(C) E(D)
out of the dark - ness You res - cued us, You have res -
D(C) A(G)
cued us. Oh,
D(C) E(D)
in - to the light of Your love for us, Lord, You res -

2. Here we stand, held by grace,
Knowing every day
Is a new beginning.
All we need found in You,
Love has made a way;
It's a new beginning.

(Bridge 2)
No sorrow deep enough to crush the hope within us,
No mountain big enough to block the path before us,
No power strong enough to take us from Your mighty hand,
For You have overcome.

2317.

He became sin
(Jesus, Messiah)

Mt 1:23; 26:26-28; 27:51; Jn 8:12; 19:17; Acts 2:36; 2 Cor 5:21; Phil 2:8-9; 1 Tim 2:6

With increasing intensity

Chris Tomlin, Daniel Carson, Ed Cash & Jesse Reeves

Chorus
A
Je-sus, Mes-si - ah,
name a-bove all
Dsus2
names;
A
Bles-sèd Re-deem - er,
Esus4
E
Em-man - u-el.
The res-cue for sin -
A
Dsus2
ners,
the ran-som from hea - ven;
Last time to Coda
A/C♯
Esus4
A
Je-sus, Mes-si - ah,
Lord of all.

1.
D.C.(v.2)
2.
Mid section
Bm7
2. His
All our hope is in You,
A/C♯
Dsus2
Esus4
all our hope is in You,
all the glo-
Bm7
A/C♯
Dsus2
ry to You, God,
the Light of the
Esus4
D.S. al Coda
World.
Je-sus, Mes-si-
Coda
D/F♯
A/E
Esus4
Dsus2
Je-sus, Mes-si - ah;
Lord of all.

2. His body – the bread, His blood – the wine,
   Broken and poured out, all for love.
   The whole earth trembled and the veil was torn.
   Love so amazing, love so amazing, yeah.

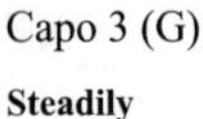

He came in flesh

(Sinless Saviour)

Is 53:3; Mt 1:23; Jn 1:14; 1 Cor 6:11, 20; Eph 1:7; 2:6; Heb 12:2; 1 Pet 2:4, 24; 2 Pet 1:19; 1 Jn 1:7; Rev 5:12

Tony Fisher, Matt Boswell & Aaron Keyes

Capo 3 (G)

Steadily

(v.2)
(v.3)
Gm7(Em) B♭/D(G/B) E♭(C) B♭(G)
hea - ven at His com - mand, en-dured the cross for all
F(D)
Chorus
B♭(G) E♭(C) Gm7(Em)
sin. He is Je - sus, sin-less Sa - viour, the spot-less Re-
F(D) E♭(C) Fsus4(D) B♭(G) E♭(C)
deem-er of man. He is Je - sus, God is with
Gm7(Em) F(D)
1.
E♭(C) F(D)
D.C.(v.2)
us; all glo-ry, all praise to the Lamb. 2. For God Him -

2. For God Himself bore all our sin in his body on the tree,
That we might die to live again, declaring Christ, our victory!
By His wounds we are healed, we are washed and received;
By His blood we are bought, we are cleansed and redeemed.

3. When very love our eyes behold, in realms of joy as yet unknown,
We lift our hands to rending skies, to Him who rose that we might rise!
This is the breaking of the dawn, when all creation will sing;
This is the Lord, our God of war, this is our Saviour, our King!

He was despised and rejected by men, a man of sorrows, and familiar with suffering. Like one from whom men hide their faces he was despised, and we esteemed him not.

ISAIAH 53:3

2319. He came so we could know
(The King has come)

Ps 48:2; 96:13; 103:6, 11, 19; Is 40:29; 55:9; Mt 5:4; Lk 19:10; Jn 8:12; Heb 1:3; Rev 11:15

With increasing intensity

Eoghan Heaslip
& Neil Bennetts

D
Em
G/B
-ness, help to the help - less, a song for those who mourn.
C
D
Em
Strength for the wea - ry, friend to the lone - ly; He's the joy
G/B
C
Chorus
of the whole earth. The King has
G
D/F#
come: the glo-ri-ous, the awe-some Son of God, the
(D.S.) come, and ev-'ry-thing with-in this heart be-lieves that
Am7
G
beau-ti-ful, the sov - 'reign Lord of love. Je - sus.
He is ev-'ry-thing we'll ev - er need. Je - sus.

D/F♯
1.
Em
C
The King has come.
G
D.C.(v.2)
2.
D
D.S.
2. He
The King has
3.
G
Mid section
D/F♯
The King has come.
This is the day,
this is the time;
1.-3.
Am
G/B
D
4.
Am
let the king-dom of our God reign.
let the
C
D/F♯
Em
king-dom of our God reign,
let the

2. He came to speak the message of new birth;
Creator, Sustainer.
He came to bring His rule upon the earth
With justice and mercy.
His ways are higher, His love is greater
Than the treasures of this world.
His grace is wider, His name is stronger;
He's the joy of the whole earth.

2320. He gave His life

Is 53:4-5; Mt 26:27; Mk 14:50; Lk 5:32; 19:10; Jn 19:30; 1 Cor 10:16; 11:26; Phil 2:7-8; 1 Tim 1:15

SELFLESS LOVE

Music: Andrew Maries

2. He did not come to call the good
But sinners to repent;
It was the lame, the deaf, the blind
For whom His life was spent:
To heal the sick, to find the lost –
It was for such He came,
And round His table all may come
To praise His holy name.

3. They heard Him call His Father's name –
Then 'Finished!' was His cry;
Like them we have forsaken Him
And left Him there to die:
The sins that crucified Him then
Are sins His blood has cured;
The love that bound Him on a cross
Our freedom has ensured.

4. His body broken once for us
Is glorious now above;
The cup of blessing we receive,
A sharing of His love:
As in His presence we partake,
His dying we proclaim
Until the hour of majesty
When Jesus comes again.

Christopher Porteous

2321. He is jealous for me
(How He loves)

Joel 2:18; Jn 3:16; 2 Cor 4:17; Eph 2:4; 1 Jn 4:16

John Mark McMillan

Steady 2

Verse

C | Am7 | G | F | C | Am7 | G

1. He is jealous for me; loves like a hurricane, I am a tree bending beneath the weight of His wind and mercy; when all of a sudden I am unaware of these afflictions eclipsed by glory. And I realise just how beautiful You are, and how

Verse 2 jump to chorus
Bridge
F
C
great Your af-fec-tions are for me. And oh, how He loves us
Am7
G
F
so, oh, how He loves how He loves us so.
1.° D.C. (v.1)
C
Am7
G
Chorus
C
Yeah, He loves us, oh, how He
Am7
G
loves us, oh, how He loves us, oh, how He

F
1. D.C. (v.2)
2. D.S.
Last time
loves. 2. And Yeah, He us.
C
C
Am7
2. We are His por - tion and He is our prize, drawn to re - demp - tion by the
G
F
grace in His eyes. If His grace is an o - cean, we're all sink - ing. So
C
Am7
hea - ven meets earth like an un - fore - seen kiss, and my heart turns vio - lent - ly in -
G
side of my chest. And I don't have time to main - tain these re - grets when I
F
Jump to chorus
think a - bout the way that He

2322. He lowers us to raise us

(All is well)

Building to chorus

1 Sam 2:7; Ps 25:13; Jer 29:11; Jn 10:29; 2 Cor 6:10; Phil 4:12; 3 Jn 1:2

Johnny Parks & Claire Hamilton

E D A D
I'm held firm in the grasp of the rock of all the a-
E Chorus A D/A
-ges. All is well with my soul;
E A
He is God, in con - trol.
D/A
I know not all His plans,
E A
but I know I'm in His hands.

2. He clothes us now then strips us,
Yet through His word equips us;
Whatever is His way, all is well.
And though our seasons change,
We still exalt His name;
Whatever is His way, all is well.

2323. Help me, Lord

Lk 15:20; 22:42; 2 Cor 1:3

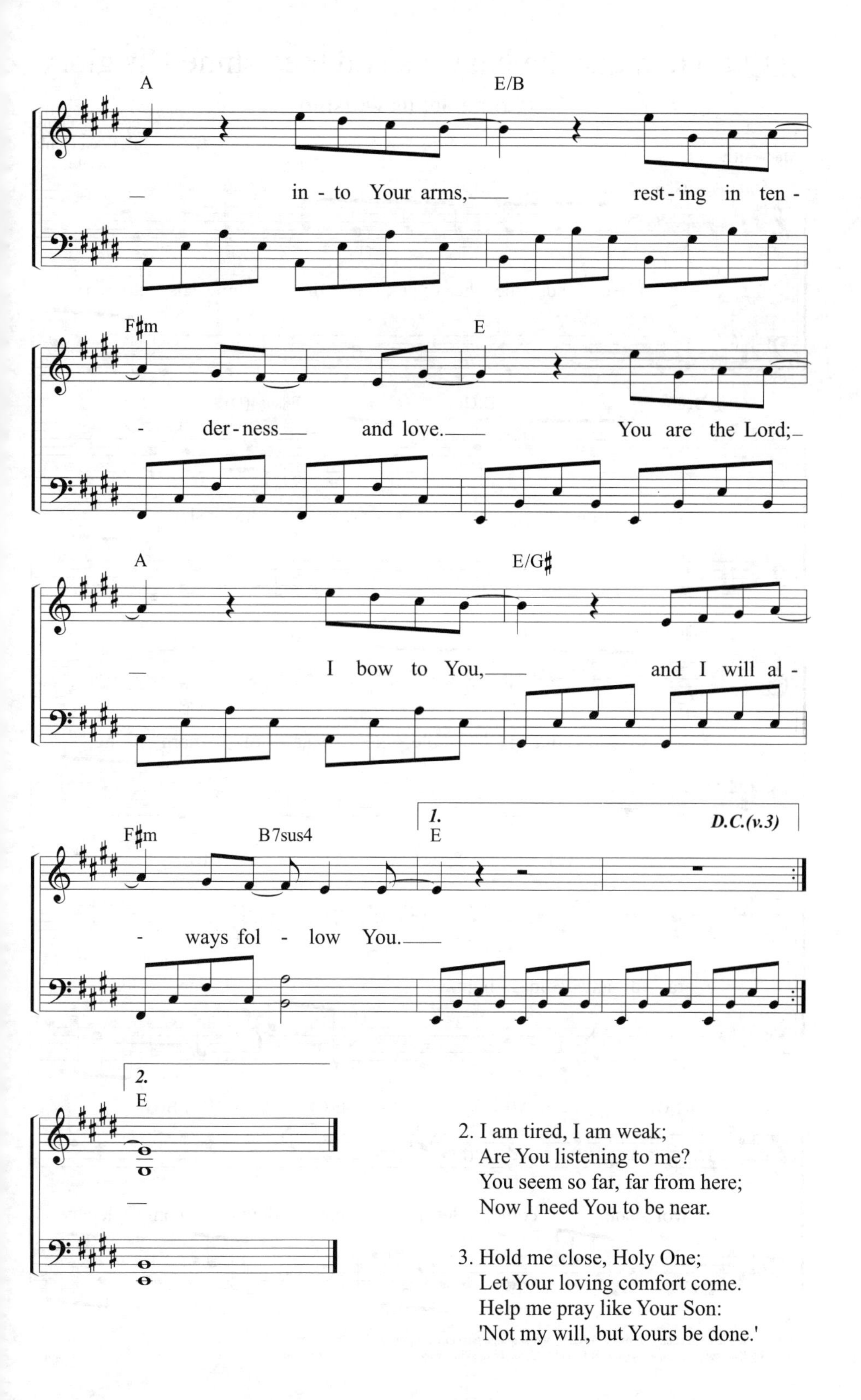
A
E/B
— into Your arms, — resting in ten-
F♯m
E
-derness — and love. — You are the Lord; —
A
E/G♯
— I bow to You, — and I will al-
F♯m
B7sus4
1.
E
D.C.(v.3)
-ways fol-low You. —
2.
E
—
2. I am tired, I am weak;
Are You listening to me?
You seem so far, far from here;
Now I need You to be near.
3. Hold me close, Holy One;
Let Your loving comfort come.
Help me pray like Your Son:
'Not my will, but Yours be done.'

2324. He made the heavens and they shine His glory

Last time to Coda
F♯m7(Dm)
A(F)
E(C)
B(G)
sing of all the Lord has done.
1st time D.C.(v.2)
Mid section
C♯m7(Am)
(G/B)
B/D♯
E(C)
B(G)
God be glo - ri-fied;
F♯/A♯(D/F♯)
C♯m7(Am)
(G/B)
B/D♯
E(C)
Je - sus
F♯(D)
D.C.(v.3) al Coda
lift - ed high.
Coda
F♯(D)
done.
B(G)
F♯(D)
A(F)
E/G♯(C/E)
His ways are migh - ty, righ - teous and ho - ly.

2. He made the world in all its countless wonder,
Composed the song creation cries.
Our God, incredible, immortal Saviour:
Jesus Christ.

3. He made the heavens and they shine His glory,
He moves the sun across the sky;
So incomparable, the star of morning:
Jesus Christ.

2325. Here is love, vast as the ocean

Ps 85:10; Zech 13:1; Mt 6:33; Jn 19:34; Rom 5:5; 1 Cor 6:11; Eph 1:12; 2:6; Col 2:14; 1 Tim 2:6

Steadily

Music: Robert Lowry
New chorus: Kate Simmonds

Verse

D G D A D G D A D D/F♯ A Em7 A D A/C♯ Bm G

1. Here is___ love,_____ vast as the o-cean, lov-ing
kind - ness as the flood, when the_ Prince___ of life, our
ran-som, shed for us_____ His pre-cious blood. Who His
love___ will not re - mem-ber? Who can cease___ to sing His
praise? He can ne - ver be for - got-ten through-out

Chorus
D/A
A
D
D/F♯
heav'n's e-ter-nal days.
Grace takes my
G
D
A
sin, calls me friend, pays my debt com-plete-ly.
D
G
D
Love res-cued me, seat-ed me with my
A
D
G2
D
King for-e-ver more.
1.,2.
D.C.
To end
A
A
D
2. On the

2. On the mount of crucifixion
Fountains opened deep and wide;
Through the floodgates of God's mercy
Flowed a vast and gracious tide.
Grace and love like mighty rivers,
Poured incessant from above;
Heaven's peace and perfect justice
Kissed a guilty world in love.

3. Let me all Your love accepting,
Love You ever all my days;
Let me seek Your kingdom only,
And my life be to Your praise.
You alone shall be my glory,
Nothing in the world I see.
You have cleansed and sanctified me,
God Himself has set me free.

William Rees (1802–83)

2326. Here I stand

(Salvation)

Is 64:6; Rom 4:5, 22; 6:7-8; Gal 6:14; Heb 7:25; 10:12, 19

Simon Brading

With energy

Verse

G

1. Here I stand, with no-thing in my hands; the best that I can of - fer is a fil-thy rag.
the righ-teous-ness of Christ is cre - di-ted to me now and for-ev - er.

F C/E (N.C.)

1. But I find
2.

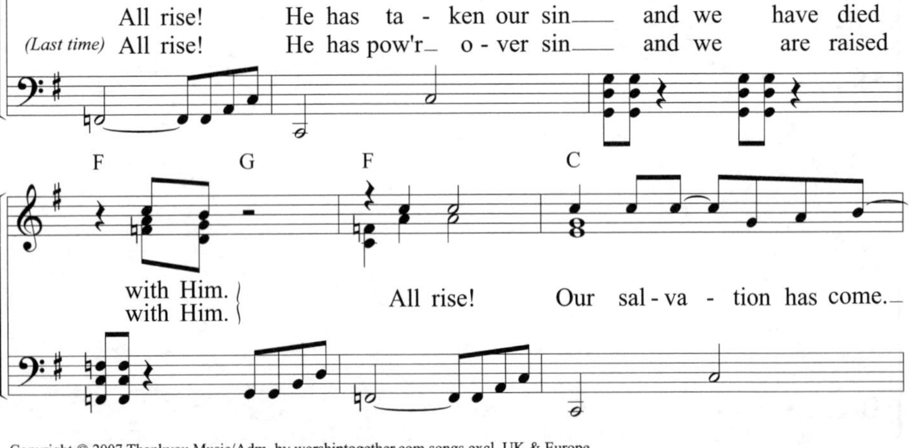

Bm
D
Chorus
G
Sal - va - tion given to us:
va - tion, gi - ven for free; the
Em7
God stepped down and lif - ted us up.
work of Christ is suf - fi - cient for me.
1.
Am7
C
We ce - le - brate, we ce - le - brate free - dom.
Gsus2
Sal -
2.
D
F
G
You are e - nough, You are e - nough, e - nough for me.
Last time to Coda
F
1.
C/E
D.C.
2. Je - sus' blood

2. Jesus' blood forever bids me come;
Tells me I'm forgiven for all time.
Now I'll boast only in His life,
Death and resurrection, and nothing else.

2327. Here's life in all its mystery

(All that matters)

Mt 7:7; Eph 5:10; Col 1:16; Heb 7:25; 1 Pet 1:8

At a steady pace

Judy MacKenzie Dunn

1.
D.C.(v.2)
2.,3.
Bm A G G/A G D/F♯ Em7 D/F♯
just a pass-ing dream? 2. Phi - know.
G G/A
Chorus
D F♯m7 Bm Bm/A
My Ma - ker is my Sa - viour, my Cre -
G2 D/F♯ Em7 G/A D F♯m7
a-tor is al-so my friend, and to find Him and His fa-
Last time to Coda
Bm Bm/A Em7 D/F♯ G2 G/A
1.
D.C.(v.3)
D G/A
- vour is all that mat-ters in the end. 3. The
2.,3.
D.S. (al Coda)
D G/A
end. My Ma -
Coda
Em7 D/F♯ G2
all that mat-ters,

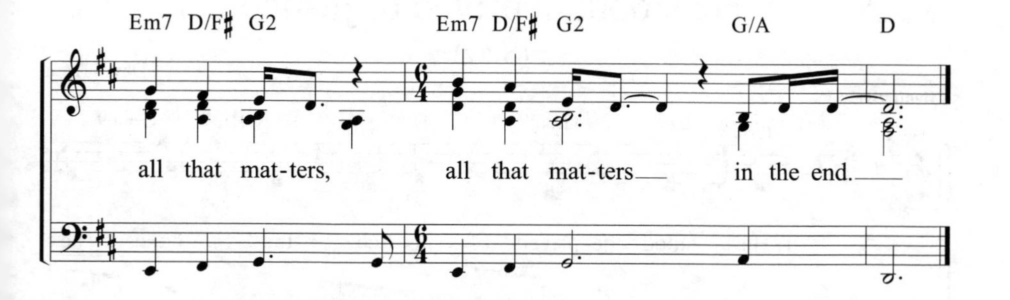

2. Philosophers philosophise
   But rarely look you in the eyes,
   And politics is compromise
   That rides the ebb and flow.
   And money talks, and fashion screams
   To fill the space inside your dreams;
   If you want something to believe,
   I'll tell you what I know:

3. The spirit of the age decrees
   We may not speak in certainties,
   But that's what Jesus is to me –
   The bedrock of my soul.
   A Saviour who can really save,
   A power stronger than the grave,
   The greatest gift I'll ever have,
   The deepest joy I know.

2328. He stood, deprived of justice

(Stay)

Is 53:7-8; Lk 19:10

David Lyon

2. He came to save His people,
And turn them back to God
To reveal a greater kingdom,
Teaching grace with every word.

3. So violently they beat Him
And punished God's own Son;
He endured humiliation,
Isolated and alone.

4. Yet whispers of forgiveness
From Saviour crucified,
And there even in the torture,
Love was burning in His eyes.

5. Surrendered to the Father
As nails tore through His hands,
He became our condemnation
And then died as guilty man.

6. He stood deprived of justice,
The Innocent accused,
And yet no retaliation
From the One that they abused.

2329. Hide me again

Ps 17:8; 18:2; Zeph 3:17; Rev 19:11

Capo 4 (C)

Chris Orange

A(F)
B(G)
C♯m(Am)
F♯m7(Dm)
— with-in — to rise — and sing. —
Bsus4(G) B(G)
Chorus
E(C)
B/D♯(G/B)
You a-lone are wor-thy, You a-lone are — good,
E/G♯(C/E)
A(F)
You a-lone are faith-ful — and — true.
E(C)
B/D♯(G/B)
You a-lone are ho-ly, You a-lone are — pure,
E/G♯(C/E)
A(F)
You a-lone are stead-fast — and — sure.

Tag
F♯m7(Dm)
E/G♯(C/E)
A(F)
Sing o - ver me.

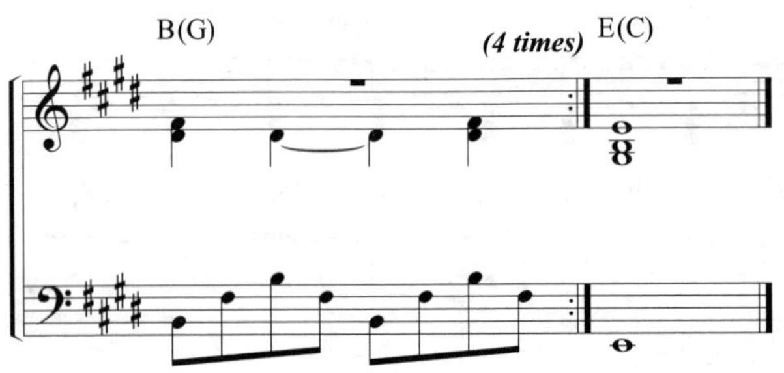
B(G)
(4 times)
E(C)

Keep me as the apple of your eye; hide me in the shadow of your wings from the wicked who assail me, from my mortal enemies who surround me.

PSALM 17:8-9

2330. Holy, holy is the Lord God Almighty

Ps 72:19; Is 6:3; Mt 6:10

Capo 3 (G)

Graham Kendrick

Relaxed feel

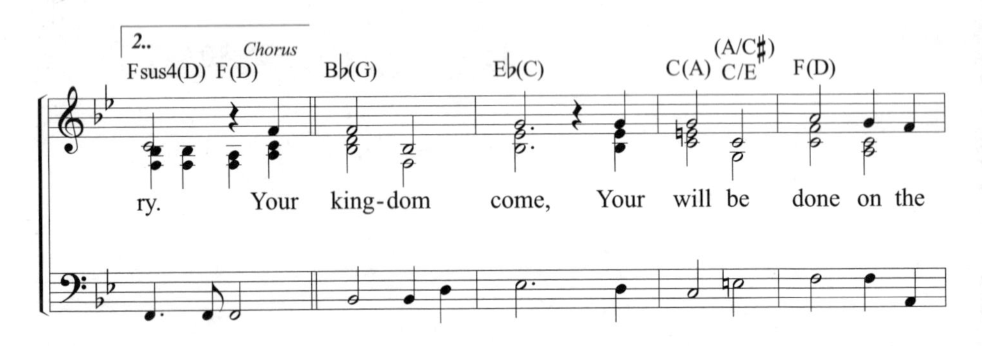

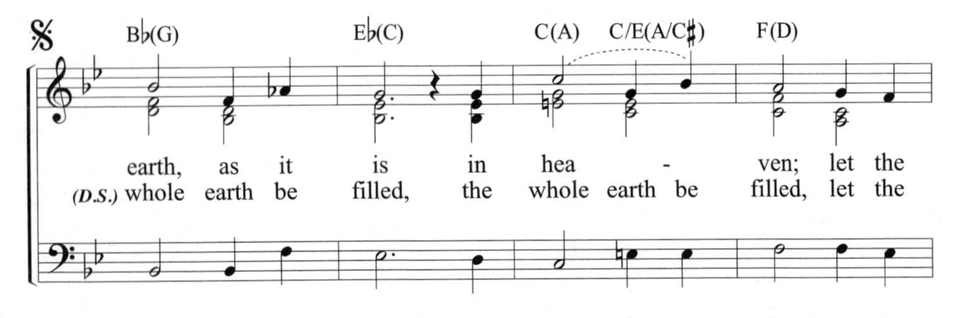

1.
B♭/D(G/B) B♭(G) E♭(C) F(D) B♭sus4(G) B♭(G)
whole earth be filled with Your glo - ry.
whole earth be filled with Your glo -
Cm7(Am) B♭(G) Cm7(Am) B♭(G)
D.C.
2. D.S. (Ch.2) 3.
B♭sus4(G) B♭(G) Gm7(Em) F2(D) E♭(C) F(D)
ry. Let the ry. Your glo -

Gm7(Em) F2(D) Cm7(Am) F(D) B♭sus4(G) B♭(G)
ry, Your glo - ry.

2331. Holy, holy, Lord God Almighty

(Hold on to You forever)

Capo 4 (C)

Moderately

Ps 139:2, 13; 1 Jn 4:19; Rev 4:8, 11

Kees Kraayenoord & Chris Eaton

A(F) E(C) B(G)
know the depths of my heart. Still You love me, still You
C♯m7(Am) A(F) 1. B(G) E(C)
save me, and I wor - ship You.
A/E(F/A) D.C.(v.1) 2. Bsus4(G)
You, for
Jump to 𝄋 3.
A(F) B(G) Bridge B(G) Bridge
who You are. Beau-ti-ful You. Beau-ti-ful
A(F) C♯m(Am)
Sa - viour, oh, how I love You, on-ly be -

2. Holy, holy, Lord God Almighty,
Glory and honour be unto You.
Love unfailing, never ending;
Glory and honour be unto You.

We love because he first loved us.

1 JOHN 4:19

2332. # Holy Spirit, come

Hos 6:3; Joel 2:23; Lk 15:20; Jn 1:32; 14:16; 1 Jn 2:27

Worshipfully

Raymond Tan

1.
Amaj7 D/A Amaj7 D/A D/E
2. Chorus
G/A A7 Dmaj7 C♯m7 Bm7 D/E
Come, a - noint me and fill me and make me whole;
noint us and fill us and make us whole;
Amaj7 Em7 A7 Dmaj7 C♯m7 F♯m7
come and touch me, em - pow - er me to
come and touch us, em - pow - er us to
1.,3. 2.,4.
Bm7 D/E G/A A7 Amaj7
do the Fa - ther's will. Come, a -
do the Fa - ther's will.
1. D.C. 2. 8va
D/A Amaj7 D2/A D D/E A

2333. Holy Spirit, come with Your fire

Acts 2:3-4, 11

Sam Blake, Stephen Gibson,
Joel Pridmore & Ian Yates

Bm7
E7
D6
— con-sume — us, — Lord, — with You. —
2° only
Chorus
A
Fill us, — Ho - ly Spi - rit,
F♯m7
E
fire, — fall — up-on — us; pow - er —
Bm7
Last time to Coda
to — dis-play — the won - ders, — the won-ders of — our God. -
F♯m E/G♯ A
Dmaj7 C♯m7 Bm9
D.C.(v.2)
—

2. Holy Spirit, open our eyes
To see the things that move You;
We need You.
Holy Spirit, burn in our hearts
With passion for the broken;
We need You.

They saw what seemed to be tongues of fire that separated and came to rest on each of them. All of them were filled with the Holy Spirit and began to speak in other tongues as the Spirit enabled them.

ACTS 2:3-4

2334. Holy, You are holy

(Santo)

Lk 1:35; Rev 5:12

Nivea Soares

Building in intensity

2. Worthy, You are worthy,
Jesus, Son of God.

D.C.(v.2)
2.
D.S.
3.
D C D A/C♯ D
sus. sus.
Mid section
F G
All glo - ry, all ho - nour to the Lamb of God.
D C D C F
All pow - er, and do-min-
1.
G D C D C
- ion be un-to You, Je - sus. All glo -
2.
D C F G D
D.C.(v.1) al fine
(inc. 1 rpt)
sus.

2335. Hope is here

(Jesus saves)

Ps 100:1; Is 61:1; Mt 18:27; Lk 19:10; Jn 14:9, 17; Eph 2:6; Jas 2:13

Tim Hughes
& Nick Herbert

Moderately

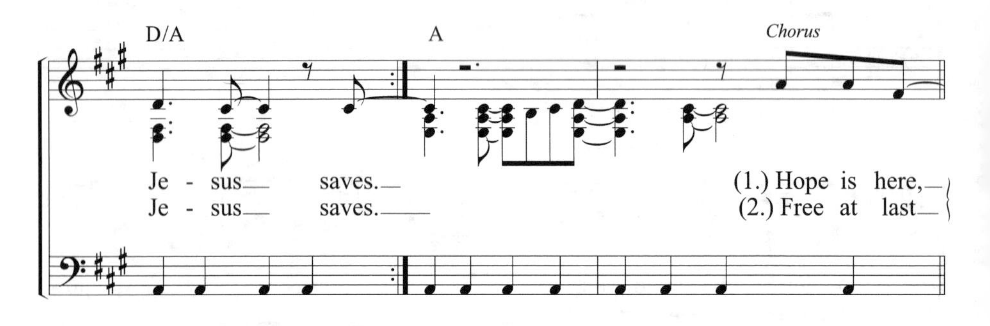

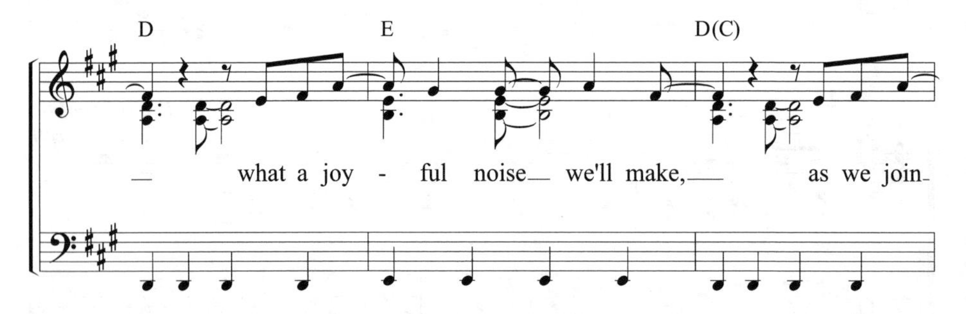

F♯m
E/G♯
E
F♯m
— with hea - ven's song — to let all — the world — know that
D
A
E
Je - sus — saves. — Raise a — shout — to let all —
Last time to Coda
F♯m
D
1.
D.C.(v.2)
— the world — know that Je - sus — saves. — 2. Free at last, —
2.,4.
D.S.S. (al Coda)
3.
Mid section
A
E
— Sing it out, — — You save, — You heal, — re-store, —
F♯m
D
— re-veal — Your Fa - ther's heart — to us. — You rose —

2. Free at last,
   Every debt has been repaid,
   Broken hearts can be remade:
   Jesus saves.
   Sing above the storms of life,
   Sing it through the darkest night:
   Jesus saves.

The Son of Man came to seek and to save what was lost.

LUKE 19:10

2336. Hope will not disappoint

(Hope)

Is 26:3; Jn 8:45; 14:27; Rom 5:5; Rev 21:4

Andrew Philip Ehrenzeller

Steadily, with a strong beat

Dm7
C
Your love is all — a-bout: — learn-ing — to trust, —
Gsus4
D
— like up-on a mo-ther, the bet-ter off we will be, —
Dm7
C
— rest-ing com - for-ta-bly, — learn-ing — to
G
Chorus
F
Am/E
trust. — There'll be no — more — cry - ing,
Dm7
Am
no — more — dy - ing, 'cause we don't — know — how — to. —

G C F Am/E
3
No more pain or sor - row, no es -
Dm7 Am
cap - ing to - mor - row, 'cause we don't know how to.
1.
D.C.(v.2)
2.,3.
G Am F G G
No more
F Am/E Dm7
guilt or shame, no more sin - ful stains, 'cause we
Am G C F Am/E
don't know how to. And e - ven death has

Last time to Coda
Dm7 Am G F Am/E
passed a - way.
Dm7 Am G F Am/E
D.S. al Coda
Coda
Dm7
Am
Am Verse F2 G
2. You keep in per - fect peace those whose minds
Am F2 G/B
keep on You, 'cause You tell the truth.
Am F2 G
Not like the world, which gives and takes a - way
Am F2 G/B
to get rich and save a lit - tle face.

2337. How great is Your love

(All glory)

Ps 99:5; 117:2; 146:6; Eph 3:20-21; Heb 10:20

Nikki Fletcher, Tim Hughes & Martin Smith

Steady 4, building

Chorus
G
Gmaj7
A
D/F♯
All glo - ry to God
who is a - ble,
all po - wer and praise;
forever the earth will proclaim: You are migh -
Last time to Coda
1.
Bm
ty, You are migh - ty.
D.C.(v.2)
2.
D.S.
D
ty, Lord.

3.
Mid section
G D A D G D
- ty. Lift Him high - er, He is migh - ty; lift Him high-
A D G A D/F♯
- er, He is God. Lift Him high - er, He is migh-
G A D/F♯
1.,2.
G D
- ty; lift Him high - er, He is God. Lift Him high -
3.
G
D.S. al Coda
Coda
G
- ty. You are migh-
A D/F♯ G
- ty.
2. So great is Your love,
It keeps all its promises;
Unshakable,
Eternity rests in Your hands.
Jesus, I surrender,
Lead me in Your ways.

Exalt the LORD our God and
worship at his footstool; he is holy.

PSALM 99:5

2338. I am broken
(Coming back)

Ps 28:2; Lk 15:20; 1 Tim 1:1

Ben Cantelon

Thoughtfully

B/D♯
D
Chorus
Bm/A
A
ne - ver, e-ver take Your place. I'm com - ing back to
(ch.2)
E/A
A
A/E
E
D/E
E
You, my love; I've had e-nough of what I've be-come. I'm
Last time to Coda
1.
Bm/F♯
F♯m
F♯sus4
F♯m
(ch.2)
Bm/D
Dmaj7
Bm6/D
D
com-ing back to You, I'm com-ing back to You.
A
F♯m
C♯m/E
D
A
F♯m
C♯m/E
D.C.(v.2)
2. I am
2.,4. D.S. (Chorus 2)
(2° al Coda)
3.
Bm6/D
D
Bm
A/D
A
Mid section
A
You. You.

F♯m/A
C♯m
D
Bm
A
F♯m
C♯m
D
Bm
A
I'm com-ing back,
F♯m
C♯m
D
Bm
I'm com-ing back to You. Yes, I'm
A
F♯m
C♯m
com-ing back, oh, I'm com-ing back to
D
Bm
A
F♯m
You. Oh, break me, mould me, heal me, re-store me;
Hold me close-ly, ne-ver let go;

2. I am reaching up to a higher ground,
But gravity has got a hold on me,
But I know Your love will see me through
This darkness.

(Chorus 2)
Take my heart and make it clean,
I'm overwhelmed as Your grace covers me;
I'm coming back to You,
Lord, I'm coming back to You.

2339. I am coming alive to You

(Coming alive)

Ps 86:8; Is 53:4; Joel 3:15-16; Mt 26:28; Jn 15:13; Acts 4:12; 1 Cor 2:9; Heb 10:20; 13:8

Steadily building

Paul Oakley

2. There is no other name;
Yesterday, tomorrow, today –
You are always the same,
You never change, Jesus.
No eye ever has seen
And no mind could ever conceive
All the good that You have
Waiting in store for us.

2340. I bow before You, God

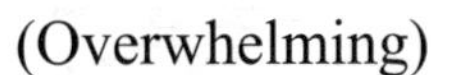

Amos 5:24; Jn 12:46

Geraldine Latty

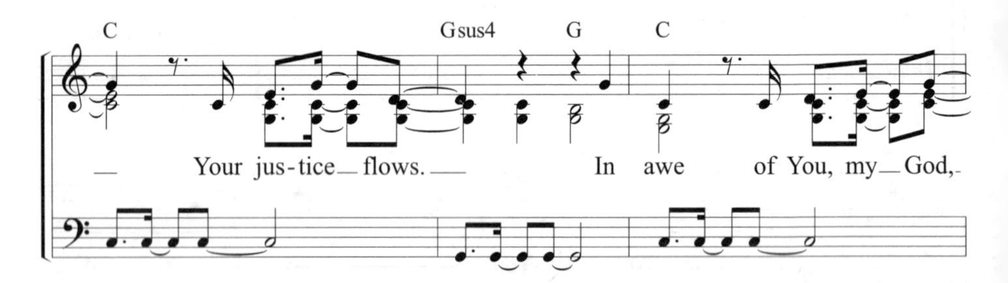

2. Today I choose You, God.
Compelled by love to follow You,
Today I choose to walk
Into Your promise, Your kingdom truth...

That's overflowing, overflowing
To the people we know and the world that You love.
It's overflowing, overflowing;
God, You poured out Your heart
So that we can take part in Your love.

3. We go with You, our God,
To speak Your words, to walk in grace.
We go with You, our God.
To show Your love in every place.

You're always loving, always loving;
Let compassion and grace give us courage to say:
You're always loving, always loving.
God, You poured out Your heart
So that we can take part in Your love.

2341. I bow down

(My heart, Your throne)

Ps 118:14

Capo 2 (D)

Raymond Tan

Flowing

Verse

E(D) C♯m7(Bm7)

I bow down be-fore Your throne, be-fore Your

Amaj7(G) A(G) Bsus4(A) E(D)

ma - je-sty; I sur - ren - der all to You, Lord,

C♯m7(Bm7) Amaj7(G) A(G) Bsus4(A) B(A)

to my Mas - ter and my King. I

C♯m(Bm) F♯/A♯(E/G♯) Bsus4(A) B(A) E/G♯(D/F♯) A(G)

lift up a psalm of praise; You are the song of my life.

Bsus4(A) B(A) *Chorus* 𝄋 Esus4(D) E(D)

I wor - ship, I

C♯m7(Bm7)
F♯m7(Em)
E/G♯(D/F♯)
A(G)
Bsus4(A) B(A)
wor - ship; my heart be-longs to You a-lone. I
Esus4(D)
E(D)
C♯m7(Bm7)
wor - ship, I wor - ship;
Last time to Coda
A(G)
B(A)
C♯m(Bm)
F♯/A♯ (E/G♯)
Lord, make my heart Your throne,
1.
A(G)
B(A)
E2(D)
C♯m7+4(Bm)
Lord, make my life Your own.
D.C.
2.
A2(G)
Bsus4(A)
A(G)
B(A)
I bow
Lord, make my life Your

E(D)
E/D(D/C)
A/C♯(G/B)
Am/C(Gm/B♭)
Am/D(Gm/C)
own.
Mid section (4 times with ad libs)
Lord make, Lord make my heart Your throne.
life Your own.
1.-3.
4.
D.S. al Coda
I
Coda
A(G)
B(A)
Lord, make my life Your own.

2342. I cling to the cross

Capo 2 (D)

Paul Baloche
& Matt Redman

Moderate 4

Verse

A(G) B(A) E(D)

I cling to the cross and ev-'ry-thing it means; I know it's the

A(G) B(A) E(D)

on - ly hope__ there is for sav - ing me. For with -

C♯m(Bm) G♯/B♯(F♯/A♯) E/B(D/A) F♯7/A♯(E7/G♯)

out Your__ great mer - cy I would be for-e-ver lost;__ with a

3rd time to Coda 𝄌

A(G) E/G♯(D/F♯) A(G) Bsus4(A) 1. A(G) B(A) E(D) A(G) B(A)

thank-ful heart_ I come and cling to the cross.

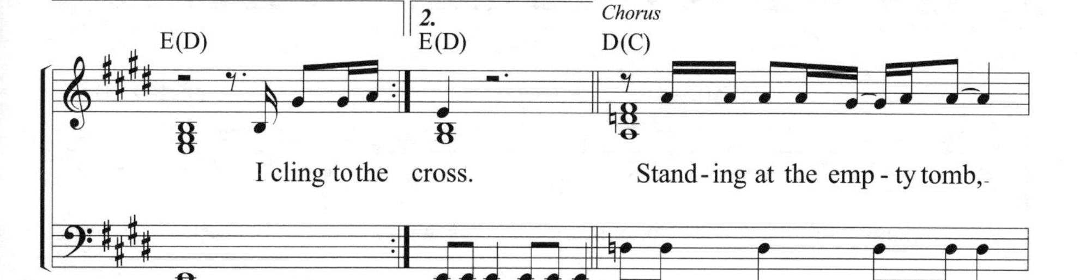

A/C♯(G/B)
E(D)
the pro-mis-es I have in You a - rise.
D(C)
A/C♯(G/B)
I was made a-live in You, ev'-ry-thing You said was true.
Am/C(Gm/B♭)
Bsus4(A)
You suf-fered, died and rose to bring us life, oh,
D.C.
Coda
B(A)
A(G)
bring us life. I cling to the
with a
E/G♯(D/F♯)
A(G)
E/G♯(D/F♯)
thank - ful heart I come, with a thank-ful heart I come

A(G)
Bsus4(A)
E(D)
and cling to the cross.
Mid section
E(D)
The world be - hind me, the cross be -
fore me. The world be - hind me, the cross be -
A/C♯(G/B)
fore me. The world be - hind me, the cross be -
E/B(D/A)
A(G)
E/B(D/A)
B(A)
fore me; no turn-ing back, no turn-ing
1.
2.
E(D)
E(D)
back. The world be - back. I cling to the cross.

2343. If faith can move the mountains

(Waiting here for You)

Mt 17:20; Eph 1:4; Heb 2:10; Rev 3:14

Capo 3 (C)

Chris Tomlin, Jesse Reeves & Martin Smith

Gently, building

Fm7(Dm)
Cm7(Am)
B♭sus4(G)
lift - ed high in
A♭sus2(F)
E♭(C)
praise. And it's You we a-dore,
Fm7(Dm)
Last time to Coda
Cm7(Am)
B♭sus4(G)
sing - ing, 'Al - le - lu-
Cm7(Am)
B♭sus4(G)
1.
E♭(C)
Cm7(Am)
B♭sus4(G)
ia.'
R.H.
E♭(C)
Cm7(Am)
B♭sus4(G)
D.C.(v.3)
2
A♭sus2(F)
3. You are ev -

Mid section
A♭(F)
Cm7(Am)
B♭sus4(G)
We will wait for You, Lord, in
A♭(F)
3
Cm7(Am)
B♭sus4(G)
step with You, Lord. We will sing, 'Al-le-lu - ia.' Sing-ing,
A♭(F)
Cm7(Am)
B♭sus4(G)
A♭(F)
'Al - le - lu - ia, al - le -
1.
Cm7(Am)
B♭sus4(G)
lu - ia.' Sing-ing,
2.
Cm7(Am)
B♭sus4(G)
lu - ia.'
D.S. al Coda
Coda
Cm7(Am)
B♭sus4(G)
Wait-ing here for You,
- le -

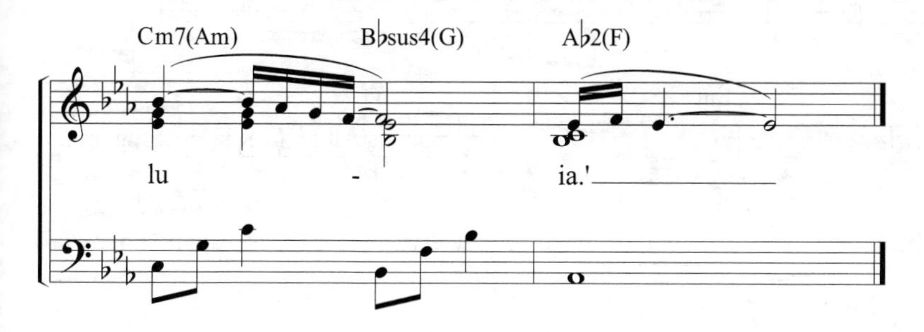

2. You're the Lord of all creation
And still You know my heart.
The Author of Salvation –
You've loved us from the start.

3. You are everything You've promised,
Your faithfulness is true,
And we're desperate for Your presence;
All we need is You.

2344. If I call, will You come?

(Faithful God)

Ps 61:1; Lam 3:23; Phil 2:10; 1 Pet 5:7; 1 Jn 2:28

Zach Neese

D
Chorus
Em D/F♯ G
God. Faith - ful God, You hold my life se -
C Dsus4 D Em D/F♯
cure, and all my days are Yours. I be -
G C Dsus4 D
lieve my God is like a fire, de-fend - ing me faith -
Last time to Coda
1.
D.C.(v.2)
Em D/F♯ G Em D/F♯ Cmaj7
- ful-ly, faith - ful-ly.
2.
Mid section
G C Em
And I know You are mine and I am Yours,

D/F♯ G C
I am Yours. And I know Your faith-ful - ness
Em D/F♯ Em D/F♯
it will en - dure, it will en - dure.
G Em D/F♯ Cmaj7 D.S. al Coda
Coda
Gsus2 G Em D/F♯ Cmaj7
Verse
Em D/F♯ G Em D/F♯ G
2. I be-lieve You still heal and de - mons still bow.
Em D/F♯ G C D
I'm con-vinced there is pow'r in trust-ing in a faith - ful God.
Em D/F♯ G Em D/F♯
So I will praise till You ap - pear and set Your foot up-on this
G Em D/F♯ G C D
shore. And I de-clare that ev - 'ry foe is sub-ject to my faith-ful God.

Because of the LORD's great love we are not consumed, for his compassions never fail. They are new every morning; great is your faithfulness.

LAMENTATIONS 3:22-23

2345. If I sang the songs the angels sing

1 Cor 13:1-8

(Never-failing love)

Stuart Townend
& Mark Edwards

D.C.(v.3,4) al Coda
E7 Asus4 A Dsus4 D G C/G G7
un - de-filed, re - joic-ing in the truth. 3. I could
Coda
Freely
a tempo
Rit.
C6 D7 G7sus4 C/G C
love, His ne-ver fail - ing love.
Ped.
8vb
C E7 Am Fm6 C E7
2. I could give to ev - 'ry child in need, I could save the pla-net
Am Fm6 C Dm/A E7/G♯ C/G D9 Dm7 B C
from our greed, I could stand for jus-tice till I bleed – and ne-ver know His love.
C E7 Am Fm6 C E7
3. I could give my mo-ney to the poor, I could preach the gos - pel
Am Fm6 C Dm/A E7/G♯ C/G D9 Dm7 B C
door to door, e-ven save a thou-sand souls or more – and still not know His love.
C E7 Am Fm6 C E7
4. When the fin - est words have passed a-way, and the best we have is
Am Fm6 C Dm/A E7/G♯ C/G D9 Dm7 B
yes - ter-day, there is one thing that is here to stay – His ne-ver - fail-ing
C6 D7 G7sus4 C/G C
love, His ne-ver - fail - ing love.

2346.
If it wasn't for the blood
Jn 14:6; Rom 5:9;
1 Cor 1:18; Col 1:20
Capo 2 (D)
Godfrey Birtill
Moderately
Verse
E(D)
1. If it was-n't for the blood I'd be dead; if it
was-n't for the blood I'd be hope - less. If it
was-n't for the blood I'd be lost; if it
was-n't for the blood, was-n't for the blood of my
Chorus
A(G)
Je - sus, Sa - viour, re - con - ci - ler,

2. If it wasn't for the blood I'd be blamed;
If it wasn't for the blood I'd be guilty.
If it wasn't for the blood I'd be vile;
If it wasn't for the blood,
If it wasn't for the blood of my . . .

2347. I hear the Saviour say

(Jesus paid it all)

Is 1:18; Ezek 36:26; Mt 26:41; 1 Jn 1:7; Rev 7:9

CHRIST I OWE

Words: Elvina M. Hall (1820–1889)
Music: John T. Grape (1835–1915)
Arr. Aaron Keyes

With thankfulness

Verse

C G/B
1. I hear the Saviour say, 'Thy strength indeed is
(2.) now indeed I find Thy pow'r and Thine a-

C F
small. Child of weak - ness watch and pray; find in
-lone can change the le-per's spots and

C G C
me thine all in all.'
melt the heart of stone.

Chorus

Am C/E
Je - sus paid it all: all to Him I

G C C/E F C G
owe. Sin had left a crim-son stain: He washed it white as

1.
D.C.(v.2)
2.
C
Csus4
Fmaj7
G
snow.
2. Lord,
snow.
Fmaj7
G
Verse
D
Bm
3. And when be-fore the throne I
A
D
A/C♯
Bm
D/A
stand in Him com - plete, 'Je-sus died my soul to
G
D
A
D
save,' my lips shall still re - peat.

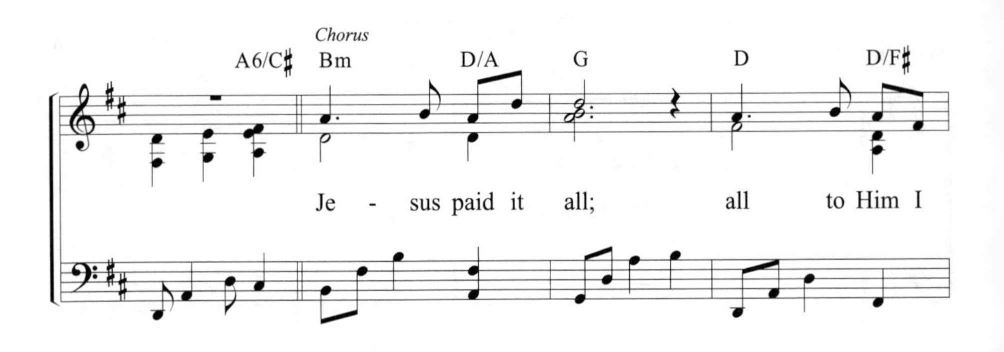
Chorus
A6/C♯
Bm
D/A
G
D
D/F♯
Je - sus paid it all; all to Him I

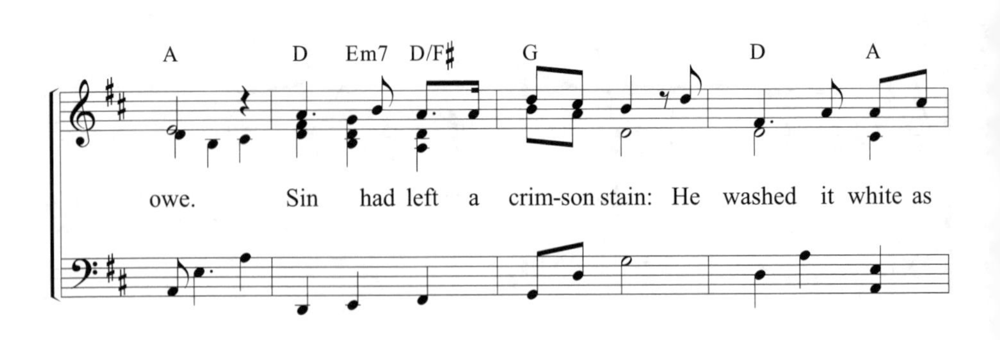
A
D
Em7
D/F♯
G
D
A
owe. Sin had left a crim-son stain: He washed it white as

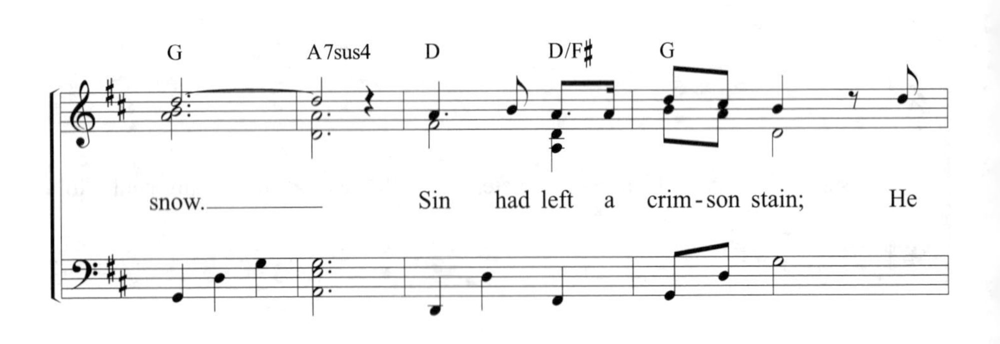
G
A7sus4
D
D/F♯
G
snow. Sin had left a crim - son stain; He

D
A
G
A7sus4
D
washed me white as snow.

2348. I hear the words

(Prophet song)

Rom 10:13; 2 Cor 12:10

Martin Smith

1.
D.C.(v.2)
C
G
love to hear the voice of God.
2.,3.
G
D
Most of all I
C
G
Gsus2
1st time D.C.(v.2)
G
love to hear the voice of God.
Chorus
G
We'll call on the name of the
hun - ger and thirst for Your
D
(2°)
Lord, for He is the One who can
word, for here we will meet You, Lord,

2. I hear the prayers of the pray-ers,
I hear the songs in the silence,
I see the joy of the dancers
And all the healing they bring;
But most of all I love to hear the voice of God.
Most of all I love to hear the voice of God.

3. We long to see heaven open
And see Your glory come down;
We long to hear words eternal,
Forever changing our hearts.
And if You'd come, we'd love to hear the voice of God.
Oh, will You come? We long to hear Your voice, O God.

2349. I know that my Redeemer lives

Job 19:25; Ps 34:8; Acts 1:11; Eph 1:14; 1 Thess 4:17; Heb 7:25; Rev 5:12

With a strong beat

Chorus & new music:
John Hartley & Chris Eaton

Verse

C F G F G C

1. I know that my Re - deem - er lives and ev - er prays for me.
(2.) - sus, I hang on ev - 'ry word, I stead-fast - ly be - lieve.

A to - ken of His love He gives, a pledge of lib - er - ty.
You will re - turn and claim me, Lord, and

(vv.3&4)

F G F G C

1.

2. Je -

2.,3.,4.
(vv.3&4)

F G C

to Your - self re - ceive.

Chorus

And we will lift You

F G Am
up, hal-le-lu - jah, ho - ly is our God.
F G Am
And we will wor-ship You and ho - nour Your name.
C/E F G
Wor-thy is the Lamb, hal-le-lu - jah, You
Am F G
reign in ma - jes - ty. Glo-ry to our God, for-ev - er the
1.
C F/C Dm/C
same. 3. Joy -

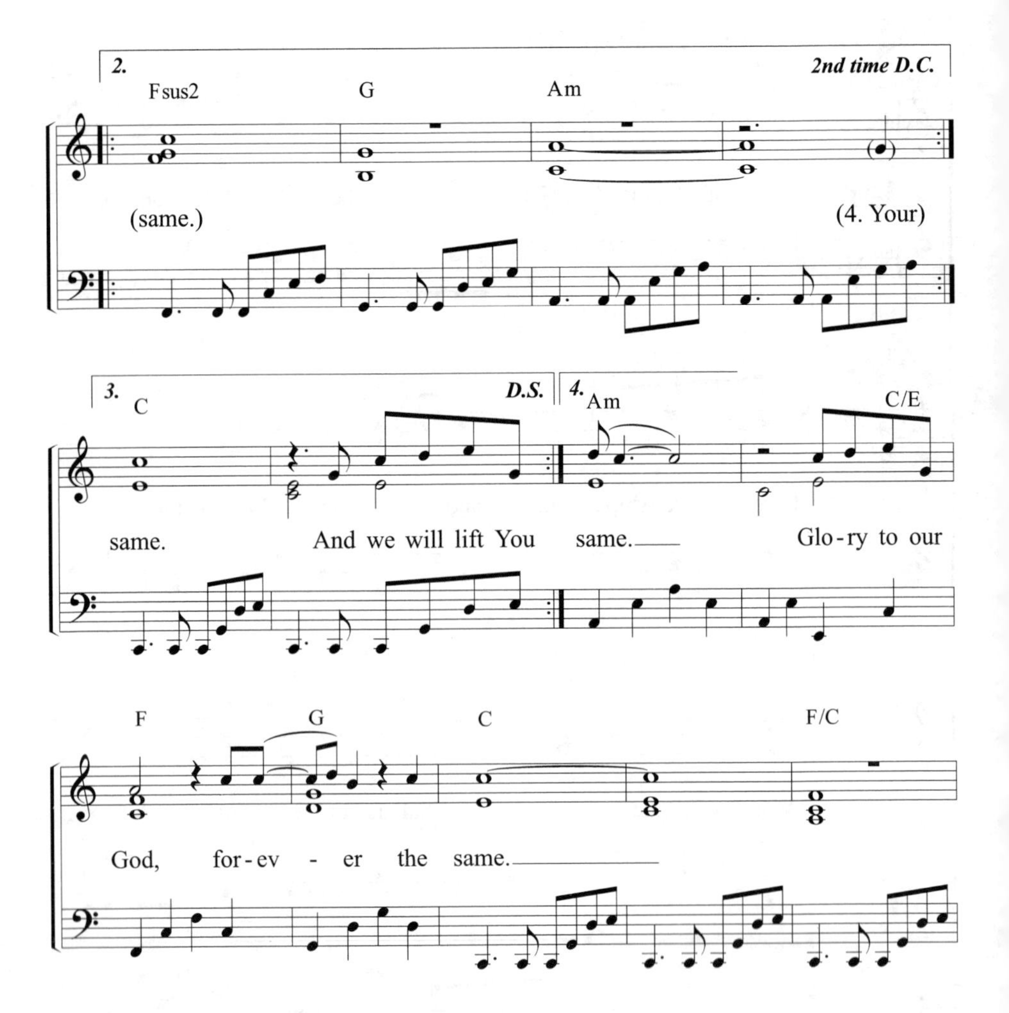

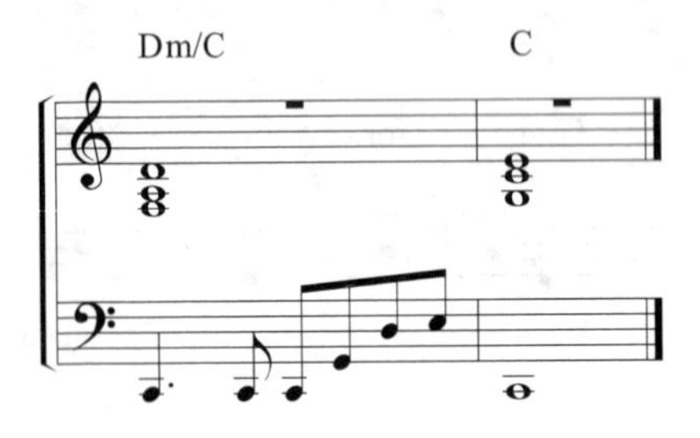

3. Joyful in hope my spirit soars
To meet You from above.
Your goodness thankfully adores,
And sure, I taste Your love.

4. Your love I soon expect to find
In all its depth and height;
To comprehend the eternal mind
And grasp the infinite.

Charles Wesley (1707–88)

2350.
I'll remember You
(Remember)
Capo 2 (D)
Lk 24:2-3; Jn 15:13; 1 Cor 7:23; 11:24-26
Tim & Rachel Hughes
Steadily
Verse
E(D)
Asus2/E(G/D)
B(no3rd)/E(A/D)
1. I'll re-mem - ber You,
I'll re-mem - ber what You did. Re-
C♯m(Bm)
A2(G)
mem-ber-ing the cross, re-mem - ber-ing the price You paid,
I'll re-mem - ber You. For
Chorus

Amaj7(G)
Bsus4(A)
E/G♯(D/F♯)
no one's e - ver loved me quite like You do,
Amaj7(G)
Bsus4(A)
C♯m(Bm)
no one's e - ver loved me quite like You;
Amaj7(G)
Bsus4(A)
E/G♯(D/F♯)
Je - sus, for Your glo - ry, I will tell the sto - ry of the
Last time to Coda
1.
D.C.(v.2)
2.
Mid section
Asus2(G)
Asus2(G)
cross.
2. And
Hal-le -
A(G)
B(A)
C♯m(Bm)
lu - jah, hal-le - lu - jah, hal-le - lu - jah for the cross.

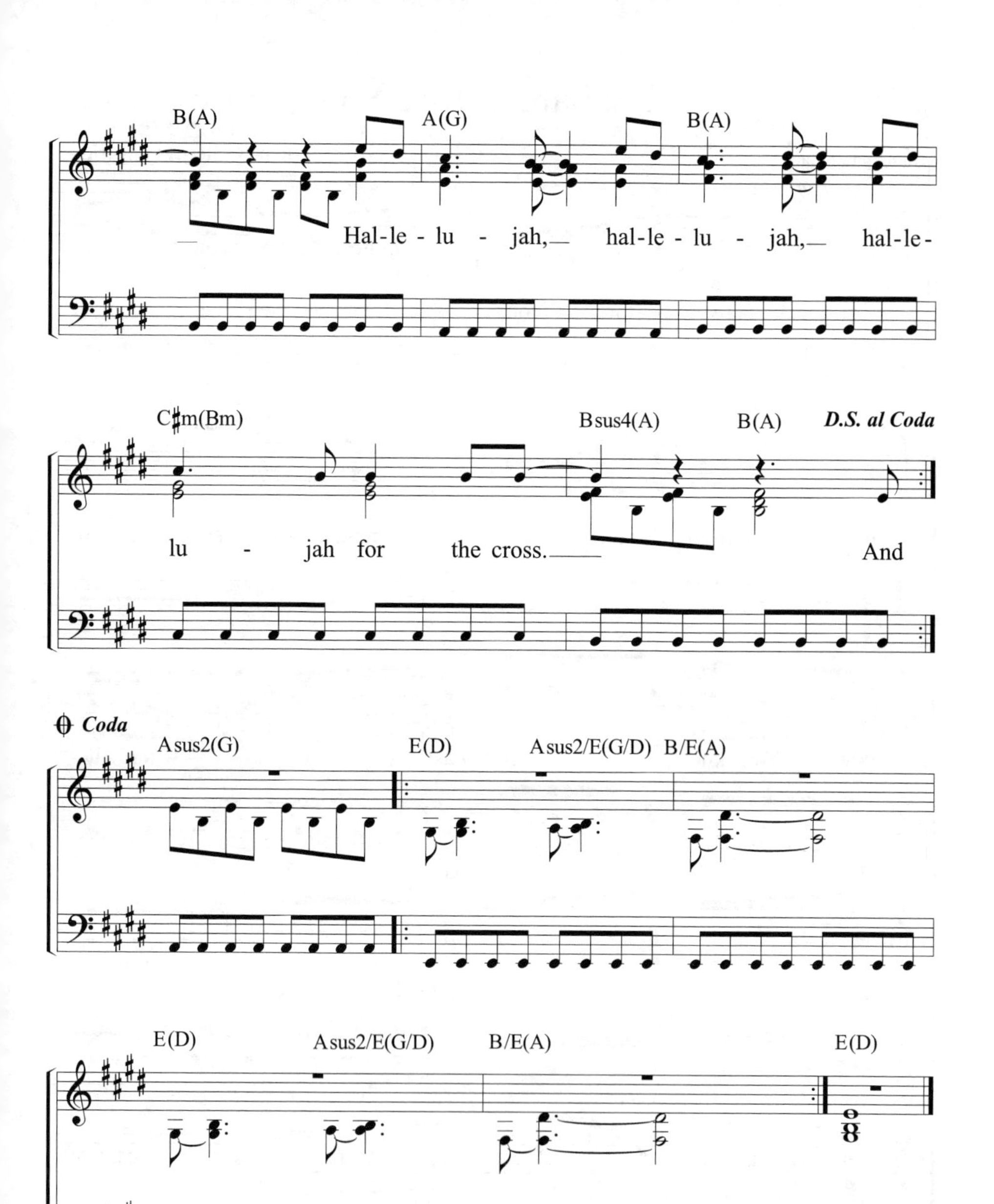

2. I will sing of You,
I will sing of what You did.
The stone lies rolled away,
Nothing but an empty grave.
I will sing of You.

2351.

I'm bare before You

(Exalt)

Ps 18:19; Jn 13:5; Rom 2:4; Col 1:14; Heb 4:13

Rend Collective Experiment

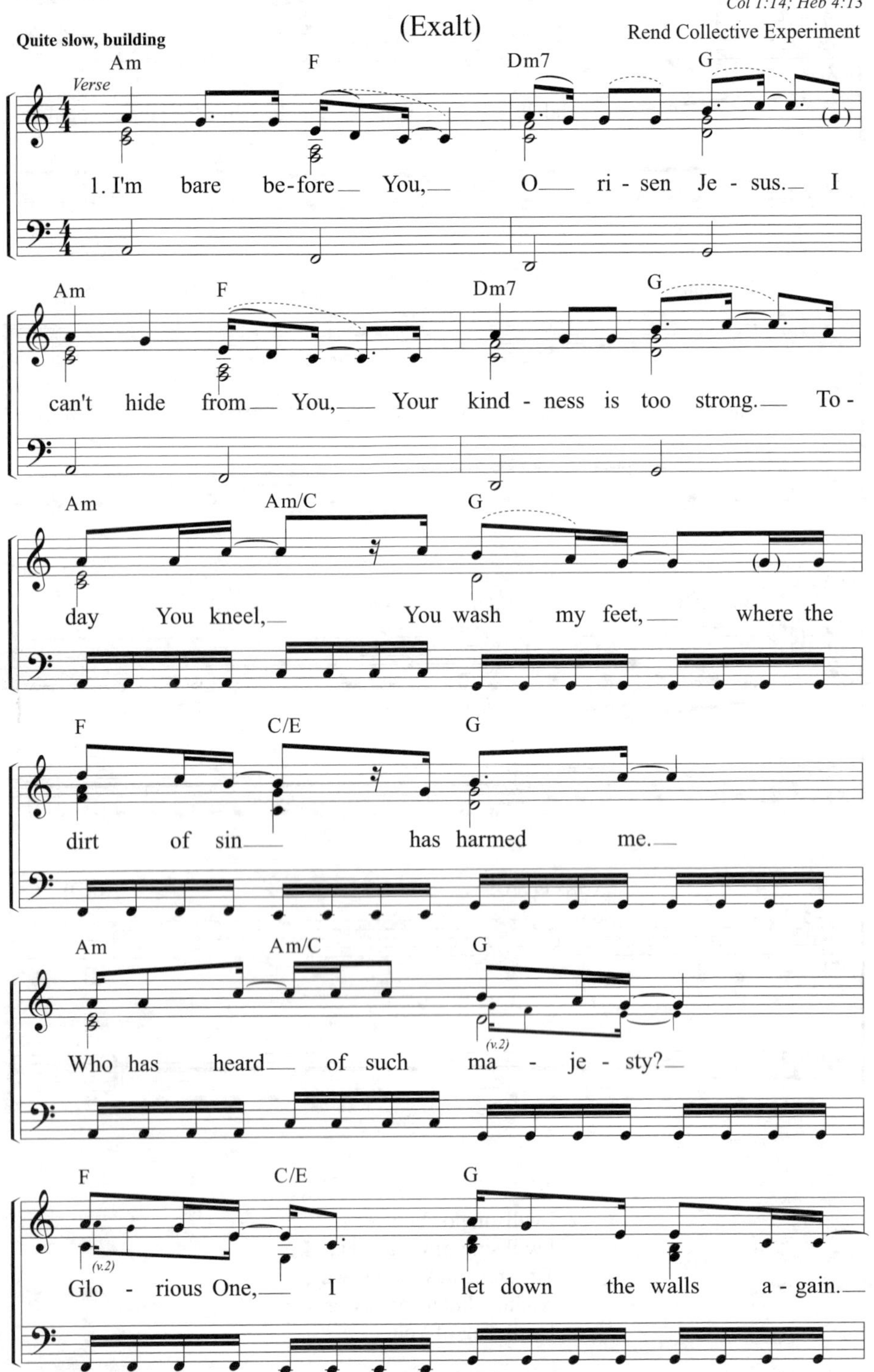

(v.2)
F
G
There's no-thing that's sweet-er than Your friend-ship;
Am
F
C
G
Chorus
there's no-thing that's great-er than Your lord-ship. I ex -
C
F
alt You, I ex - alt You, I ex -
Dm7
G
alt You and en - joy You. I ex -
(D)
Am
F
(small notes D.S.)
alt You, I ex - alt You, I ex -

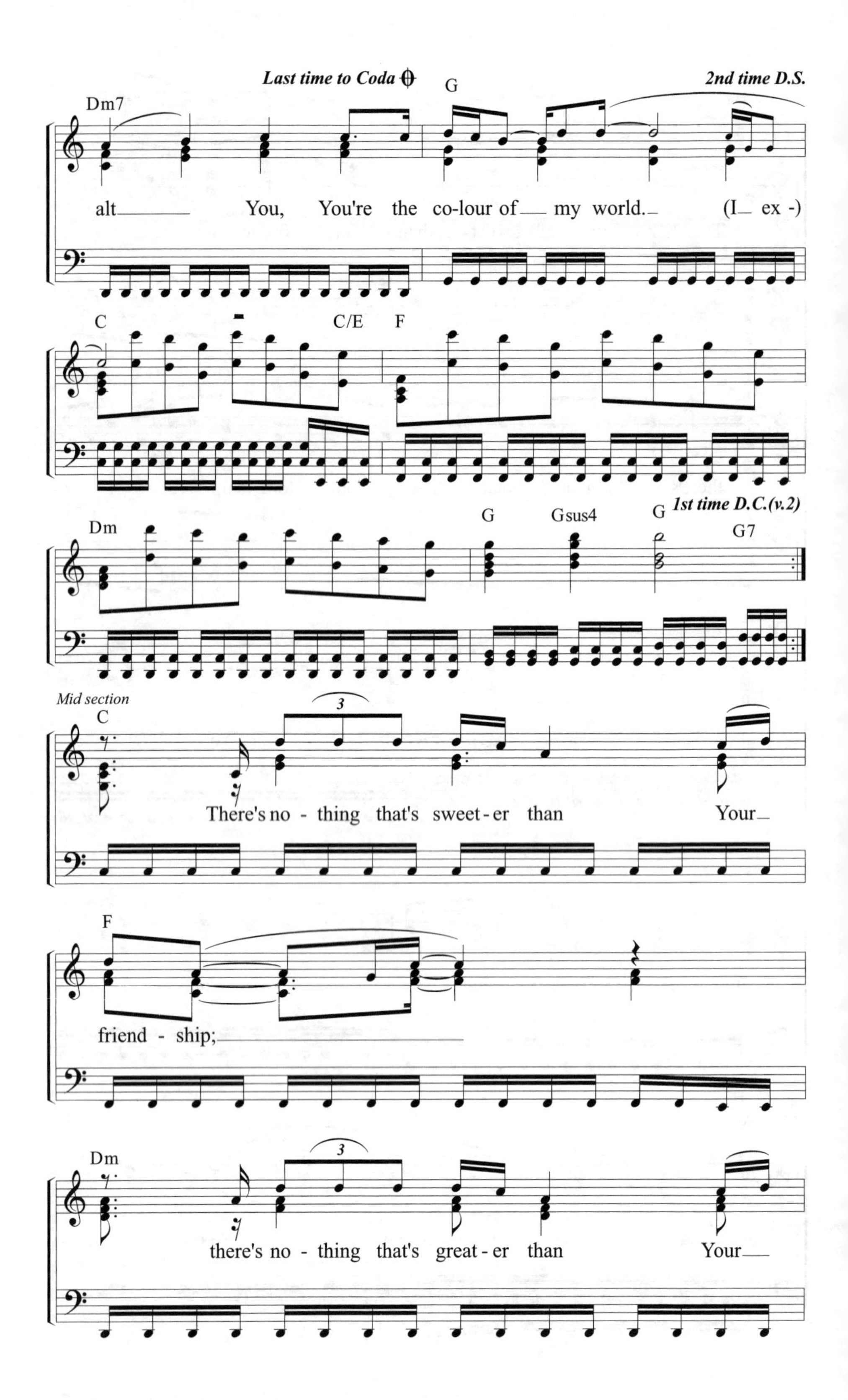

Last time to Coda
2nd time D.S.
Dm7
G
alt You, You're the co-lour of my world. (I ex-)
C
C/E
F
Dm
G
Gsus4
G
1st time D.C.(v.2)
G7
Mid section
C
There's no - thing that's sweet-er than Your
F
friend - ship;
Dm
there's no - thing that's great-er than Your

2. You are my sight, my life's guide;
Though I'm blind, You brighten the way.
The troubles they are many,
And I feel I'm losing,
But You rescue me in Your time.
Glorious One, You redeem all my mistakes;
There's nothing that's stronger than
Your overwhelming grace,
And Your truth is my wide open space.

2352. I'm casting my cares aside

(Today is the day)

Ps 118:24; Mt 6:34; Eph 6:14; Phil 3:13; 1 Pet 5:7

Paul Baloche
& Lincoln Brewster

Driving rock

Verse

C(no3rd) Am7 F2

1. I'm cast-ing my cares a-side, I'm leav-ing my past

C(no3rd) Am7 F2 C(no3rd)

be-hind, I'm set-ting my heart and mind on You,

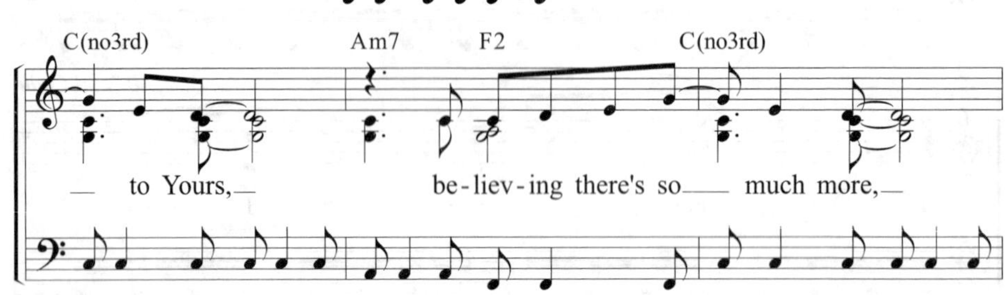

Dm7
F2
Chorus
C
is good. To-day is the day You have made,
Gsus4
Am7
F2
I will re-joice and be glad in it. To-day is the day
C
G/B
Am7
You have made, I will re-joice and be glad in it.
F2
Dm7
Last time to Coda
C/E
I won't wor - ry a-bout to-mor-row, I'm
F2
Gsus4
C
trust-ing in what You say: to-day is the day,

1.
D.C.(v.2)
C/E F C C/E F
to-day is the day. 2. I'm put-ting my fears
2.
Mid section
C/E F C Am G F
I will stand up - on Your truth. (I
C Am G F C Am
will stand up - on Your truth.) All my days, I'll live
G F
1.
C Am G F
for You. (All my days, I'll live for You.) I
2.
Dm7 F
D.S. al Coda
my days I'll live. To-day is the day
Coda
C/E
to-mor - row, giv-

2. I'm putting my fears aside,
I'm leaving my doubts behind,
I'm giving my hopes and dreams to You, Jesus.
I'm reaching my hands to Yours,
Believing there's so much more,
Knowing that all You have in store for me
Is good, is good.

2353. I'm gonna dance on the streets

(Dance on the streets)

Mt 1:20-21; Lk 1:35; Acts 2:33; Rev 22:1, 20

Mike Burn

Lively

Verse

G

I'm gon - na dance on the streets, ___

A

I'm gon-na sing in the rain, ___ for the Spi - rit of God

C D G

___ is poured ___ out a - gain. ___

G

I'm gon - na shout it a - loud, ___

A

I'm gon-na let the world know ___ that the ri - ver of God

C D G
has start - ed to flow.
Chorus
C D G
And we sing Je - sus, Je - sus, come!
C D G
Oh, we will lift Your name on high.
C D Em
You are the Son of God, sa - ving One.
A C Am7 D
Je - sus, Je - sus, come!

1.
2.
G/B
C
I'm gon - na dance on the streets,
Je - sus,
Am7
D
G/B
C
Je - sus, come!
Je - sus,
Am7
D
G
Je - sus, come!

God has raised this Jesus to life, and we are all witnesses of the fact. Exalted to the right hand of God, he has received from the Father the promised Holy Spirit and has poured out what you now see and hear.

ACTS 2:33-33

2354. I'm laying out all the pieces of my life

(Keep the faith)

Lev 9:24; 1 Kings 18:38; Rom 8:37; 12:1-2; 2 Tim 4:7

Tenderly

Martin Smith, Nick Herbert & Tim Hughes

Verse

F♯m E/G♯ A

1. I'm lay-ing out all the pie-ces of my life;

F♯m E/G♯ A

on the al-tar, I'm Your sac-ri-fice.

Bm7 A E

Let Your fire fall, I'm wait - ing here.

Bm A E A/C♯

Come and take it all, this heart of fear.

Omit 3°

D2 ***D.C.(v.2)*** D2

Chorus

A

We will o-ver-come; when

D/A
A
You are with us, we are strong, and
D/A
A
E/G♯
love will be our great - est song. We'll keep the faith
Last time to Coda
1.
D.C.(v.3)
D/F♯
A/E
E
and stand for - e - ver.
2.,4.
D.S. (al Coda)
(small notes 2°)
3.
Mid section
E
E
A
Bm7
- ver. We will o - ver - ver. We be - lieve in
E
D
A
Bm7
E
D
A
Bm7
God Al - migh - ty, we be - lieve in You. We will trust in

E D A Bm7 E D D/F♯
God Al-migh-ty, we will trust in You. We be-lieve in
A/E E D/F♯ A/E E
God Al - migh - ty, we be - lieve in You.
D/F♯ A/E E D/F♯
We will trust in God Al - migh - ty, we will trust in You.
A/E E
D.S.
We will o-ver -
Coda
E A/C♯
- ver. We'll keep the
D/F♯ A/E E D/F♯
faith and stand for - e - ver. Live the faith and stand for-

A/E
E
e - ver.
Verse
F♯m
E/G♯
A
2. All I want is to do my Fa - ther's will,
and be a voice to a world that's stand - ing still.
I must keep the
Bm7
faith, not back - ing down.
We must keep the
Bm
A/C♯
D2
faith: this is our time.
Verse
3. If not us, who will shout Your song of praise
for ev-'ry soul to be saved in Je - sus' name?
So we must keep the
faith, not back - ing down.
We must live the
faith: this is our time, oh.

2355. Immortal, invisible

2 Sam 7:22; Ps 104:1-2; Dan 7:9; Rom 16:27; 1 Tim 1:17; 6:16

New music & Chorus: John Hartley, Chris Eaton & Chris McClarney

(v.2)
(v.3)
Am
C
G
al-migh-ty, vic - to-rious, Thy great name we praise.
1. D.C.(v.2)
2.,3.
Dsus4 D
Dsus4 D
Chorus
Em
love. Lord, there is none like You,
C
G
D
(oh,) my Je - sus, my Je - sus. No-thing com-pares
Em
C
G
to You, oh, my Je - sus, my Je -
1. D.C.(v.3)
3. D.S.
2.,4.
Dsus4 D
Dsus4 D
Dsus4 D
- sus. - sus. Lord, there is none - sus. Oh,

Mid section
G D Em
Im - mor - tal, in - vi - si - ble, God on - ly wise;
C G D
in light in - ac - ces - si - ble
Em C G
hid from our eyes. Most bles - sèd,
D Em C
most glo - ri - ous, An - cient of Days:
G D 1. Em
al - migh - ty, vic - to - ri - ous, Thy name we praise.

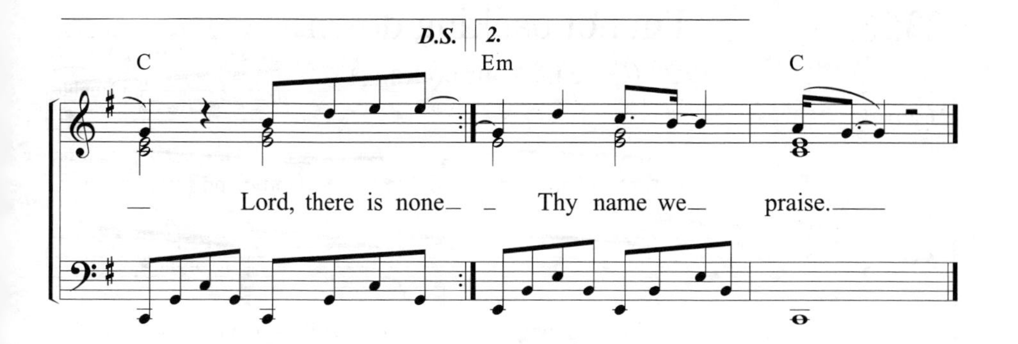

2. Unresting, unhasting, silent as light;
   Nor wanting, nor wasting, Thou rulest in might.
   Thy justice, like mountains, soaring above;
   Thy clouds, which are fountains of Your goodness and love.

3. To all life Thou givest, both great and small;
   In all life Thou livest, true life of all.
   Great Father of glory, pure Father of light,
   Thine angels adore Thee, all veiling their sight.

W. Chalmers Smith (1824–1908) adpt.

2356. I'm not backing down

(Give us Your courage)

Num 6:25; Lk 1:37; Jn 20:22; Acts 1:8; Eph 6:14

Tim Hughes

Moderately

(v.2)

Em C
I'm not back-ing down, I will stand my ground,

G D Em
lift-ing high the name of Je-sus. Hold-ing out Your light

C G D
to a world in need, liv-ing out the love of Je-

Am7 *Bridge* G/B C
-sus. Though the bat-tles rage,

Am7
G/B
C
Chorus
(small notes 2°)
Your bles-sing still will come.
To the ends
G
of the earth we will go, to the ends
of Your word we will stand, for the truth
D
(small notes 2°)
Am
of the earth we will go; fill us with pow-er,
of Your word we will stand; give us Your cou-rage,
Last time to Coda
1.,3.,5.
2. D.C.(v.2)
C
fill us with pow-er. For the truth
give us Your cou-rage.
4.
Mid section
D
C
G/B
Would You breathe on us, would You breathe on

2. Be our strength and song
Till the battle's won,
Cause Your face to shine upon us.
Stretch Your hand to save,
Our God never fails;
Nothing is impossible for You.

2357. I'm ready to rise

(Wake up)

Ps 57:8-9, 11; Is 6:3; Mt 16:25

Rock feel

Stuart Garrard, Tim Hughes & Martin Smith

Em7
Am
F
strong - er, shout it out and wor - ship Him.
G
Am7
Dm7
All that we have will give You praise.
G
Am7
Yes, we were born to give You praise.
F
Last time to Coda
1.
D.C.(v.2)
2.
Mid section
And
G
Am7
F
sing!
Oh, my soul, rise and

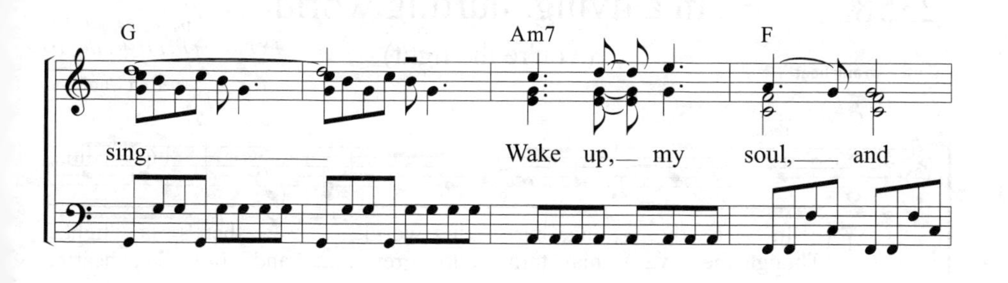

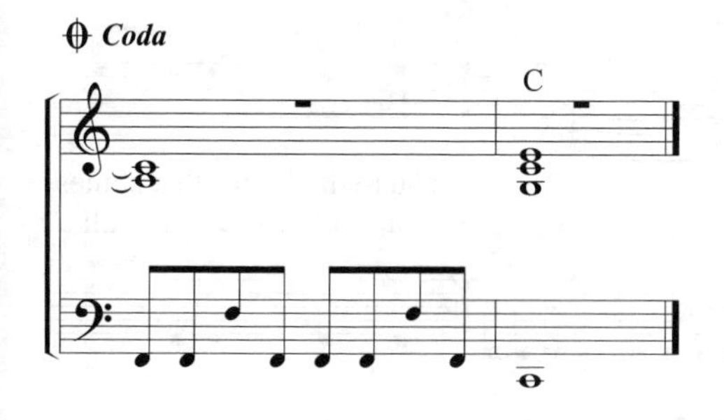

2. You light up my heart,
You light up the skies,
You've covered the earth in glory.
The wonder of You,
The wonder of You.
You never give up,
You never let go,
You give me a crown of mercy.
The beauty of You,
The beauty of You.

2358. In a dying, hurting world

(You're the light)

Amos 5:24; Mt 11:5; Lk 1:37; Jn 1:5; 11:44; Heb 1:3

With a strong beat

Ben Cantelon

Verse

C

1. In a dy - ing, hurt - ing world there's a light that shines for all to see.
Though the sky may turn to grey and bro - ken hearts be - gin to fade a - way,

F/A Am F/A 1. Am

2. Am Gsus4 G Gsus4

Your love shines through, day-light breaks through the long-est of nights.

G F Dm

Chorus

F

You're the light that shines in dark - ness, shi - ning bright for all the world to see.
ra - di - ant in all Your glo - ry; no - thing is im - pos - si - ble for You,

C

2. God of mercy, God of grace,
Let justice flow like we have never known.
Give us courage, give us faith,
Faith for miracles we've longed to see.
The deaf will hear You,
The blind will see You.
Let the dead man arise!

2359.

In all I do

(This is my worship)

Mt 5:16; Rom 12:1; Eph 5:10; Col 3:23-24; Jas 1:17

Nathan Fellingham

Am
Em
that You have not gi - ven; I'll ho - nour You, Lord,
G
C
Dsus4
D
Chorus
C
with my whole life. This is my wor - ship, this is my wor-
Em
G
Dsus4
- ship: liv-ing for Your glo - ry, O God. In all of my deal-
C
Em
- ings, let me be pleas - ing; it is Je-sus
1.
G
Dsus4
D
D.C.(v.2)
Christ whom I serve. 2. With ev - 'ry gift

2. With every gift Your mercy brings,
I will work towards Your cause.
To share good news with every heart
Is Your charge to those You've called.
Your love is so vast,
Your grace so compelling,
And all that is good is sourced in You.
Now as I draw near,
You call me to share in
The wonder of all the Godhead's love.

Whatever you do, work at it with all your heart, as working for the Lord, not for men, since you know that you will receive an inheritance from the Lord as a reward. It is the Lord Christ you are serving.

COLOSSIANS 3:23-24

2360. I need Thee every hour

Mt 11:28; Jn 14:27; 1 Cor 10:13

Annie S. Hawks (1835–1918)
& Robert Lowry (1826–99)
Arr. Paul Hughes

NEED

2. I need Thee every hour,
Stay Thou nearby;
Temptations lose their power
When Thou art nigh.

3. I need Thee every hour
In joy or pain;
Come quickly and abide,
Or life is vain.

4. I need Thee every hour;
Teach me Thy will,
And Thy rich promises
In me fulfil.

5. I need Thee every hour,
Most holy One.
O make me Thine indeed,
Thou blessed Son.

2361.
In every circumstance
(You reign)
Ps 23:1, 4; Lam 3:23; 5:19; Mal 3:6; 2 Cor 12:9; Phil 4:12
Capo 3 (D)
Jamie Thomson
Joyfully
Verse
F(D)
1. In ev - 'ry cir - cum-stance You reign, e - ver-last -
Dm7(Bm)
(v.2)
- ing, You won't change; Lord, I trust
B♭(G)
in You, my heart it knows Your name.
C(A)
F(D)
You are my God, You ne - ver fail, in dark-est days
Dm7(Bm)
You still pre - vail, I know Your faith -

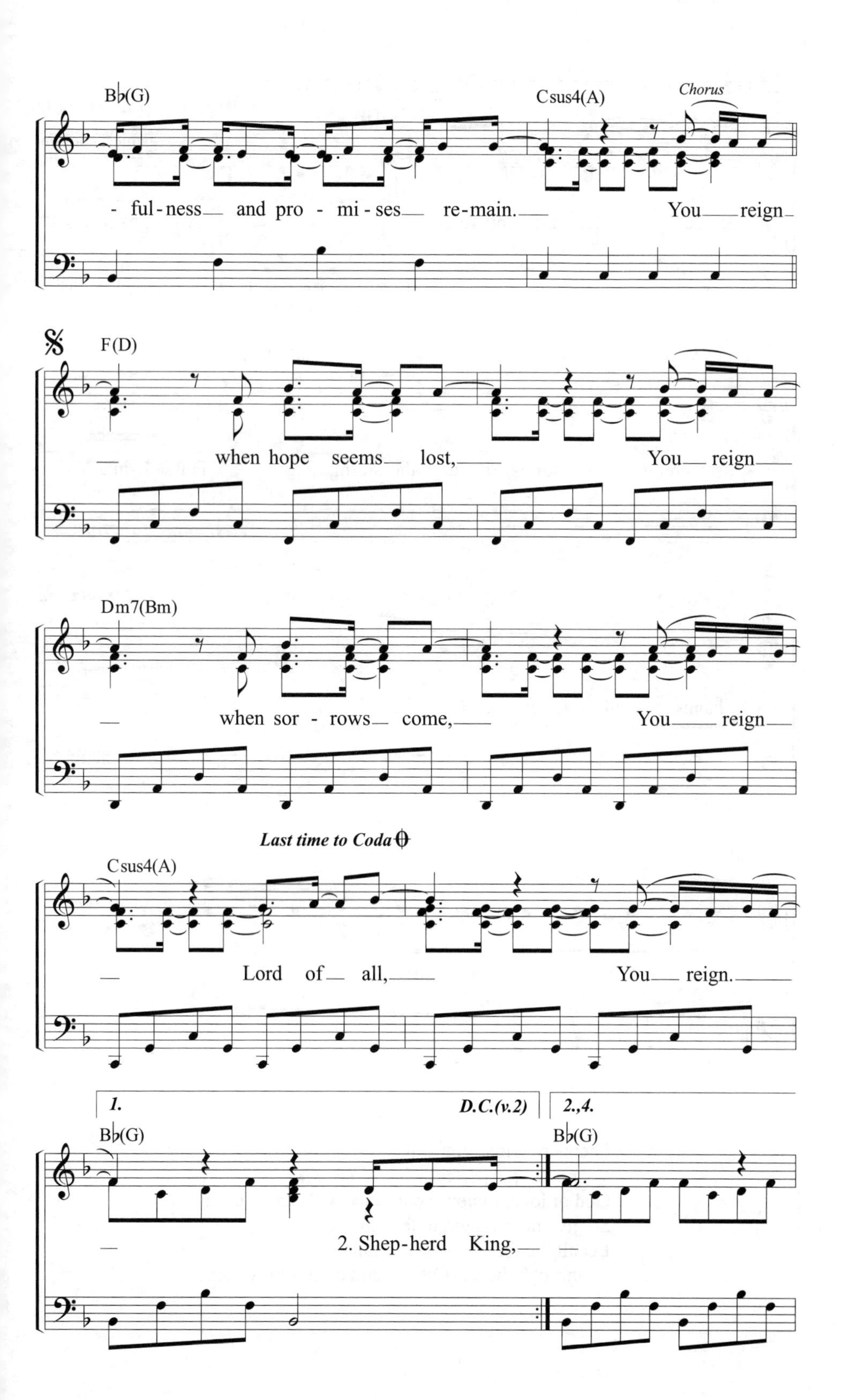
B♭(G)
Csus4(A)
Chorus
- ful - ness and pro - mi - ses re - main.
You reign
F(D)
when hope seems lost,
You reign
Dm7(Bm)
when sor - rows come,
You reign
Last time to Coda
Csus4(A)
Lord of all,
You reign.
1.
D.C.(v.2)
2.,4.
B♭(G)
2. Shep - herd King,
B♭(G)

2. Shepherd King, You walk with me,
Your power is perfect when I'm weak,
God of love, I know Your grace will light the way.
So give me strength to face today,
Let all the fear give way to faith,
So through the tears of life and times of joy I sing.

I the LORD do not change.

MALACHI 3:6

2362. In our hearts, Lord
(Awakening)

Ps 57:8-9; Mt 4:16; 6:10

Chris Tomlin
& Reuben Morgan

Worshipfully

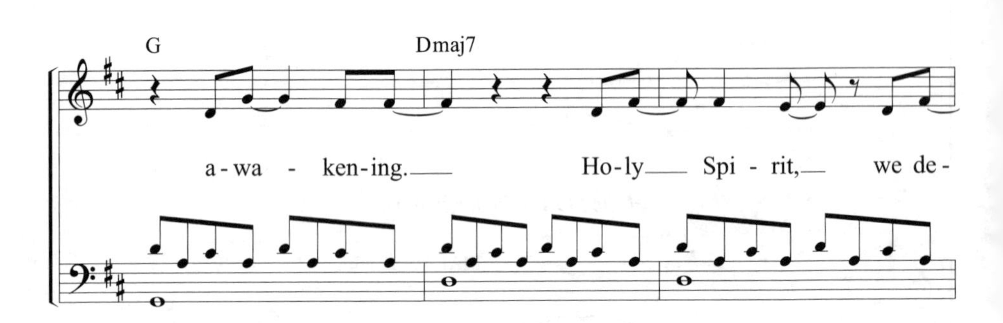

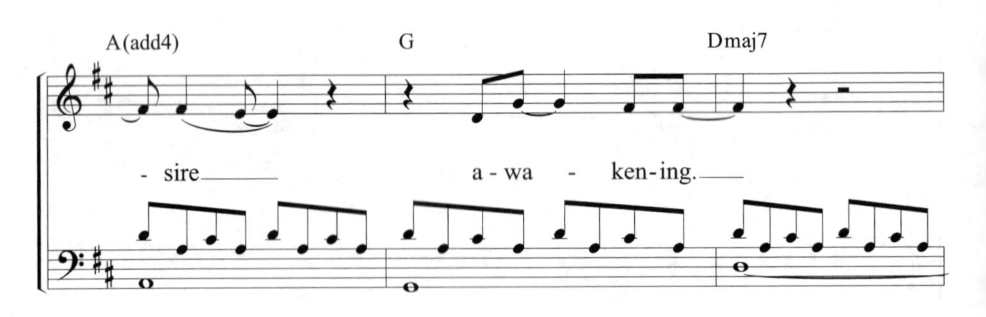

Dsus2
A
Gsus2
my soul, and sing.
For the world You love, Your will
Bm7
Dsus2
1.
A
be done; let Your will be done in me.
D.C.(v.2)
2.
A
D.S.
3.
A
2. In Your
For You, and You
G
Em7
Bm7
Dsus2
Em7
G
A
Mid section
8va
Like the ri-sing sun

G
Em7
Bm7
that shines, from the dark-ness comes a light;
Dsus2
Em7
G
I hear Your voice and this is my a-wa-ken-ing!
1.
E9sus4
A
2.
F♯m/A
Ano3rd
Like the ri-sing sun
G
F♯m7
Bm7
A2/C♯
D
1
A
2
A
G
Like the ri-sing sun that shines, a-wake,
8va

2. In Your presence, in Your power,
Awakening.
For this moment, for this hour,
Awakening.

2363. In the beginning was darkness and nothing

(Breath of God)

Gen 1:1-3; Ezek 37:1, 10; Joel 2:23; Lk 7:7; Jn 1:1; 20:22

Capo 4 (G)

Vicky Beeching

With increasing intensity

Bridge
C♯m7(Am)
B/D♯(G/B)
E(C)
Just say the word and my wea - ry soul will be re -
F♯(D)
Chorus
B(G)
F♯/A♯(D/F♯)
newed. Breathe on me, O breath of God, and
C♯m7(Am)
B/D♯(G/B)
E(C)
F♯(D)
B(G)
fill me with life a - new. Breathe on
F♯/A♯(D/F♯)
C♯m7(Am) B/D♯(G/B)
me, O breath of God, and set this
Last time to Coda
E(C)
F♯(D)
B(G)
1.
Emaj9(C)
heart on fire for You.

F♯(D) G♯m7(Em) F♯(D) Emaj9(C) F♯(D)
D.C.(v.2)
2.
B(G)
Mid section
E(C) F♯(D) G♯m7(Em)
Re - vi-val fire, fall down
F♯(D) E(C) F♯(D) G♯m7(Em) F♯(D)
like the rain. Re - vi-val fire, set my soul a-blaze. Re-
E(C) F♯(D) G♯m7(Em) F♯(D) E(C)
vi - val fi - re, fall down like the rain. Re - vi - val
F♯(D) G♯m7(Em) F♯(D) E(C) F♯(D)
fi - re, set my soul a - blaze,

2. Bones in a valley were changed into an army,
Raised by Your Spirit's powerful touch.
Here in Your presence, I'm needing Your refreshing;
Lord, please revive my heart with Your love.

2364. In the early morning light

(Because He lives)

Mt 28:1, 6; Acts 4:30; 1 Cor 15:19-20

Noel & Tricia Richards

Steadily

C
G/B
C
F
lives, be-cause He lives, we have a hope that will re-main.
Gsus4
G
C
G/B
Be-cause He gives e-ter-nal life to those who
Last time to Coda
1.
D.C.(v.2)
3.
D.S. al Coda
C
F
Gsus4
G
Gsus4
G
call up-on His name. Be-cause He
2.
Mid section
Gsus4
G
F
Am
G
F
Am
Je - sus lives, Je - sus lives,
G
F
Am
G
F
Am
Je - sus lives, Je - sus lives,

2. As we journey through this world,
Singing God's great song;
Age to age the story told
Of the risen One.
Holy fire, breathe on us
Resurrection power;
Signs and wonders follow us
Every waking hour.

2365. In the end

(O resplendent Light)

Ps 36:7; 119:114; 1 Thess 4:17; Rev 21:4

Jeremy Bush & David Crowder

Capo 1 (C)

2.
Ab(G)
Bridge
Gbmaj7(F)
Ab(G)
— em-brace. — In His sha-dow there — is peace, — in His
Gbmaj7(F)
Ab(G)
Gbmaj7(F)
arms there — is rest, — in His word there — is hope,
Ab(G)
Gbmaj7(F)
Ab(G)
Chorus
— in His hands there — is grace. — In the end —
(2°) (peace) —
Gbmaj7(F)
Ab(G)
Gbmaj7(F)
— no hurt - ing, in the end — no yearn-
Ab(G)
Gbmaj7(F)
Ab(G)
- ing, in the end — no suf - fer - ing, — no —

2. In the end, in love our souls will rise,
 All the nations, all the sides;
 No fear in me for that dark place,
 For I will be in His embrace.

3. Till the end, when all of this is gone,
 And all that's living has moved on,
 The sun and moon will rise and set,
 The wind will bring the seas unrest.

4. Till the end, in love our souls can rise,
 All the nations, all the sides;
 No fear in me for this dark place,
 For I am held in His embrace.

(Chorus 2)
Till the end there's hurting,
Till the end, there's yearning,
Till the end there's suffering,
Here waiting, here waiting, oh.
(Till the end, oh, till the end.)

2366. In the name of the Father

(Our God saves)

Ps 30:11; Is 40:31; Mt 12:21

Paul Baloche
& Brenton Brown

2.
Bridge
D
grace. Hear the joy-ful sound of our of-fer-ing as Your
Aadd4
saints bow down, as Your peo-ple sing. We will
Bm7
rise with You, lift-ed
on Your wings, and the
G2
world will see that
Chorus
our God
D
saves.
Our God
A
saves,
there is
Bm7
hope
in Your
G2
name.
1st time only
In the name of the
2.
Mourn-ing
D
turns

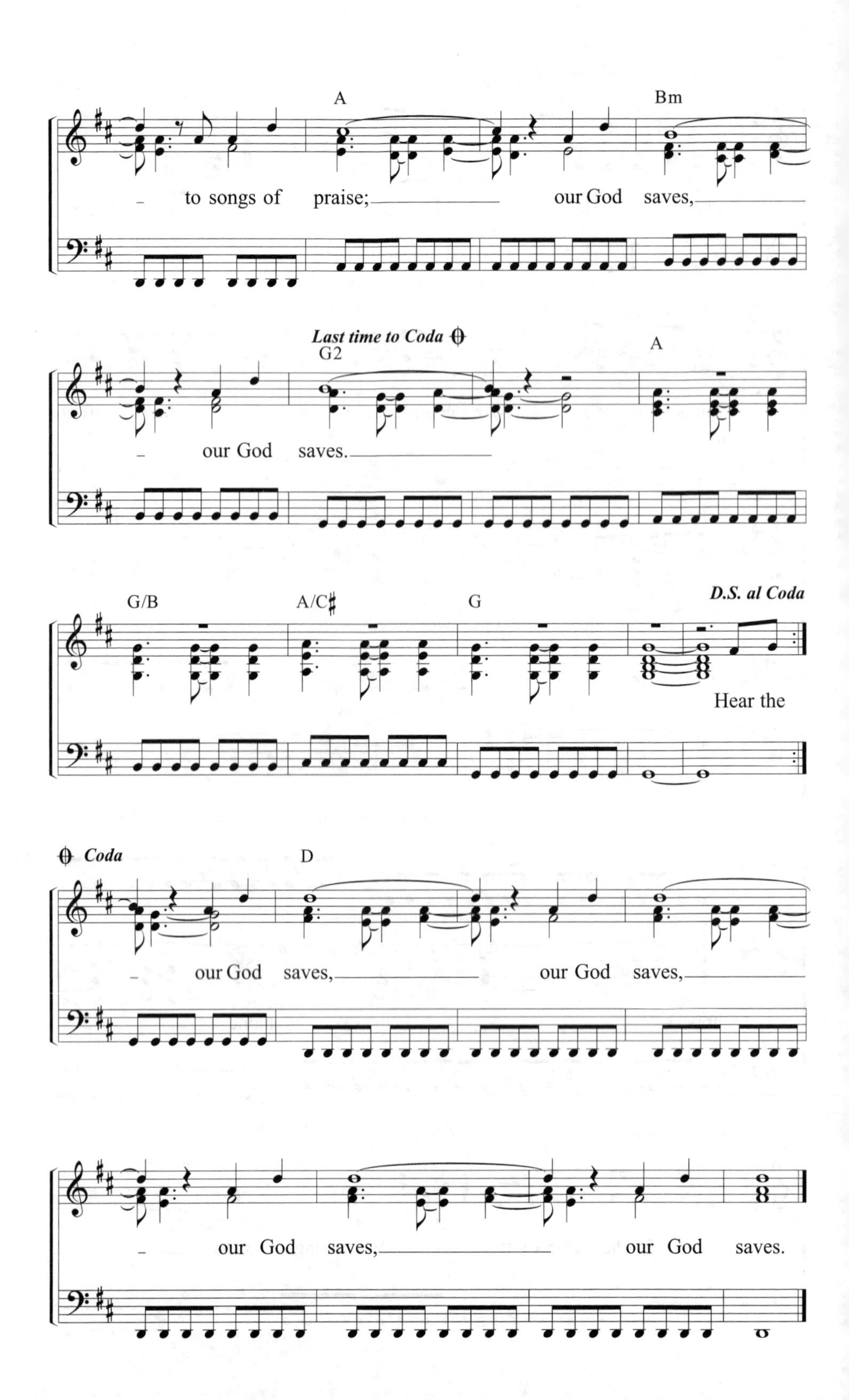
A
Bm
to songs of praise; our God saves,
Last time to Coda
G2
A
our God saves.
G/B
A/C♯
G
D.S. al Coda
Hear the
Coda
D
our God saves, our God saves,
our God saves, our God saves.

In his name the nations will put their hope.

MATTHEW 12:21

2367. In this land

2 Chron 7:1, 14

Capo 2 (D)

Jeremy Ng

2. In this land I will serve;
This is where I'll pour out my love.
In this land I will pray:
May Your glory fill this place.

2368. In this moment
(God is coming)

Ps 7:10; 1 Cor 1:7; 4:5; 2 Pet 3:12; 1 Jn 2:8

Tim Hughes
& Martin Smith

With anticipation

D
A
C♯sus4
so I will wait for You.
C♯
Bridge
D
A
For my God is com-ing; we can hear
F♯m7
E
D
the hea - vens roar. Hold on, get rea-dy for the
F♯m
E
Chorus
glo - ry of the Lord. Here You come,
A
D/A
A
run - ning to find me.
to light up the dark - ness,

Last time to Coda
D/A
Bm7
A
King of the u - ni - verse,
yes, our God is the God who saves.
for - e - ver glo - ri - ous,
yes, our God is the God who saves.
1.,3.,5.
E
Here You come,
2.
E
D.C.(v.2)
2. In our world
4.
E
Here You come,
A
D/F♯
D
A
D/A
Bm7
A
E
Mid section
D
E
F♯m
Bm7
Great is the Lord,

1.
E F♯m Bm7 F♯m/A F♯m E6
You are Lord; God is great.
2. D.S. (inc. rpt) al Coda
E6
Here You come,
Coda
E
D E F♯m Bm7 E F♯m Bm7
Bm7 F♯m/A F♯m
Verse
D A D E F♯m
2. In our world that's torn a - part, give us cou - rage, give us heart.
D A E
On - ly You can raise the dead to life. Take our voi -
D A D E F♯m
- ces, keep us strong; we'll shake the earth with hea - ven's song.
D A C♯sus4
You a - lone can take what's wrong and make it right.

2369. Into this broken world You came

Jn 1:4; 1 Cor 7:23; Heb 9:26

(Never stop singing)

Tim Hughes, Paul Evans, Martin Smith, Ben Cantelon & Jon Dean

Brightly

Chorus
G
D
Once and for all the price is paid.
C
G
We can't stop sing-ing. A - ma - zing love
D
C
has won the day. We'll ne-ver stop sing-ing.
Em7
G
C
We'll shout it out, we'll live it loud. We
Am7
can't stop sing-ing, we'll ne-ver stop sing-ing Your
C
D
Em7
praise.
(not 1°)
(We'll ne-ver stop sing-ing Your

2. In You the best is yet to come:
A brighter day.
In You the best is yet to come.
The King of love is here.

2370. In Your name

2 Chron 30:9; Jn 14:14

David & Yvonne Lyon

Last time to Coda
Gsus4
F
look up - on our need, and let Your love re - main.
pro - mi - ses re - vealed; an - swer us a - gain.
1.,3.,5.
2.
D.C.
Csus4
C
Csus4
C
C
F2
4.
Mid section
C
C
Dm7
You move in ways
You choose, yet si - lence is not ab - sence.
C
Dm7
C
You reach the dark - est place, and cause our hearts to trust.

1.
2.
D.S. (inc. rpt) al Coda
Coda
Fsus2
Fmaj9
an - swer us a - gain.
C
G/B
Am
C/G
F2
C

2371. I praise You for who You are

Mt 1:21; Rom 1:4

Mike Burn

E
A
Je - sus – the on - ly name I praise.
A
Chorus
D
I will praise You in the morn - ing, I will
A/C♯
A
D
praise You through the day, I will praise You in the night - time, giv-ing
E
A/C♯
D
thanks You keep me safe. I will praise You through the good times,
A
E/G♯
F♯m
Esus4
E
praise You through the pain.

1.,3.
D Bm A E A G D
Yours is the name I love and the name I praise, I
Last time to Coda
D.C.
A G D A G D A G D
praise, I praise. I
2.
D.S. al Coda
Coda
E A/C♯ A
love and the name. I will

'You are to give him the name Jesus, because he will save his people from their sins.'

MATTHEW 1:21

2372. I see Your face

(Beautiful)

Acts 2:23-24, 33; Rom 1:20; 1 Thess 4:14, 17; Rev 19:9; 21:4, 9

Phil Wickham

Esus4
E
A
D
You're beau - ti - ful.
4th time jump to v.4
5th time to Coda
F♯m7
E
A
Verse
2. I see Your pow - er in the
3. I see You there, hang - ing
D
F♯m7
moon - lit night, where pla - nets are in mo - tion and
on a tree; You bled and then You died and then You
Esus4
E
A
ga - la - xies are bright. We are a - mazed in the
rose a - gain for me. Now You are sit - ting on Your
D
F♯m7
(small notes v.3)
light of the stars; it's all pro - claim - ing who You are:
hea - ven - ly throne, and soon we will be com - ing home:

Esus4
E
D.S.
A
You're beau - ti - ful.
You're beau - ti - ful.
4. When we ar - rive at e -
D
F♯m7
ter - ni - ty's shore, where death is just a me - mo - ry and
Esus4
E
A
tears are no more, we'll en - ter in as the
D
F♯m7
wed - ding bells ring; Your bride will come to - ge - ther and we'll
D.S. al Coda
Coda
Esus4
E
A
Tag
sing: You're beau - ti - ful.
I see Your face, You're

D
F♯m7
beau - ti - ful,
You're
beau - ti - ful,
You're
Esus4
E
A
beau-ti - ful.
I see Your face,
You're
D
F♯m7
beau - ti - ful,
You're
beau - ti - ful,
You're
To repeat
Last time
Esus4
E
Esus4
E
A
beau-ti - ful.
beau-ti - ful.

2373. Is there anyone here?

(I am Yours)

Is 40:28; Rom 2:4; 5:9; Phil 2:11; 1 Pet 2:9

Aaron Keyes, Gary Sadler & John Hartley

Strong rock style

2. So who will declare
The glory of God?
Who will cry out, unashamed,
'He is glorious'?
Till every eye sees,
Till every heart knows,
Let everyone stand in praise,
Everyone stand and say:

2374. Is there a place rest can be found?

(Hear my cry)

Ps 22:2; 61:1, 3; 88:1; 91:5

Capo 2 (D)

Gently

Wayne Drain &
Noel & Tricia Richards

Verse

E(D) Esus2(D) A2/C♯(G/B) B2/D♯(A/C♯)

1. Is there a place rest can be found,

E(D) Esus2(D) A2(G) E(D) Esus2(D)

peace for the trou - bled mind? Is there a light to

A2/C♯(G/B) B2/D♯(A/C♯) E(D) Esus2(D) A2(G)

show me a way, grace for a - no - ther day?

Chorus

F♯m7(Em) B7sus4(A) E(D) E2/G♯(D/F♯) E(D) A(G)

Hear my cry, heed my pray'r.

2. Is there a love that never fades,
Constant through all my life?
Is there a hope when I am alone,
Courage to face the night?

2375. It doesn't matter what you've done

(Not guilty any more)

Zech 3:4; Lk 4:18; Rom 8:1; 1 Cor 6:11

Aaron Keyes & Andy Lehman

Ballad style

D
E
A
you, mer - cy is yours. You're not bro - ken a - ny more,
Amaj7
C♯m
you're not cap - tive a - ny more: I love
3rd time to Mid section
1.,3. (Fine)
D
E(D)
A
you, mer - cy is yours. 2. Can you be-lieve that this is
2.
A
Amaj7
D
Bridge
There is now there -
A
Amaj7
D
D.S. al Coda
- fore no con-dem-na - tion for those who are in Je-sus.

2. Can you believe that this is true?
Grace abundant I am giving you.
Cleansing deeper than you know,
All was paid for long ago.

2376.
I treasure Your voice
(Bones)
Ps 31:10; Is 58:10; Ezek 37:11, 14; Lk 11:2
Capo 1 (G)
David Gate
Steady 4
Verse
A♭(G)
I treasure Your voice, I
Fm7(Em)
cherish Your name,
E♭(D)
all I desire is Your
D♭(C)
presence again. I
1.
2.,3.
Chorus
D♭(C)
There's no strength in these bones, so
Lord, come fill me. I can't
Fm7(Em)
do it alone, so

D♭(C)
Lord, be near me. For Your king-dom come,
Last time to Coda
1.
D.C.
E♭(D)
Lord, work through me and be glo-ri-fied. I
2.,3.,5.
D.S. (3rd time al Coda)
4.
Mid section
There's no
Not for
D♭(C)
here, but for there, with the lost and the lone-ly. Not for
Fm7(Em)
here, but for there, with the bro-ken and the hun - gry. Not for

D♭(C)
here, but for there, with the lost and the lone - ly. Not for
E♭(D)
D.S.
here, but for there. There's no
Coda
D♭sus2(C)

2377. It's falling from the clouds

(Cannons)

Ps 8:3; 19:1; 148:3; Rev 4:11

Moderately, with strength

Phil Wickham

Bm
A
moon and the stars de - clare who You are. And I'm
Last time to Coda
D
Gmaj7
Bm
so un - wor - thy, but still You love me; for- e - ver my heart will
1.
A
D
G
sing of how great You are.
D.C. (v.2)
3.
D.S. al Coda
Bm
Em
A
sing of how great You are.
2.
Mid section
A
G
D
A
sing of You. All glo-ry, ho-nour, pow-er is Yours. A - men. All

G
D
A
glo - ry, ho - nour, pow - er is Yours. A - men. All
Em
Bm
Asus4
A
glo - ry, ho - nour pow - er is Yours for - e - ver. A - men.
D.S.
Coda
Asus2
A
We're sing - ing
A
sing of how great You are.
1.
D
G
Bm
Em
2.
A
G
D
2. Beautiful and free,
The song of galaxies,
It's reaching far beyond the Milky Way.
Let's join in with the sound,
C'mon, let's sing it out,
As the music of the universe plays, we're singing.

2378. It's in view of Your mercy

(In view of Your mercy)

2 Sam 7:22; Rom 12:1; Phil 2:9; Tit 3:4

Claire Hamilton
& Ben Cantelon

Strong rhythmic feel

Bm
A
G
re-spond - ing to Your love.
Chorus
A
Bm7
We come and wor - ship You, Al - migh-
G
D
A
- - ty God, our hearts re - spond-
Bm7
G
- ing to Your love.
We lift
A
D/F♯
G
Your name a - bove all o - ther names,

2. It's in view of Your kindness we come,
It's in view of Your kindness we come,
It's in view of Your kindness we come
And worship You, our God.

2379. It's just impossible to find the words

(My wonder)

Contemporary Britpop feel

Paul Oakley

Em G D
- ther love that I could live for, and I will ne-
than I could e - ver dream of. No one could e -
1.
A Em G A
- ver be the same a - gain: You've got my heart.
2.
A G Em A
- ver take Your place.
G D/F♯
(1.,3.) You a - lone could be the fire in my heart,
(2.) You a - lone can turn my life in - side out
G
1.
A G D/F♯ G A
so fan the spark in - to a flame for Your name.
to the won - der of Your

G D/F♯ G A
D.C.
2.
A G
name. You a-lone could be the
D/F♯ G A G
fire in my heart, so fan the spark in-to a flame
D/F♯ G A G D/F♯ G A G
for Your name, ev-'ry day.
D/F♯ G A
D.S.
3.
A G D/F♯ G A G
flame ev-'ry day,
D/F♯ G A G D/F♯ G A G D/F♯ G A D
for Your name.

I pray that out of his glorious riches he may strengthen you with power through his Spirit in your inner being, so that Christ may dwell in your hearts through faith.

EPHESIANS 3:16-17

2380. It's time for us to live the songs we sing

Gm7(Em) Dm7(Bm) C(A) Gm7(Em) Dm7(Bm)
moun-tains are shak - ing; could this be a great a - wa-ken-
C(A)
Chorus
Fsus4(D) F(D)
- ing? Break our hearts with the
C/E(A/C♯) Dm(Bm)
things that break Yours, wake us up to see
B♭(G) Fsus4(D) F(D)
through Your eyes. Break our hearts with the
C/E(A/C♯) Dm(Bm)
Last time to Coda
things that break Yours, and send us out to shine

(D.S.)
shine.
B♭(G)
3rd time D.S.S.
1.
Dm7(Bm)
C(A)
Gm7(Em)
in the dark - ness.
D.C.(v.2)
2.
Dm(Bm)
Mid section
B♭(G)
2. It's
Here I am, send me
F(D)
C/E(A/C♯)
to be Your hands and feet.
Here I am,
D.S.
send me.
I will go.
The

2. It's time to move outside our comfort zone,
To see beyond our churches and our homes;
To change the way we think and how we spend,
Until we look like Jesus again.

2381.
It's Your blood that saved me
(To You be the glory)
Heb 10:19-20; Rev 11:15
Capo 1 (Bm)
Sim Walker & Chris Sayburn
Moderately
Verse
Cm7+4(Bm) Bb(A) Ebsus4(D)
1. It's Your blood that saved me,
Cm7+4(Bm) Bb(A) Ab2(G)
it's Your blood that ne - ver fails.
Cm7+4(Bm) Bb(A) Eb(D) Fm(Em) Eb/G (D/F#)
Your sa - cri-fice for all, made per - fect on the
(v.2)
Ab(G) Eb/G (D/F#) Fm(Em) Bbsus4(A) Eb(D)
cross, You o - pened up the way to e-ter - nal life.
Chorus
Cm(Bm) Bbsus4(A) Eb(D) Cm(Bm) Bbsus4(A)
To You be the glory, to You be the

Last time to Coda
Fm(Em)
Cm(Bm)
B♭/D(A/C♯)
Gm7(F♯m)
praise; as we crown You with glo-ry, we de-clare:
1.
A♭(G)
B♭(A)
E♭(D)
God of hea-ven, You reign.
2.
A♭(G)
B♭(A)
Cm(Bm)
B♭/D(A/C♯)
D.S.
God of hea - ven, You reign. To You be the
4.
A♭(G)
B♭(A)
E♭(D)
B♭/D(A/C♯)
Cm(Bm)
D.S. al Coda
God of hea-ven, You reign. To You be the
3.
A♭(G)
B♭(A)
E♭(D)
Mid section
B♭sus4(A)
God of hea-ven, You reign. For-e - ver, for-e-

Cm7(Bm) A♭(G) 1. B♭sus4(A)
- ver, for-e - ver You shall reign. For-e -
2. B♭sus4(A) B♭sus4/D(A/C♯) Cm7(Bm)
For-e - ver, for-e - ver, for-e -
A♭(G) B♭sus4(A) B♭sus4/D(A/C♯)
- ver You shall reign. For-e - ver, for-e -
Cm7(Bm) A♭(G) B♭sus4(A) D.S.S.
- ver, for-e - ver You shall reign.
Coda
A♭(G) B♭(A) E♭(D)
God of hea-ven, You reign.
2. You alone are worthy,
You deserve our highest praise.
In awe we stand amazed,
That You would take our place;
You opened up the way
Into eternal life.

The seventh angel sounded his trumpet, and there were loud voices in heaven, which said: 'The kingdom of the world has become the kingdom of our Lord and of his Christ, and he will reign for ever and ever.'

REVELATION 11:15

2382. I wanna soar with You

Is 40:31; Eph 6:14; Phil 4:13

Rend Collective Experiment

A
G2
through. I can't stand still, what-e-ver
D
A
G2
hits, I'll keep mak-ing move - ments to You - oo.
G
Chorus
D/F♯
I'm run - ning fast and free to You,
A
D/F♯
'cause You are the move - ment and fight in me.
G
D/F♯
A
(Fine)
I'm run - ning fast and free to You, 'cause You are my home,

D/F♯
G2
D
where I wan-na be; come, move in me.
A
G2
Where I wan-na be;
1.
D.C.(v.2)
D/F♯
A
D/F♯
come, move in me.
2. I wan-na
2.
Mid section
D
A
D/F♯
Bm7
come, move in me.
I won't walk a-
G2
D
A
way, won't walk a - way.

2. I wanna float with You,
The current's driving me,
But I'll paddle hard too,
When the waves and rapids overcome.
I wanna stand firm
When my mind's weak and my emotions squirm.
I must stand true,
Whatever hits, I'll keep making movements to You.

2383. I want my life to give You glory

(Shine on me)

Mt 5:16; 2 Cor 4:6; Eph 5:14

Simon Parry
& Dan Weeks

F♯m7
D
E
A
so the world will see You.
Shine, shine, shine, shine,
C♯m7/G♯
F♯m7
shine, shine, shine on me
so the world
Bm7
A/C♯
D
Esus4
will know You're the on - ly way to be free.
1.,3.
E
A
C♯m7/G♯
F♯m7
D
So won't You shine on me.
D.C.(v.2)
Last time to Coda
2.
A
C♯m7/G♯
F♯m7
D
E

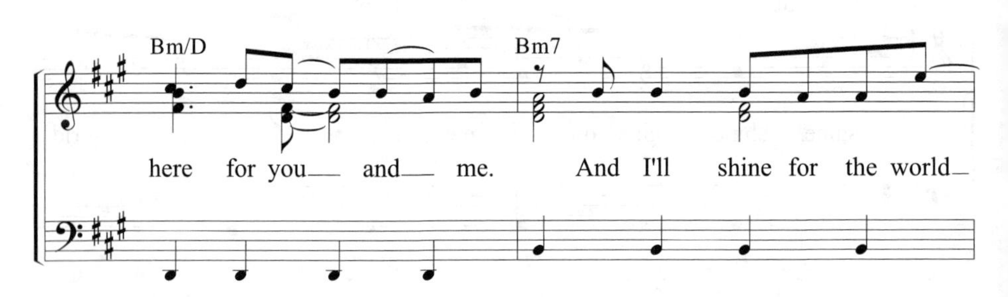

2. I want my friends to know You as Saviour,
   I want my town to see You're the light,
   I want this world to see You in glory,
   I wanna go where You will send me to...

Let your light shine before men, that they may see your good deeds and praise your Father in heaven.

MATTHEW 5:16

2384. I want to be like Jesus

(Like Jesus)

Eph 5:10; Col 3:17

Aaron Keyes
& Paul Oakley

Rhythmic

D *Chorus*

I want to be like Je - sus, I want to do the
I want to look like Je - sus, show the world there's a

1. G 2. G D

things He does. God a - bove who loves us, there's a

God a - bove who loves us. (Fine)

𝄋 *Verse*

1. Ev - 'ry - thing I
liv - ing now to

(v.2)

A G 1. D 2. D

say and do, ev - 'ry - thing I am,
wor - ship You with ev - 'ry - thing I can.

A 1. G

You're the on - ly hope we have, You're the great - est

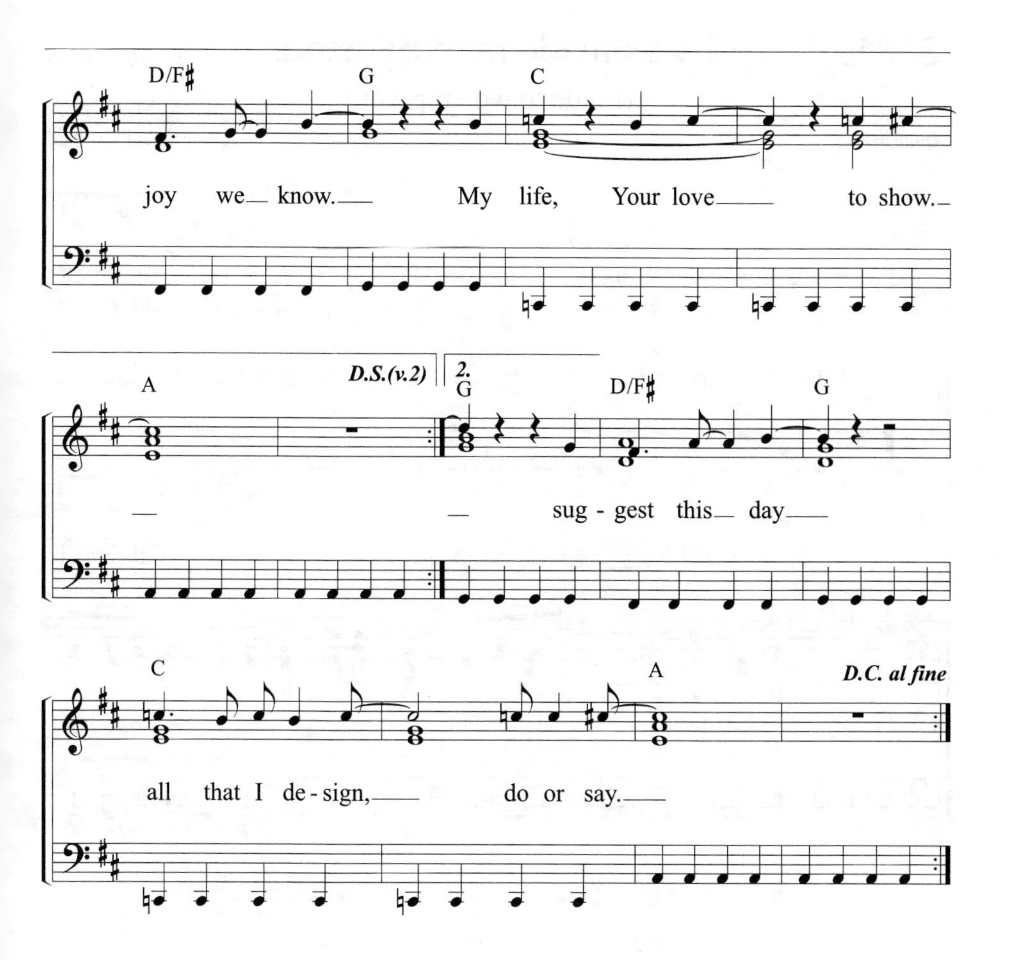

2. Lord, I want to think and speak, be and do,
Everything and only that which pleases You.
So come take control, suggest this day
All that I design, do or say.

2385. I was made by holy hands

(Made to worship You)

Ps 139:14; Jn 10:3

Adam Carmichael, Ken Riley
& Matthew Chambers

Quite quick

C
D
C
called our names, to join as one to praise You,
Chorus
G
D
Lord. I'm made to wor - ship You with
live to ho - nour You with
Last time to Coda
1.,3.,5.
Em
C
all I have with - in me, and ev - 'ry - thing I am.
ev - 'ry breath You give me. I'm
2.
C
D.C.(v.2)
I'll made to wor - ship, made to wor - ship.
4.
C
(C)
made to wor - ship, made to wor - ship You,

G/B
Am7
made to wor - ship You.
D/F♯
1.
2.
made to wor - ship You,
Mid section
C
G/B
(small notes 2°)
We were made for more than the world can e-ver give;
Am7
1.
D/F♯
no-thing can com-pare to life in You.
2.
D/F♯
D.S.(with rpt) al Coda
G
Am7
G/B
G
I'm made to wor - ship

2. God on high, Your love came down
To save a wretch like me.
With all my heart I bow, I worship and adore
The Lord of life.

2386.
I will cast my cares
(Redeemer)
Ps 18:2; 19:14; 119:154; Mk 10:45; Lk 1:47; Jn 1:3; 1 Cor 1:31; 1 Pet 2:24; 5:7
Cathy Burton
Steadily
Verse
1. I will cast my cares upon You, God, laying all my burdens at Your cross; I will not be proud of all I've done, but I'll boast in You.
heart into Your hands, for You are the author of my life, and with ev'ry breath You give to me I will trust in You.
2. I will place my
D.C.(v.2)
Chorus
You are my Redeemer, You are my heal-

G
C2
- er,
You are my Sa - viour,
D2
G
You are my God.
You are my de -
C2
D2
Em
fen - der,
the source of ev - 'ry hour.
D/F♯
C2
D2
You are my rea - son,
You are my God.
1.,3.
(Fine)
D.C.(v.2)
Em
G
C
Em
G
Cmaj7
2. I will place my Je -

2.
Gsus4 G Gsus4 G
Mid section
Am7
Je - sus, my Re-deem-
C2 G D Dsus4 D
- er, ran - somed now I stand.
Am7 C2 G
Je - sus, my Re-deem - er, You have won me back.
D Am7 C
My Re-deem - er, my Sa - viour, my Com-
Em D
D.S. al fine
- for - ter and Re - scu - er. You are my Re -

Cast all your anxiety on him because he cares for you.

1 PETER 5:7

2387. I will celebrate

Ps 72:13; 91:2; 1 Cor 7:23

(Celebrate the beauty)

Moderately

Chris McClarney, Kees Kraayenoord & John Hartley

(v.3)
D2
F♯m7
E
need. In Your pre - sence I'm ac-cep - ted and I'm
D2
A
Dsus2
clean, Je - sus. Oh,
Chorus
A
E
thank You, e - ver I will thank You. You
F♯m7
took a-way my shame, for - e - ver I am changed
D
A
by Your love. Thank You,

E
Je-sus, I a - dore You; I will ne - ver be the same,
F♯m7
D
all glo - ry to Your name, Je-sus.
1.,3.
A
D
A
D
(Fine)
D.S.(v.3)
3. I will
2.
C♯m
Mid section
F♯m
D2
And when I think a-bout the price You paid, thank
A
E/G♯
C♯m
F♯m
You. I see the cross, I see the emp-ty grave,

3. I will sing my song to praise Your majesty,
I will worship You for all eternity,
I will lift Your name for all the world to see,
Jesus, Jesus.

2388.

I will choose to praise You

(Choose a hallelujah)

Deut 30:19; Ps 86:11; Lk 14:28, 33

Cathy Burton & David Gate

Moderately

D2
choose the song of hea - ven, and I
ev - 'ry road be-fore me, I will
F♯m7
choose a ha - le - lu - jah;
choose the path that's cost - ly;
for You are high
Eadd4
a-bove a-ny-thing that
1.
D2
turns my love from You.
A2
D.C. (v.3)
2.,4.
D2
turns my love from You.
A2
D.S.
And with
3.,5.
D2
turns my love from You.
Last time to Coda
A

E
Mid section
F♯m7
Give me a heart that is on - ly de-vo - ted to You:
D
E
un - di - vi - ded and faith -
F♯m7
D
- ful to all that is true,
E
F♯m7
D
de-ter - mined to see Your king - dom break through,
D.S. al Coda
E
break through.
So I

2. I give You all that I am,
   My life I place in Your hands.
   For Your worship I was made,
   To give my life in praise to You.

3. I am Your creation,
   Made to give You glory.
   So I'm finding every way I can
   To serve You, Lord.

2389. I will lift up the name of the Lord

Ps 40:1-3

Last time to Coda
E
B
E
lift up the name of the One who lift-ed me.
Verse
A
E
A
Oh, I praise You, Je -
E
A
E
sus, for You al - ways hear my cry.
A
E
G♯
Ev - 'ry day that You give me
C♯m
A
F♯m7
breath, I'm gon-na lift Your name on

Bsus4
B
D.C. al Coda
high.
I will
Coda
B
I will lift up the name of the One who lift-ed
E
A
E
me.
I'm gon-na lift up the name of the One
B
E
who lift - ed
me.

2390.
I will wait for You to move
(My deliverer)
Ps 32:6-7; 40:2; 71:3, 19; Is 60:18
Chris Tomlin, Daniel Carson, Matt Maher & Jesse Reeves
Moderately
Verse
D
E
1. I will wait for You to move, for Your migh-
D A E D
- ty hand to save; when the trou - bled wa - ters rise,
E D A E
(v.2)
You are my hid - ing place, You are
D A E Bm7
Bridge
A
my hid - ing place.
Your walls are sal-va-tion,
F♯m7 Esus4 E Bm7
Your gates are praise! Your walls are

Chorus
A/C♯
D2
Esus4
E
sal - va - tion, Your gates are praise! My de -
Dsus2
A
Esus4
E
li - ver - er, my de - li - ver - er, my de -
Last time to Coda
li - ver - er is the Lord.
1.
2.
D.S.
3.
2. Who is like My de -
Mid section
Oh, oh.

2. Who is like You, mighty God?
Who can take me from Your hand?
As I walk with You in freedom,
You're the rock on which I stand,
You're the rock on which I stand.

2391. Jesus Christ, You never change

(Morning Star)

Heb 13:8; Rev 4:8; 22:16

Al Gordon & Tim Hughes

Steadily *Verse*

A Bm A/C♯

1. Je - sus Christ, You ne - ver change, yes - ter - day, to -
Morn - ing Star, the ris - ing sun, with You the best is

D E F♯m

day the same. Christ has died, Christ is ri - sen,
yet to come.

(v.2) (v.2)

D E

Christ will come a - gain.

Chorus

A

King for - e - ver

E F♯m

more, it's You I'm liv - ing for, it's You I'm liv - ing

D A E

for. Bright - est Morn - ing Star, how

Last time to Coda 𝄌

Bm D

beau - ti - ful You are, how beau - ti - ful You are.

1. D.C.(v.2)

A Bm F♯m D

3. D.S. al Coda 2. Mid section

E F♯m7 D

I am Yours, Je - sus, Yours.

E F♯m7 D D.S.

I am Yours, al - ways Yours.

𝄌 *Coda*

A Bm

Can you hear the fu - ture sounds

see the star that's break - ing through: e -

2. Can you hear the future sound
That rises up to shake the ground?
All around the world we sing
The anthem of the coming King.
God who was,
God who is,
God who is to come.

Capo 2 (D)

Godfrey Birtill

2393. Jesus, there is no one like You

(How I love You)

Is 53:4; Phil 2:9

Ben Cantelon

G
for words aren't e - nough to tell just how
D/F♯
Asus4
A
Chorus
much I love Your name.
How I
G
A
Bm
love You, my Lord.
How I
G
A
Dsus2
D
love You, my Lord.
(Fine)
D
Last time D.S. al fine
Mid section
A
And no - thing else could e -
(last time) (How I)

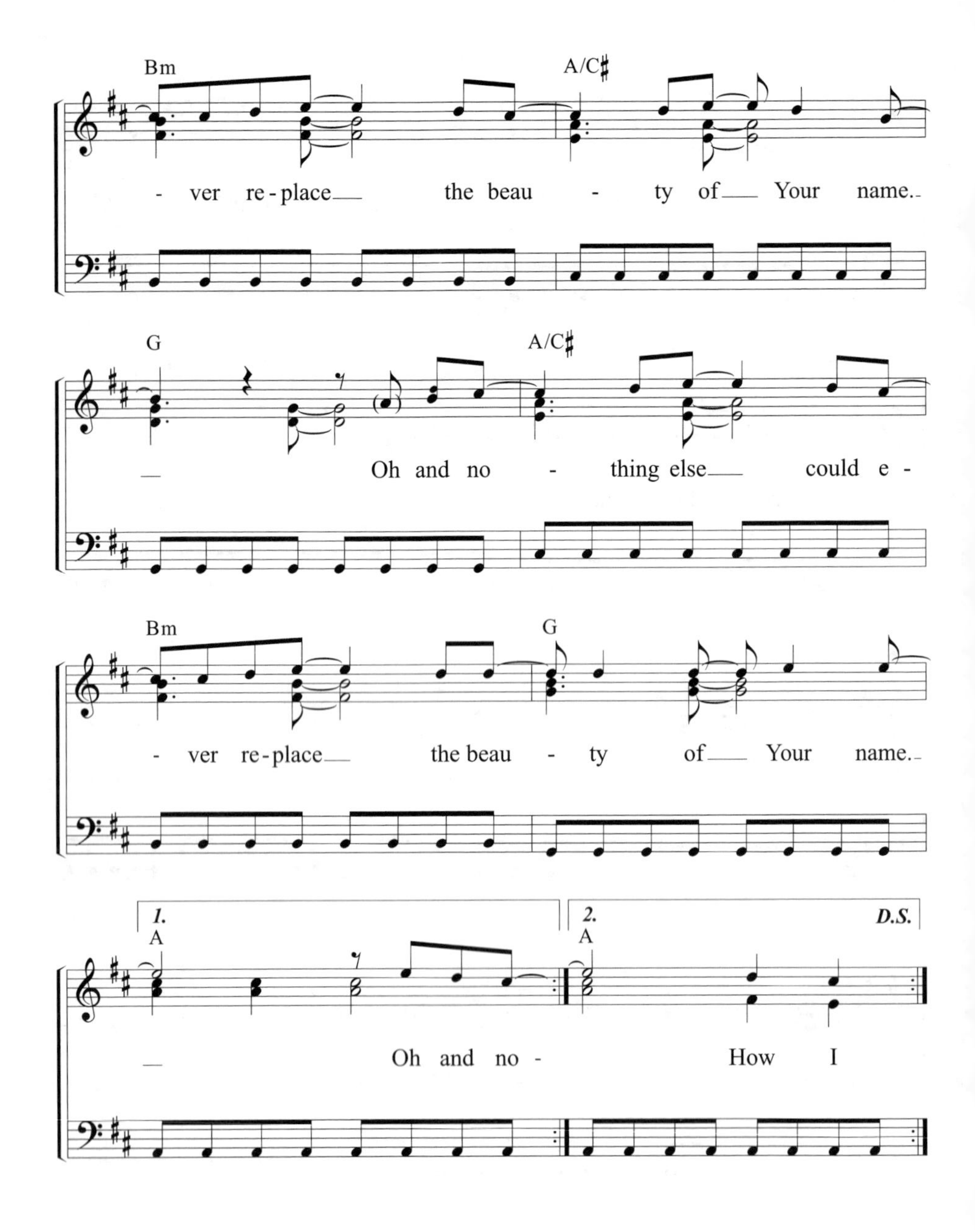

2. You, O Lord,
Are the One that I adore;
Sovereign King,
Yet You welcome me.
How can it be?
I worship You
With everything I say and do;
All glory and praise
Be unto the name
Above all names.

Surely he took up our infirmities and carried our sorrows, yet we considered him stricken by God, smitten by him, and afflicted.

ISAIAH 53:4

2394. Jesus, what an awesome wonder You are

2. Saviour, what an awesome wonder You are;
O Saviour.
Saviour, what an awesome wonder You are;
O Saviour, O Saviour, O Saviour:
What a wonder You are.

3. Father, what an awesome wonder You are;
O Father.
Father, what an awesome wonder You are;
O Father, O Father, O Father:
What a wonder You are.

4. Healer, what an awesome wonder You are;
O Healer.
Healer, what an awesome wonder You are;
O Healer, O Healer, O Healer:
What a wonder You are.

2395. Jesus, You are here

(Won't stay silent)

Lk 11:1; Rom 8:26

Paul Baloche, Steven Curtis-Chapman, Stuart Garrard, Israel Houghton, Tim Hughes, Graham Kendrick, Andy Park, Matt Redman, Martin Smith, Michael W. Smith, Chris Tomlin, Darlene Zschech

Capo 3 (G)

Rock

E♭(C)
Gm(Em)
F(D)
pray'r - ful peo - ple? Shake us up to - day,
E♭(C)
Chorus
B♭(G)
Lord. We're call - ing out, on our knees,
F(D)
A♭/C(F/A)
E♭(C)
des - p'rate, Lord, for You to be in our ci-
B♭(G)
F(D)
A♭/C(F/A)
- ties, in our streets, lift - ed high for all to see.
1.,2.,4.
Last time to Coda
E♭(C)
Gm(Em)
F/A(D/F♯)
B♭(G)
We won't stay si - lent a - ny more, we won't stay

1st time D.C.(v.2)
2nd time to Mid section
3.
D.S. al Coda
Gm(Em)
F/A(D/F♯)
E♭2/B♭(C/G)
E♭(C)
si - lent a - ny more.
We're call - ing out
Mid section
B♭(G)
F(D)
A♭(F)
Oh,
won't stay si - lent, won't
E♭(C)
B♭(G)
F(D)
stay si - lent.
Oh,
won't
A♭(F)
E♭(C)
B♭(G)
stay si - lent, won't stay si - lent.
Oh,
F(D)
A♭(F)
E♭(C)
won't stay si - lent, won't stay si - lent.

Gm(Em)
F/A(D/F♯)
E♭/B♭(C/G)
Oh, won't stay si - lent.
E♭(C)
D.S. al Coda
We're call - ing out
Coda
B♭(G)
Gm(Em)
F/A(D/F♯)
We won't stay si - lent a - ny more,
E♭/B♭(C/G)
Gm(Em)
F/A(D/F♯)
we won't stay si - lent a - ny more,
B♭(G)
Gm(Em)
F/A(D/F♯)
E♭2(C)
we won't stay si - lent a - ny more.

2396. Jesus, You are holy

(None like You)

2 Sam 7:22; Ps 9:1; Rev 5:12; 21:4

Eoghan Heaslip, Nick Herbert & Nicole Brown

(ch.2)
Em7
C2
G
sav - ing Lord,
Je - sus,
Last time to Coda
1.
D/F♯
Em7
C2
there is none like You, none like You.
G
Am7
B♭
C
D.C.(v.2)
2. Je - sus,
2.,4.
D.S. (chor 2) (al Coda)
3.
C2
C2
Mid section
Glo - ri - ous, I will praise,
Cmaj7
D
Em
I will sing; with this song of love I bring,

2. Jesus, You are worthy,
There is none like You.
Jesus, You are worthy,
You make all things new.

(Chorus 2)
Glorious, powerful,
Jesus, there is none like You,
None like You.

2397.
Jesus, You are strong to save
(We lift You up)
1 Cor 1:30; Phil 2:8-9; Heb 4:15
Brenton Brown
Capo 2 (G)
Moderately
Verse
A2/C♯(G/B) Dmaj7(C) Esus4(D) E(D)
1. Je - sus, You are strong to save,
there's no bat-tle You can't win;
strong-er e-ven than the grave,
F♯m7(Em)
we turn to You a - gain.
A(G)
Chorus
And we lift You up,
(2. So)
D2(C)
we lift You high - er, 'cause You de - serve our high - est praise.

Esus4(D)
E(D)
A(G)
D2(C)
Esus4(D)
F♯m7(Em)
We'll sing it out, we'll sing it loud - er: Je-sus, name
Last time to Coda
1.
D2(C)
Esus4(D)
E(D)
A/C♯(G/B)
D(C)
a - bove all names.
A/E(G/D)
Esus4(D)
E(D)
A/C♯(G/B)
D(C)
D.C.(v.2)
3.
D.S. al Coda
2.
A/E(G/D)
(D)
Esus4
E(D)
A(G)
A(G)
Oh, we will lift You up,
Mid section
D(C)
E(D)
D(C)
E(D)
C♯m7(Bm)
You con-quered temp - ta - tion, o - be - di - ent to death.

2. For only You have overcome
Every trial this world can bring.
Humbly You defeated sin,
Then died that we might live.

2398.
Jesus, You endured my pain
(Because of Your love)
Is 53:4; Lk 4:18; Jn 1:3; 15:13; 1 Jn 1:7
Capo 3 (D)
Phil Wickham
Steadily, building
Verse
F(D) Fmaj7(D) F(D) Fmaj7(D)
1. Je - sus, You en - dured my pain,
Dm(Bm) Dm7(Bm) Dm(Bm) Dm7(Bm)
Sa - viour You bore all my shame, all be-cause of
B♭(G) B♭maj7(G) B♭(G) B♭maj7(G) F(D) Fmaj7(D) F(D) Fmaj7(D)
Your love. Ma-ker of the u - ni - verse,
(v.2)
Dm(Bm) Dm7(Bm) Dm(Bm) Dm7(Bm) B♭(G) B♭maj7(G)
bro-ken for the sins of the earth, all be-cause of Your love,
(small notes 2°)
B♭(G) B♭maj7(G) Dm(Bm) Dm7(Bm) C(A)
Chorus
all be-cause of Your love. Be -

F(D)
C(A)
Dm(Bm)
cause of Your cross my debt is paid; be - cause of Your blood my
B♭(G)
F(D)
C(A)
sins are washed a-way. Now all of my life I free-ly give, be-
Dm(Bm)
1.,4.
B♭(G)
F(D)
(Fine)
cause of Your love, be - cause of Your love I live.
C(A)
Dm(Bm)
B♭(G)
D.C.(v.2)
2.
B♭(G)
D.S.
3.
B♭(G)
Gm(Em)
cause of Your love. Be - cause of Your love I live.

2. Innocent and holy King,
You died to set the captives free,
All because of Your love.
Lord, You gave Your life for me,
So I will give my life for You,
All because of Your love,
All because of Your love.

Greater love has no-one than this, that he lay down his life for his friends.

JOHN 15:13

2399.
Jesus, You rescued me
(This is Your grace)
Jn 10:3; Eph 2:8; 1 Pet 2:9; 4:16
Capo 2 (G)
With pace
Jo Petch
Verse
F♯m7(Em) D(C) A(G)
Je - sus, You rescued me, You turned
You called my name, led me out of the dark -
E(D) F♯m7(Em) D(C) A(G)
my life a - round with sal - va - tion's song.
- ness in - to light and a brand new day.
Bm7(Am) Bridge F♯m(Em)
You take me as I am;
Bm7(Am) D(C)
there's no - thing I can do to earn
Esus4(D) A(G) Chorus E(D)
Your love. This is Your grace;

Bm(Am)
D(C)
grace that's sav - ing me, and set - ting me free.
E(D)
A(G)
E(D)
I'm not a - shamed,
Bm(Am)
I'm not a - shamed to say Your name: Je-
D(C)
1.,3.
E(D)
F♯m7(Em)
C♯m7(Bm)
- sus, You're ev - 'ry-thing to me.
Dmaj7(C)
F♯m9(Em)
C♯m7(Bm)
Dmaj7(C)
1st time D.C.
Last time to Coda
2.
E(D)
D.S. al Coda
Coda
A(G)
- 'ry-thing

2400. Jesus, You're the hope I cling to

(Christ in me)

Ps 61:3; Mt 26:28; Acts 2:23-24; 2 Cor 4:6; Phil 3:9; Col 1:27; 3:3

Capo 3 (G)

Steadily, building

Lou & Nathan Fellingham
& Gary Sadler
Mid section words: Edward Mote (1797–1874)

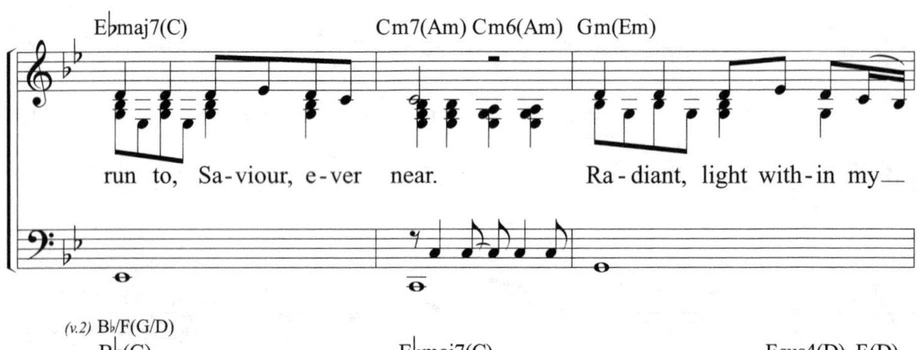

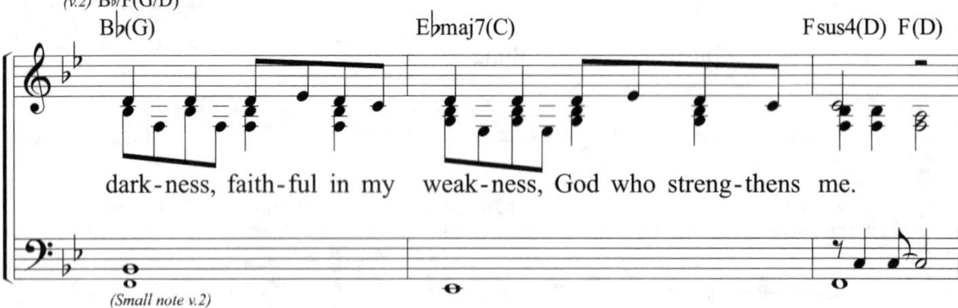

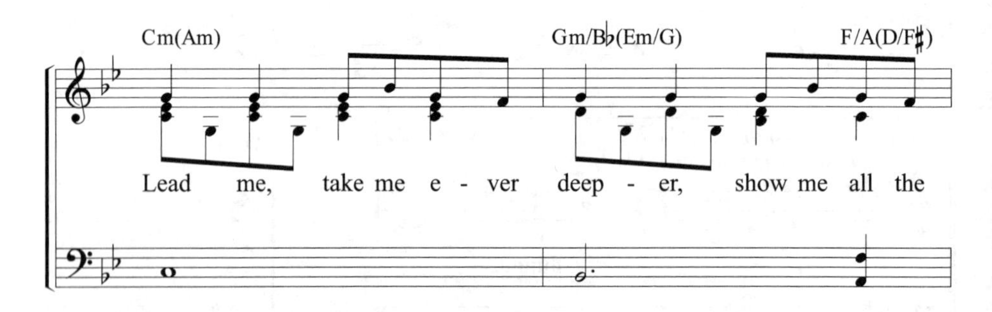

Chorus
B♭(G) Fsus4(D) F(D) B♭(G) E♭(C)
rich - es of this my-ste - ry. Christ in me,
Fsus4(D) F(D) Gm(Em) E♭(C)
my hope and my glo - ry, my cer-tain - ty.
Fsus4(D) F(D) B♭(G) E♭(C)
My heart bows down,
1.
Fsus4(D) F(D) Gm(Em) E♭(C)
sur-ren-dered in wor - ship to my God and King.
Fsus4(D) F(D) D.C.(v.2) 2.,3. Fsus4(D) F(D) D7/F♯(B/D♯)
sur - ren - dered in wor -

Last time to Coda
Mid section
Gm(Em)
E♭(C)
Fsus4(D) F(D)
Cm(Am)
- ship to my God and King. My hope is built on no -
Gm(Em)
Cm(Am)
- thing less than Je - sus' blood and right -
B♭(G)
Cm(Am)
- eous - ness. I dare not trust my fee -
Gm(Em)
E♭/G(C/E)
F/A(D/F♯)
- ble frame, but whol - ly lean on Je - sus' name.
D.S. al Coda
Coda
F(D)
Fsus4(D) F(D)
Dm(Bm)
Dm2(Bm)

2. Jesus, You're the holy promise,
Poured Your blood out for us,
Rose again to life.
All my sins are now forgiven
And my life is hidden,
Saved through Jesus Christ.
Jesus, when I stand in glory,
With Your throne before me,
I'll be found in You.

2401. Joyful, joyful, we adore You

(The One who saves)

ODE TO JOY

Ps 30:3; 36:9; Jn 1:29; 2 Pet 1:19; 1 Jn 3:5; Rev 22:5

Music: Ludwig van Beethoven (1770–1827)
Verse words: Henry J. van Dyke
Arr., new words & chorus: Brenton Brown & Jason Ingram

Capo 7 (G)

Quite fast

Last time to Coda
1.,3.,5.
2. D.C.(v.3)
4. Mid section
A(D)
the grave.
a - way.
You are the light
G(C)
Je - sus, You
D(G)
are my res - cue,
A/C♯(D/F♯)
Je - sus, You
Bm7(Em)
are my res - cue;
G(C)
I give You ev -
D(G)
- 'ry - thing I am.
A/C♯(D/F♯)
Play 4 times then D.C. (v.3) al Coda
Coda
You are the One
G(C)
who takes
(G/C)
D/G
all our sins
1.
A(D)
a - way.
2.
A(D)
a - way.
2. Melt the clouds of sin and sadness,
Drive the dark of doubt away.
Giver of eternal gladness,
Fill us with the light of day.
3. You are giving and forgiving,
Ever blessing, ever blessed.
Fountain of the joy of living,
Ocean depths of happy rest.

2402. King over all

Mal 3:6; Heb 13:8; Rev 19:6; 22:13

Capo 3 (D)

With strength

Nicki Rogers
& Eoghan Heaslip

Chorus
F/A(D/F♯)
B♭sus2(G)
Csus4(A)
F/A(D/F♯)
B♭sus2(G)
First and the last, the Al-pha O-me - ga, pre-sent and past,
Csus4(A)
Dm(Bm)
B♭sus2(G)
all-know-ing Sa - viour, gi-ver of life, awe-some Cre-a - tor,
D.S. for last chorus repeat
Last time to Coda
Csus4(A)
Dm(Bm)
B♭sus2(G)
Csus4(A)
You are for - e - ver the same; Lord, You will ne - ver change.
1st time D.C.
F/A(D/F♯) B♭sus2(G)
C(A)
F/A(D/F♯) B♭sus2(G)
Csus4(A)
Mid section
Dm(Bm)
Csus4(A)
B♭sus2(G)
(2°)
Yes, we love You for all You've

1.
Dm(Bm)
Csus4(A)
Bbsus2(G)
done; Lord, we thank You for Your great
2.
D.S. (with repeat) al coda
Bbsus2(G)
Bb(G)
love. Yes, we love Your great love.
Coda
F/A(D/F#)
Bbsus2(G)
C(A)
F/A(D/F#)
Bbsus2(G)
1.
Cno3rd(A)
2.
Cno3rd(A)

2403. Kyrie eleison

Mt 25:35, 40; Lk 10:27; 18:38-39

Stuart Townend
& Keith Getty

Unhurried

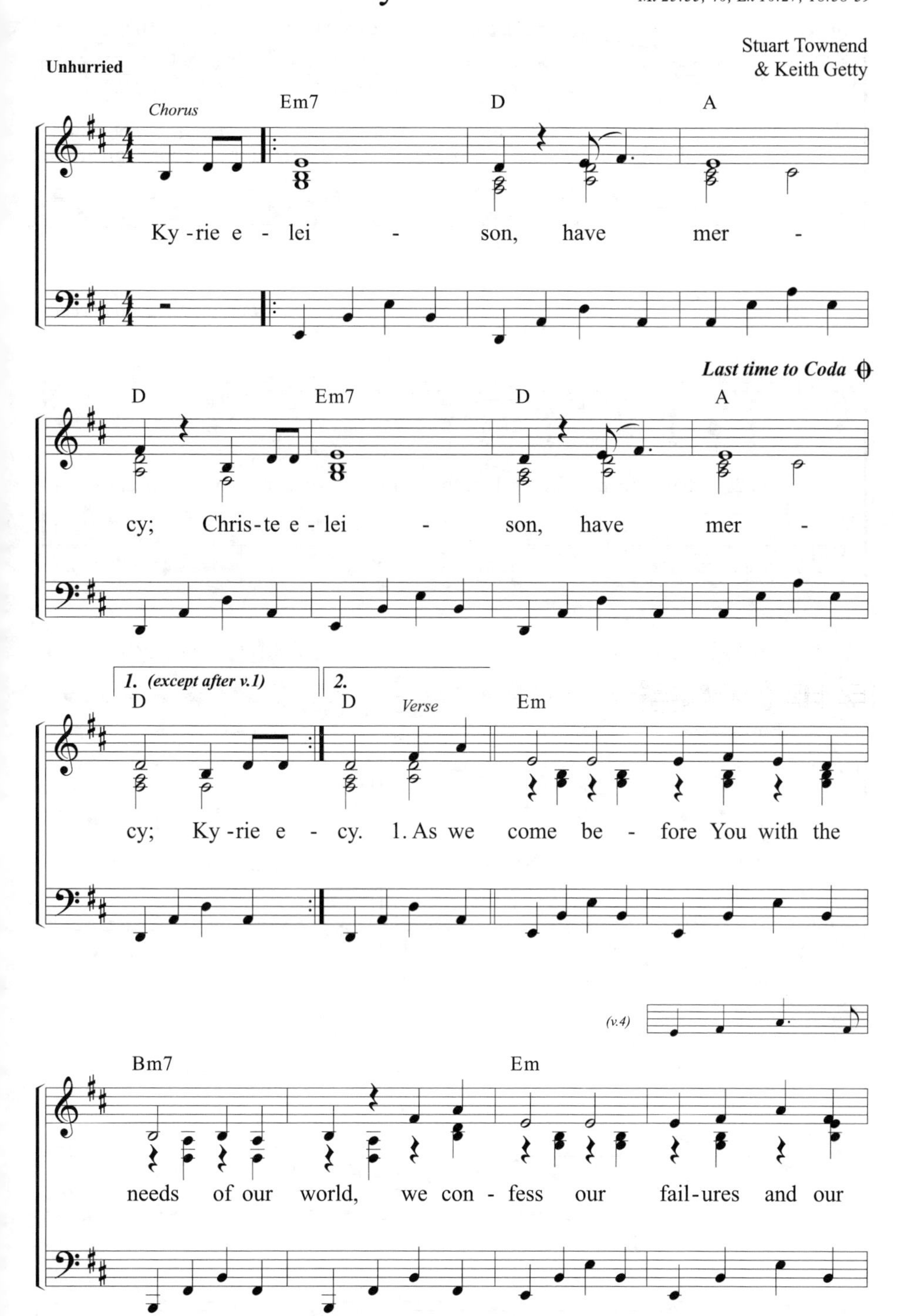

Bm7
Em
sin, for our words are ma - ny yet our

Bm7
Em
deeds have been few. Fan the fire of com - pas - sion once a -

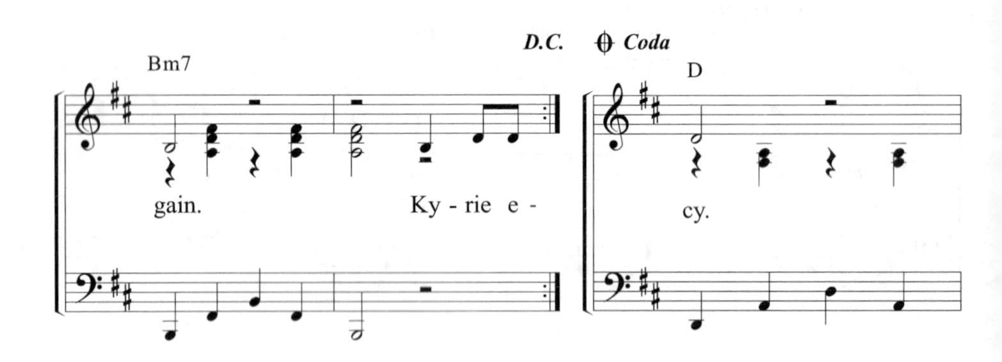
D.C.
Coda
Bm7
D
gain. Ky - rie e -
cy.

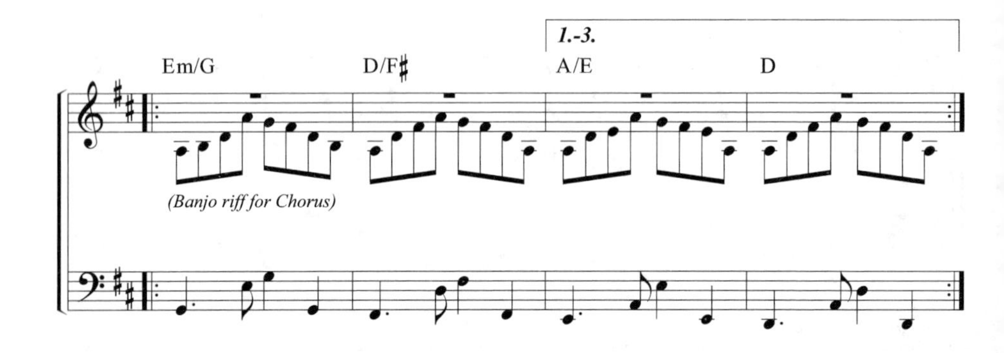
1.-3.
Em/G
D/F♯
A/E
D
(Banjo riff for Chorus)

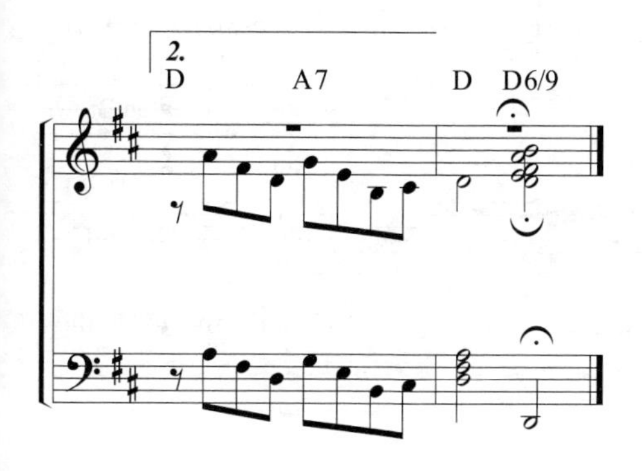

2. When the cries of victims go unheard in the land,
   And the scars of war refuse to heal,
   Will we stand for justice to empower the weak,
   Till their bonds of oppression are no more?

3. If we love our God with all our heart, mind and strength,
   And we love our neighbours as ourselves,
   Then this law of love will heal the nations of earth
   And the glory of Christ will be revealed.

4. Lord, renew our vision to be Christ where we live,
   To reach out in mercy to the lost;
   For each cup of kindness to the least in our midst
   Is an offering of worship to the throne.

2404. Lead me

Ps 61:2; Is 28:16; 43:2; 1 Cor 10:4; 1 Pet 2:6

1.
2.
D.C. al fine
G6
A
D
D
ages,___ You will stand. When the stand.

2405. Let no one caught in sin

(Christ is risen)

Mt 26:39; 28:6; 1 Cor 15:55; Eph 5:14; Heb 12:1-2

Matt Maher
& Mia Fieldes

Gently building

D
(small notes 5°-8°)
ri-sen from the dead, tram-pling o - ver death by death. Come, a-
ri-sen from the dead, we are one with Him a - gain. Come, a-
Last time to Coda
1.,3.,5.-7.
D.S. (al Coda)
G
Bm7
A/C♯
(small notes 4°-7°)
wake, come, a-wake, come and rise up from the grave. Christ is
wake, come, a-wake, come and
2.
Bm7
A
D
G/D
D
rise up from the grave.
D.C.(v.2)
4.
Mid section
Em/D
Bm7
A
D/F♯
G
2.Be-neath rise up from the grave. O death,
Bm7
A
D/F♯
G
Bm7
A
where is your sting? O hell, where is your vic - to-ry?

2. Beneath the weight of all our sin,
You bowed to none but heaven's will;
No scheme of hell, no scoffer's crown,
No burden great can hold You down.
In strength You reign;
Forever let Your church proclaim:

2406. Let our lives become a song for You

(All that really matters)

Mt 5:14, 16; Jn 14:6; Rom 12:1; Eph 5:2; Phil 3:14; 1 Tim 6:19

Moderately

Matt Redman
& Jonas Myrin

C G Dsus4
counts is found in You. What else would we
C G Em Dsus4 C2
live for? You're the way, the life, the truth, and
3rd time D.S. al Coda
Last time to Coda
Am (small notes 3°) G Em Dsus4
all that real-ly mat-ters is You. Je - sus, it's You.
(Yes,)
G Em 1. Dsus4 D.C.(v.3) 2. Dsus4
3. Let our lives
Mid section
Em C G
(1.,3.) King of glo - ry, be the cen - tre. King of glo - ry, You'll
(2.,4.) We shall have no o - ther trea-sure: all that counts is You

2. Let our lives become an offering,
Ever-pleasing to Your heart.
The glory of Your name, our highest call.

3. Let our lives become a light for You,
Like a city on a hill.
We'll glorify Your name forever more.

2407. Let our praise be Your welcome

(Here for You)

2 Chron 7:1; Is 55:11; Acts 2:2; Rev 15:4

Capo 5 (G)

Matt Maher, Matt Redman, Tim Wanstall & Jesse Reeves

With anticipation

C/E(G/B)
F(C)
Dm7(Am)
You are our one de - sire.
You a-lone are ho - ly,
G/B(D/F♯)
C/E(G/B)
1.
F(C)
on-ly You are wor - thy;
God, let Your fire fall down.
D.C.(v.2)
2.
F(C)
D.S.
3.
F(C)
2. Let our down.
To down.
Mid section
C(G)
Csus2(G)
We wel-come You with praise, we
(3.) ev - 'ry heart a - dore, let
C(G)
Csus2(G)
Am7(Em)
wel-come You with praise.
Al - migh-ty God of love, be
ev - 'ry soul a - wake.
Al - migh-ty God of love, be

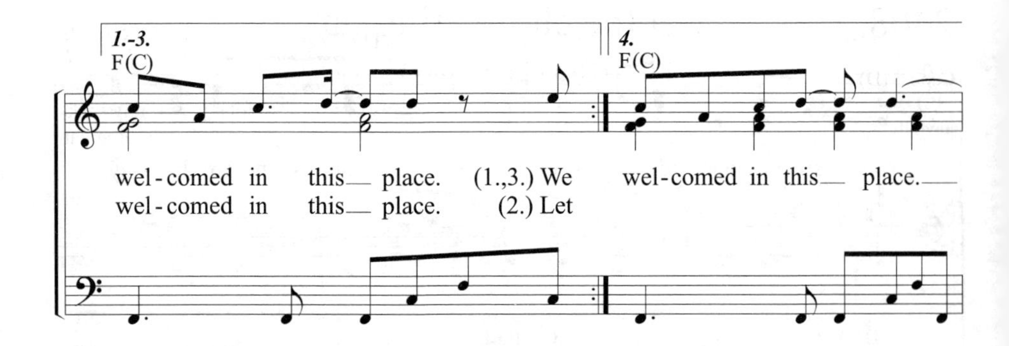

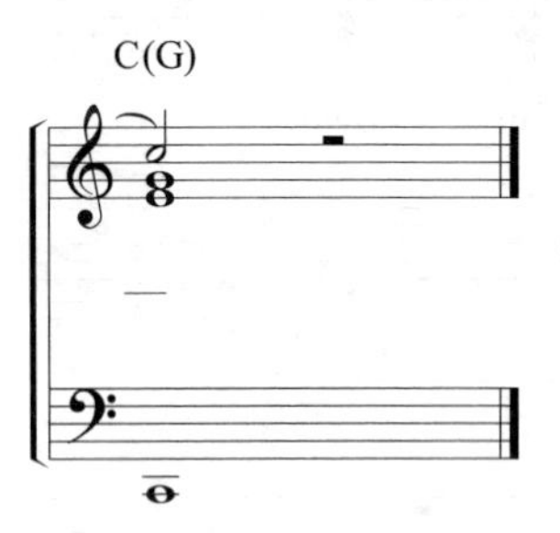

2. Let our shout be Your anthem,
Your renown fill the skies;
We are here for You,
We are here for You.
Let Your word move in power,
Let what's dead come to life;
We are here for You,
We are here for You.

2408. Let the chords ring out

(Brand new day)

Rom 6:4; 1 Cor 7:23; 1 Thess 4:14

Capo 2 (D)

Johnny & Cathy Parks
& Matt Redman

Joyfully

B(A)
E(D)
day, it's a brand new day. I'll
C♯m(Bm)
F♯(E)
take this ri-sen life You give; for You I'll live.
1.,4.
Last time to Coda
B(A)
E6(D)
F♯(E)
E(D)
D.C.
2.
D.S.
3.
2. So I'm
It's a brand new

2. So I'm letting go of all that's gone,
I'm soaking up this bright new dawn.
You have changed me, Lord.
The sun is rising in my life
Because the Son has paid the price.
You have changed me, Lord,
You've changed me, Lord.

2409. Let the words of my mouth

(All for You)

Ps 19:14; Col 3:23

Paul Baloche &
Graham Kendrick

Capo 4 (C)

Moderately

F♯m(Dm)
C♯m(Am)
A(F)
work be - side You and learn of You,
C♯m(Am) B(G)
A(F)
C♯m(Am)
A(F)
Je - sus, till all I do speaks of You.
D.C. (al Coda)
Coda
E(C)
A/E(F/A)
Let the
You, be for You, Lord, all for
E(C)
A/E (F/A)
E(C)
You, all for You.

2410. Let voices sing

(Great church)

Ps 40:2; Mt 16:18; Acts 2:17; 1 Cor 7:23; 2 Cor 5:7; Eph 1:4; 1 Thess 4:16; Heb 4:15; 12:1; 1 Pet 2:6, 9

Johnny & Cathy Parks
& Claire Hamilton

2. The ancient hymns declare His name,
Our hallowed King was without blame;
The helpless Babe, the suffering Christ
Who made Himself the highest price.
This Cornerstone will never shake,
This Spire of Hope will never break.
On the Rock, our feet stand fast:
This is a great church that will last!

3. We walk on hills of power and peace,
We stand beside the poor and weak.
We'll live by faith and not by sight;
Where there's darkness, we'll bring light.
God's purpose since the dawn of time
Is Christ revealed to all mankind.
Then we'll hear the trumpet blast:
This is a great church that will last!

2411. Life is but a breath

Ps 19:12; 51:10; 119:105; Mt 5:16

(Let it shine)

Capo 3 (G)

Lou & Nathan Fellingham
& Gary Sadler

Cm7(Am)
Gm7(Em)
F(D)
guide, let Your truth be my light, let my
me, love and grace set me free. By Your
Last time to Coda
Gm7(Em)
Cm7(Am)
C/E(A/C♯)
heart be con - sumed; let me live all for
pow'r I'm re - newed; I will live all for
1.
Fsus4(D)
F(D)
B♭(G)
You.
D.C.(v.3)
2.,3.,4. D.S. (chorus 2.,1.,2.)
5.
Fsus4(D)
F(D)
Fsus4(D)
F(D)
B♭(G)
You. Let Your You.

2. Every single day,
Trusting in the word You've spoken.
Obedience and faith,
Walking in the way You've chosen.
Oh, I wanna shine for You.
Oh, I wanna shine for You.

3. Work within my heart,
Purify my deepest motives.
Show me who You are,
Draw me to a life of worship.
Oh, I wanna shine for You.
Oh, I wanna be for You.

2412. Lift up a joyful song

(God of light)

Ps 68:4; Mt 5:13-14; 17:20; Lk 1:37; Acts 26:18; 2 Cor 5:7; Rev 17:14

Andy & Wendy Green

Asus4
D
Dsus4
work through our lives. God of light,
D
Bm7
re-kin-dle the fire; the hope and the
Last time to Coda
G
3
Asus4
A7sus4
vi-sion that's dimmed, let it burn once a-gain in our
D
Dsus4
1.
D.C.(v.2)
G/D
hearts.
2.
Mid section
G
A
Moun-tains can be moved; Lord,

G/B
A/C♯
G
no - thing is im - pos - si - ble for You. Moun - tains can be moved;
A
G/B
A/C♯
D.S. al Coda
we walk by faith and not by sight. God of light
Coda
G/B
D/F♯
G
3
The hope and the vi - sion that's dimmed, let it
A7sus4
D
D7sus4
D
D7sus4
burn once a - gain in our hearts.
D
D7sus4
D
D7sus4
D
2. Lord, we'll stay close to You.
You're the voice that's true
In a world that is screaming out lies.
Help us be salt and light,
Living out our lives
Showing Jesus through all that we do.

2413.
Lift up His name
(Holy is our God)
Capo 3 (G)
Ex 3:14; Heb 7:3; Rev 4:8; 15:3-4; 19:6
Robin Mark
With energy
Verse
B♭(G) E♭2(C) Cm7(Am) Fsus4(D) F(D)
1. Lift up His name with-in the sanc-tu - a - ry,
B♭(G) E♭2(C) Cm7(Am) Fsus4(D) F(D)
lift up His name a - mong the peo - ple who are
E♭(C) B♭(G)
ga - thered here to sing His praise, who are
E♭(C) F(D)
ga - thered here to sing His praise.
Chorus
B♭(G) E♭(C)
Ho - ly is our God. Ho - ly is Your name;

F(D)
E♭(C) F(D) Gm(Em) F(D)
might-ty are Your works and deeds and
B♭(G) E♭(C)
won-drous are Your ways. All that You have made
Last time to Coda 1.
F(D) E♭(C) F(D) Gm(Em) F(D)
shall re-turn and give You glo - ry, Lord.
D.C.(v.2) 3. D.S. al Coda
B♭(G) E♭2(C) B♭(G) E♭2(C) Gm(Em) F(D)
glo - ry,
2.
Mid section
Gm(Em) F(D) Gm(Em) E♭/G(C/E) B♭/F(G/D) F(D)
glo - ry, (Lord.)

D.C.(v.3)
Coda
Gm(Em) F(D) Eb(C) F(D)
glo - ry, give You
Gm(Em) F(D) Eb(C) F(D) Gm(Em) F(D) Bb(G)
glo - ry, give You glo - ry, Lord.
Verse
Bb(G) Eb2(C) Cm7(Am) Fsus4(D) F(D) Bb(G)
2. The earth, the sky, the sea and all with-in them, this u - ni-verse,
Eb2(C) Cm7(Am) Fsus4(D) F(D) Eb(C)
be-yond the sight of mor - tal man, all sub-ject to His
Bb(G) Eb(C) F(D)
reign; all cre - a - tion sub-ject to His reign.
Verse
Bb(G) Eb2(C) Cm7(Am) Fsus4(D) F(D) Bb(G)
3. The great I Am, no end and no be-gin - ning, You were and are
Eb2(C) Cm7(Am) Fsus4(D) F(D) Eb(C)
and e - ver-more You shall be. All my days are in Your
Bb(G) Eb(C) F(D)
hands; all my days are in Your hands.

2414. Lift up, lift up your eyes

Ps 123:1; Rev 17:14; 22:20

(The kingdom is coming)

Sam Blake, Stephen Gibson,
Joel Pridmore & Ian Yates

C
Em
Sing,
sing,
Last time to Coda
Am
our God reigns for - e - ver, our God
1.
D.C.
2.
Dm2
F
reigns.
Lift
reigns for - e - ver.
Mid section
F2
G/B
Am
G/B
The king-dom is com - ing,
1.
C2
G
(2°)
(the) hea-ven's draw - ing near.

2.
G
F
King of kings is here.
The king-dom is com-
G
Am
- ing, the king-dom is com - ing, the king-dom is com -
G/B
C
1.
- ing, the king-dom is com - ing, (2°) (the) hea-ven's draw - ing near.
G
2.
D.S. al Coda
G
King of kings is here.
Coda
Dm2
F
G
Am
G/B
reigns.
Oh,
oh,
(Fine)
C
G
oh.

2415. Light's glittering morning fills the sky

Mt 27:66; 28:6; Jn 20:13; 1 Cor 15:55; Heb 7:25; 1 Pet 1:18; 2:9

EASTER SONG

Geistliche Kirchengesang, Cologne 1623
Arr. Paul Hughes

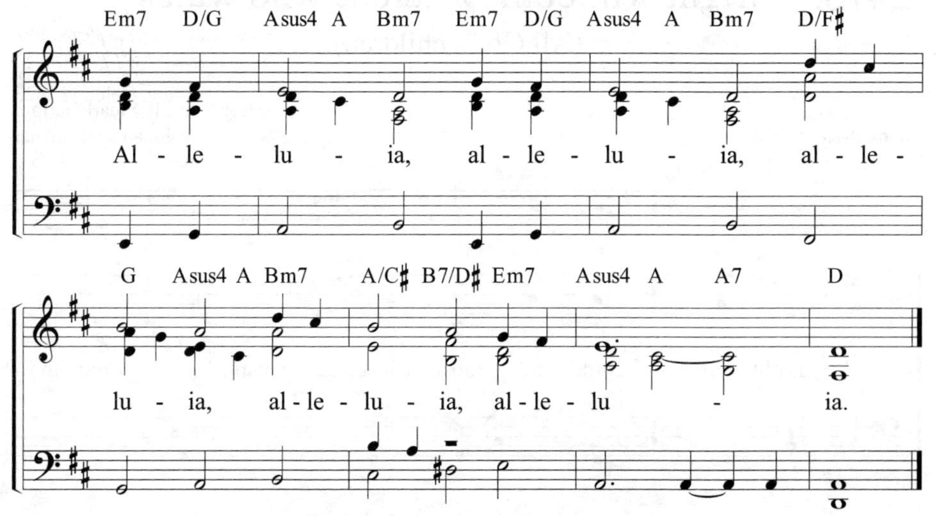

2. For Christ the Lord, the mighty King,
Closes with death and draws its sting;
Alleluia, alleluia!
He tramples down the powers of night,
Brings out His ransomed saints to light.
Alleluia, alleluia,
Alleluia, alleluia, alleluia.

3. His rocky tomb the threefold guard
Of watch and stone and seal had barred;
Alleluia, alleluia!
But now in royal triumph high
He comes from death to victory!
Alleluia, alleluia,
Alleluia, alleluia, alleluia.

4. Hell's gates are broken down at last,
Our days of mourning now are past;
Alleluia, alleluia!
'Weep not,' an angel voice has said,
'Jesus is risen from the dead!'
Alleluia, alleluia,
Alleluia, alleluia, alleluia.

5. All praise be Yours, O risen Lord,
From death to endless life restored;
Alleluia, alleluia!
To Father, Son and Spirit be
All power and praise eternally!
Alleluia, alleluia,
Alleluia, alleluia, alleluia.

From the Latin,
J. M. Neale (1818–66)

2416. Light will come to those who wait

(All God's children)

Ps 22:27; 72:11; Is 30:18; 60:1; Ezek 38:20; Mt 24:35; Phil 2:10; Rev 18:21

Martin Smith, Stuart Garrard & Jonathan Thatcher

Reflectively

(v.2)

Verse

F C

1. Light will come to those who wait. From the

F C

sha - dows, souls a - wake, for these are the days

(v.3)

G F

when the na - tions will bow at the com-ing King.

C

1. D.C.(v.2) 3.

2. All our for these are the days

G
F
when in - jus - tice will fall
at the com-ing King.
C
Jump to chorus
2.
Chorus
F
All God's chil - dren,
Dm
C
G/B
we will sing: hal - le - lu - jah, hal - le - lu - jah.
1.
F
Dm
C
G/B
D.C.(v.3)
3. Hope will
2.
F
Dm
C
All God's chil - dren, we will sing: hal - le - lu - jah, hal - le -

G/B
F
B7/F♯
lu - jah. All God's chil - dren, we will sing: hal - le -
C
G/B
F
lu - jah, hal - le - lu - jah. Hal - le - lu - jah, hal - le -
Dm
C
1.
G/B
lu - jah, hal - le - lu - jah, hal - le - lu - jah. Hal - le -
2.
G/B
Mid section
F
lu - jah. There will come a day when this
Dm7
C
all will fall a - way, we'll be sing - ing, sing - ing hal - le - lu -

2. All our kingdoms fall with the mountains,
And our empires crash into the sea,
For these are the days when the nations will rise
For the coming King.

3. Hope will come to those who wait,
As the heart of heaven breaks,
For these are the days when the least of us all
See the coming King;
For these are the days when injustice will fall
At the coming King.

2417. Longing for light, we wait in darkness

(Christ, be our light)

Mt 5:16; 6:10; 25:35; Jn 1:5; 14:27; 1 Cor 1:18; 2 Cor 4:6; 1 Pet 2:5, 9; 4:10

Flowing

Bernadette Farrell

2. Longing for peace, our world is troubled.
   Longing for hope, many despair.
   Your word alone has power to save us.
   Make us Your living voice.

3. Longing for food, many are hungry.
   Longing for water, many still thirst.
   Make us Your bread, broken for others,
   Shared until all are fed.

4. Longing for shelter, many are homeless.
   Longing for warmth, many are cold.
   Make us Your building, sheltering others,
   Walls made of living stone.

5. Many the gifts, many the people,
   Many the hearts that yearn to belong.
   Let us be servants to one another,
   Making Your kingdom come.

2418. Look inside the mystery

(Glorious)

Rom 8:23

Capo 5 (G)

Moderately

Paul Baloche
& Brenton Brown

Chorus
F(C)
G/F(D/C)
Glo - ri - ous: my eyes have seen the
F(C) G/F(D/C) C(G) F(C)
glo - ry of the Lord. Glo - ri - ous:
G/F(D/C) F(C) G/F(D/C) C(G)
He stands a-bove the ru - lers of the earth.
1. D.C.(v.2)
2.,3.
Mid section
G(D)
Glo - ri - ous, glo - ri-
Am(Em) F(C) G(D)
- ous. Lord, You are glo - ri-

C(G)
Cmaj7(G)
Am(Em)
F(C)
(ous.)
C(G)
Cmaj7(G)
Am(Em)
Oh,
You are glo -
F(C)
1.
D.S.
To end
C(G)
- ri - ous.
Glo - ri -
Verse
C(G)
Em(Bm)
Am(Em)
2. Look be - yond the tomb - stone, see the liv - ing God;
Gsus4(D)
F(C)
see the re - sur - rec - ted ru - ler of my heart.
C(G)
Em(Am)
Am(Em)
No one else a - bove Him, none to match His worth; the
Gsus4(D)
F(C)
hope of His re - turn - ing fills the u - ni - verse.

We know that the whole creation has been groaning as in the pains of childbirth right up to the present time. Not only so, but we ourselves, who have the firstfruits of the Spirit, groan inwardly as we wait eagerly for our adoption as sons, the redemption of our bodies.

ROMANS 8:22-23

2419. Looks like tonight the sky is heavy

2 Chron 7:13; Joel 2:23; Jn 7:38

(Rain down)

Martin Smith
& Stuart Garrard

D
Bridge
'Cause it's liv - ing wa - ter we
Dmaj7
D
de - sire, so flood our hearts with ho - ly fire.
Chorus
A
Rain down. All a-round the world
D
we're sing-ing: rain down.
Last time to Coda
A
Can You hear the earth is sing-ing? Rain

down. My heart is dry but still I'm sing-ing:
D
rain down, rain it
1. D.C.(v.2) 2 Mid section
G
down. 2. Back to the start down. Do not
D/F# A E/G# C
shut, do not shut, do not
G/B D G
shut the hea - vens. But o - pen

2. Back to the start, my heart is heavy.
Feels like it's time to dream again.
Well, I see the clouds, and yes, I'm ready
To dance upon this barren land,
Hope in my hands.

2420. Look up to the skies

Ps 19:1; 148:3; Rom 1:20

Judy Gresham

2. The sun rising up reminds us to say,
'Be glad and give thanks to the Lord God today.'
And when evening falls, the moon's silver light
Will shine for His praise through the darkness of night.

3. The mountains so high, the valleys so low,
The fruit on the trees and the flowers that grow;
The birds of the air, the creatures that crawl
Give glory to God, who reigns over them all.

2421.
Lord, hear our cry
(Hear us from heaven)
2 Chron 7:14; Is 35:5; Mt 6:12; 11:5
Capo 4 (G)
Jared Anderson
Tenderly
Verse
G♯m(Em) E2(C) (D/F♯) F♯/A♯ (C/E) E/G♯ G♯m(Em) E2(C)
Lord, hear our cry; come, heal our land.
(D/F♯) F♯/A♯ (C/E) E/G♯ G♯m(Em) E2(C) (D/F♯) F♯/A♯ (C/E) E2/G♯
Breathe life in-to these dry and thir-sty souls.
(G/B) B2/D♯ E2(C) F♯sus4(D) F♯(D) G♯m(Em) E2(C) (D/F♯) F♯/A♯ (C/E) E/G♯
Lord, hear our prayer:
G♯m(Em) E2(C) (D/F♯) F♯/A♯ (C/E) E/G♯ G♯m(Em) E2(C)
for-give our sin. As we call on Your name,
F♯/A♯(D/F♯) E2/G♯(C/E) B/D♯(G/B) E2(C)
would You make this a place for Your glo-ry to dwell?

F♯sus4(D)
Chorus
B(G)
O - pen the blind eyes, un - lock the deaf
F♯/A♯(D/F♯)
C♯m7(Am)
B/D♯(G/B)
ears, come to Your peo - ple as we draw near.
E2(C)
E/F♯(C/D)
B(G)
Hear us from hea - ven, touch our ge - ne - ra -
F♯/A♯(D/F♯)
C♯m7(Am)
B/D♯(G/B)
tion. We are Your peo - ple cry - ing out in des -
E2(C)
D.C.
(Fine)
B(G)
F♯/A♯(D/F♯)
C♯m7(Am)
pe-ra - tion.

1.
E2(C)
2.
E2(C)
Mid section
B(G)
Hear us from hea - ven, hear us from hea-
F♯/A♯(D/F♯)
C♯m7(Am)
1.-3.
E2(C)
- ven, hear us from hea - ven.
Hear us from hea -

4.
D.S. al fine
E2(C)
O-pen the blind

2422. Lord, I come
(Lord, I need You)

Capo 4 (G)

Jer 33:16; Mt 11:28; Rom 5:20; 1 Cor 10:13; 2 Cor 3:17; Col 1:27

Jesse Reeves, Kristian Stanfill, Matt Maher, Christy Nockels & Daniel Carson

Prayerfully

Verse B(G) Esus2(C) B(G) F♯/A♯(D/F♯)

1. Lord, I come, I con - fess. Bow-ing

G♯m7(Em) F♯sus4(D) Esus2(C) B(G) Esus2(C)

here, I find my rest. And with-out You I fall a-

B(G) F♯sus4(D) F♯(D) Esus2(C)

-part; You're the One who guides my heart.

Chorus B(G) E(C) B(G) F♯/A♯(D/F♯)

Lord, I need You, oh, I need You;

G♯m7(Em) E(C) B(G) F♯(D) B/D♯(G/B) E(C)

ev - 'ry hour I need You. My one de-fence, my

B/F♯(G/D) E/G♯(C/E) B/F♯(G/D) F♯(D) B(G) Esus2(C)
right - eous-ness, oh, God, how I need You.
B(G)
Verse
Esus2(C)
2. Where sin runs deep, Your grace is
B(G) F♯/A♯(D/F♯) G♯m7(Em) F♯sus4(D)
more; where grace is found is where You
Esus2(C) B(G) Esus2(C) B(G)
are. And where You are, Lord, I am free. Ho-li-
F♯sus4(D) F♯(D) Esus2(C) B(G) Esus2(C)
ness is Christ in me. Where You are, Lord, I am

B(G)
F♯sus4(D)
F♯(D)
B(G)
free. Ho - li - ness is Christ in me.
Chorus
Bsus4(G)
B(G)
E(C)
B(G)
F♯/A♯(D/F♯)
Lord, I need You, oh, I need You;
G♯m7(Em)
E(C)
B(G)
F♯(D)
B/D♯ (G/B)
E(C)
ev - 'ry hour I need You. My one de-fence, my
Last time to Coda
B/F♯(G/D)
E/G♯(C/E)
B/F♯(G/D)
F♯(D)
B(G)
right - eous-ness, oh, God, how I need You.
Mid section
Bsus4(G)
E(C)
(G/B)
B/D♯
F♯sus4(D)
G♯m7(Em)
So teach my song to rise to You

B/D♯(G/B)
Esus2(C)
when temp - ta - tion comes my way, and when I
E(C)
B/D♯(G/B)
F♯sus4(D)
G♯m7(Em)
can - not stand, I'll fall on You;
Esus2(C)
F♯sus4(D)
B(G)
Je - sus, You're my hope and stay. And when I
E(C)
B/D♯(G/B)
F♯sus4(D)
G♯m7(Em)
can - not stand, I'll fall on You;
Esus2(C)
F♯sus4(D)
B(G)
Bsus4(G)
D.S. al Coda
Je - sus, You're my hope and stay. Lord, I

Coda
B(G)
B/D♯(G/B)
E(C)
B/F♯(G/D)
E/G♯(C/E)
You. My one de-fence, my right - eous-ness; oh,

B/F♯(G/D)
F♯(D)
B(G)
God, how I need You.

2423. Lord, I come
(Glorified)

Ps 8:4; 31:5; 114:7; Rom 12:1

Shaun Griffiths

2. Into Your hands I commit my life,
Day by day, as a living sacrifice.
Who am I, that You would care for me?
I glorify the One who died for me.

2424. Lord, I come to You
(Glory to You)

Mt 6:10; 28:19; Acts 2:4; Eph 5:18

Neil Bennetts
& Eghan Heaslip

Steady 4

Last time to Coda
1.
D/F♯
A
G
D/G
D
bring glo-ry to You,
Je-sus.
D.C.(v.2)
2.
Gsus2
D
G
Asus4
Gsus2
Je-sus.
Mid section
A
Bm7
Take me
and fill
1.
G
A
Bm7
Gsus2
me,
and send
me
to the world.
2.
Gsus2
A
Bm7
Gsus2
Oh,
oh,
oh,

2. Lord, I am surrendered
To Your will, Your ways, Your heart;
Use me now to bring
Your kingdom on the earth.

'Go and make disciples of all nations, baptising them in the name of the Father and of the Son and of the Holy Spirit, and teaching them to obey everything I have commanded you. And surely I am with you always, to the very end of the age.'

MATTHEW 28:19-20

2425. Lord, let Your presence come

2 Chron 7:1; Jn 1:29; Acts 2:3-4; Rom 5:5; 12:1; 1 Pet 2:5-6

Chris & Jennie Orange

Flowing

Verse

D2 E A E/G♯

1. Lord, let Your pre - sence come, let glo - ry fill Your

A D2 E A E/G♯

house. Christ, the e - ter - nal King, come mi - ni - ster in

A E D2 Bm7 A/C♯

pow'r. We o - pen up our hearts, for You are

D2 E A

with us now.

Chorus

Come,

E/G♯ F♯m7 D2 A E/G♯

Ho - ly Spi - rit, come, Ho - ly

Ped.

2. Christ is the cornerstone,
Precious Lamb of God.
He made us living stones,
A house where glory dwells.
We offer up our lives,
A living sacrifice.

3. Hope does not disappoint,
For love has been poured out
Through the eternal King,
His Spirit given now.
We lift our hands in faith;
Come fill us with Your power.

2426. Lord, send us to the lost

Capo 3 (Em)

Is 58:7; 61:1; Mic 6:8; Mt 9:36; 16:24; 25:40; 28:19; Eph 4:30

Steadily

Adam Daubney

Gm(Em) *Verse* Dm(Bm)

1. Lord, send us to the lost, where brok - en - ness a -

E♭(C) B♭(G) B♭/A(G/F♯)

bounds, where we can show the Fa - ther's heart,

Gm(Em) Dm(Bm)

where we can feed the poor, where we can warm the

E♭(C) B♭(G) B♭/A(G/F♯)

cold, and com - fort those who weep and mourn.

E♭(C)
F(D)
Chorus
B♭(G)
Dm(Bm)
the earth. With mer - cy, with jus - tice, Lord, send
E♭(C)
Gm(Em)
F(D)
B♭(G)
us to the lost; with lives that re-sound
Last time to Coda
1.
Dm(Bm)
E♭(C)
Gm(Em) F(D)
with the mes - sage of the cross.
D.C.(v.2)
2.,4.
D.S.
E♭(C)
F(D)
Gm(Em) F(D)
With mer -
3.
Gm(Em) F(D)
Dm(Bm)
Mid section
What - e - ver we do for the least,
With gifts un - seen and works un - told,

2. Lord, open up our eyes
To see the Father's heart,
To know what grieves Your Spirit, Lord;
That we take up our cross,
Dying unto ourselves,
We do the things that please Your heart.
Jesus, with Your compassion,
Help us display Your love.

He has showed you, O man, what is good. And what does the LORD require of you? To act justly and to love mercy and to walk humbly with your God.

MICAH 6:8

2427. Lord, there's none like You

Is 58:7; Jer 10:6-7; Phil 2:9; Rev 4:8; 5:11-12

Capo 2 (G)

Moderately

Chris & Jennie Orange

2. Lord, I'll follow You,
My life is in Your hands;
Come shape me for Your plans. *(Repeat)*

(Chorus 2)
To save the lost and feed the hungry,
Clothe the naked, hold the lonely:
This will be the message that we live. (Repeat)

2428.

Lord, we delight

(Faithfulness and providence)

Eph 2:8-9; Col 1:14, 26; Jas 1:17

G Bm A G
pro-vi-dence, and we re-joice be-cause of Your great love.
Gmaj7 G6 Bm A D
A-live in Christ by grace a-lone and not by works that
G Bm A
man could own, and we re-joice be-cause of Your great
G Gmaj7 1° D.C.(v.2) D Dsus4
love.
D Dsus4 D
2. Now we are saved,
And forgiven is our sin.
The sacrifice of Jesus
Is more than we deserve.
God of all truth,
This mystery revealed:
You're King of all creation,
Yet lover of our souls.

2429.
Lord, we draw near to You
(We exalt You)
Mt 5:14, 16; 6:33;
Heb 4:16; 10:22
Gareth Robinson
Simply
Verse
G D
1. Lord, we draw near to You through the
G/B C G D
blood of Your Son. You've for - gi - ven our sin and
(v.2)
G/B C G D
made us ho - ly. Now with praise in our hearts, and with
G/B C G D
full con - fi - dence as the child - ren of God, we
(v.2)
(v.2)
G/B C Em D C
Chorus
give You glo - ry. We bow down. We ex -

2. You provide for our needs and You hear when we pray,
As You dwell in our hearts and we seek Your kingdom.
Now a light for this world, we will shine out for You,
With the fire of Your love, in the grace of Your wisdom.
We bow down.

2430. Lord, we have heard of Your fame

(Stretch out Your hand)

Hab 3:2; Acts 4:30-31; 1 Cor 12:27; Phil 2:9

With anticipation

Gareth Robinson & Nicole Brown

Verse G

1. Lord, we have heard of Your fame,

C/G Em7

we stand in awe of Your deeds. Re - new them in our day,

Dsus4 *1. D.C.(v.1)* D *2.,3.* D

make them known. As we

Am G/B

speak Your words, as we do Your works, O

C Dsus4 D *Chorus*

Lord, re - mem - ber mer - cy. Stretch out Your

G D G/B C
hand to heal, to save, re-store; per-form Your
Last time to Coda
Em7 C G/B
signs and wonders in the po - wer of Your name.
1. D.C.(v.2) 2.,4. D.S. 3.
D D D G/B
Stretch out Your In the
Mid section
D G/B D Em7
po - wer of Your name. Je - sus,
D.S. (with repeat) al Coda
(4 times)
C G/B D D
Your name is al - ways high - er. Stretch out Your

Coda
G/B D G/B
In the po - wer of Your name. Je - sus, in the
D G/B D G
po - wer of Your name.
Verse
G
2. Yours are the hands that heal, Yours are the words of life;
C/G Em7
we are Your hands and feet, Your voice of hope.
Dsus4 D Am
As we speak Your words, as we
G/B C Dsus4
do Your works, O Lord, o - pen the flood - gates.

2431. Lord, what I wouldn't give

(What I wouldn't give)

Capo 2 (D)

Andy Flannagan

Gently

2432. Lord, You are wonderful

(Daring to believe)

Is 42:8; Lk 4:18, 21, 40; 5:31; Jn 14:16

Spirited

Godfrey Birtill

D7
pre - sent, the King of hea-ven's here to-day, heal-ing the
bro - ken and the nee - dy; let all di - sea - ses flee at Your
(D.S.)
way, Yah - weh, Yah - weh, Yah - weh! Your
Chorus
G
name! We are dar - ing, dar-ing to be - lieve for mi-ra -
way, Yah - weh! Your way, Yah - weh, Yah - weh, Yah -
D7sus4 G D7sus4 G
cles, for mi-ra - cles. We are dar - ing, dar - ing to be -

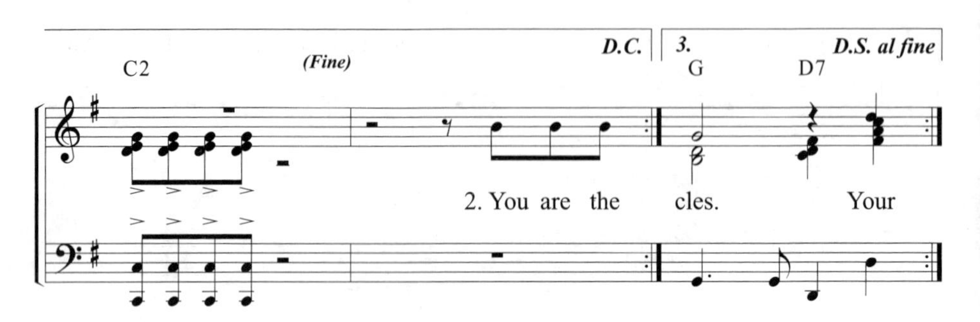

2. You are the strengthener, our holy comforter,
You are the standard, the great deliverer.
Through You, salvation, sanctification.
O great Physician, giving the vision.
To draw the future to the present,
The King of heaven's here today,
Healing the broken and the needy;
Let all diseases flee at Your name!

3. King of eternity, our blessèd surety,
Our place of safety, our holy sanctuary.
Jesus triumphant, perfect redemption;
The resurrection – our great inheritance.
To draw the future to the present,
The King of heaven's here today,
Healing the broken and the needy;
Let all diseases flee at Your name!

When the sun was setting, the people brought to Jesus all who had various kinds of sickness, and laying his hands on each one, he healed them.

LUKE 4:40

2433. Lord, You were rich

Mt 1:23; Lk 2:7; 2 Cor 8:9, Eph 1:11; Phil 2:7; Col 1:27; Rev 21:19

BERGERS

French traditional melody
Arr. Paul Hughes

Reflectively

2. You are our God beyond all praising,
   Yet, for love's sake, became a man
   Stooping so low, but sinners raising
   Heavenwards by Your eternal plan.
   You are our God beyond all praising,
   Yet, for love's sake, became a man.

3. Lord, You are love beyond all telling,
   Saviour and King, we worship You;
   Emmanuel, within us dwelling,
   Make us and keep us pure and true.
   Lord, You are love beyond all telling,
   Saviour and King, we worship You.

Frank Houghton (1894–1972)

2434. Loved before the dawn of time

(Salvation's song)

B/D♯(G/B)
Emaj7(C)
B/F♯(G/D)
cho-rus of cre-a-tion giv-ing praise to Christ a-
1.,3.
(F♯m)
A♯m7+4(no5)
D♯7(B)
D.C. (al fine)
2.
F♯sus4(D)
F♯(D)
Mid section
B/D♯(G/B)
Emaj7(C)
lone. lone. Sing-ing glo-ry, ho-nour,
B/F♯(G/D)
E/G♯(C/E)
B/F♯(G/D)
(F/G)
Amaj7/B
B7(G)
Emaj7(C)
wis-dom, pow-er to the Lamb up-on the throne;
C♯m7(Am)
B/D♯(G/B)
Emaj7(C)
C♯/E♯(A/C♯)
F♯(D)
F♯/E(D/C)
Hal-le-lu-jah, I will lift Him high. Sing-ing
(G/B)
B/D♯
Emaj7(C)
(G/D)
B/F♯
E/G♯(C/E)
B/F♯(G/D)
(F/G)
Amaj7/B
B7(G)
glo-ry, ho-nour, wis-dom, pow-er to the Lamb up-on the throne;

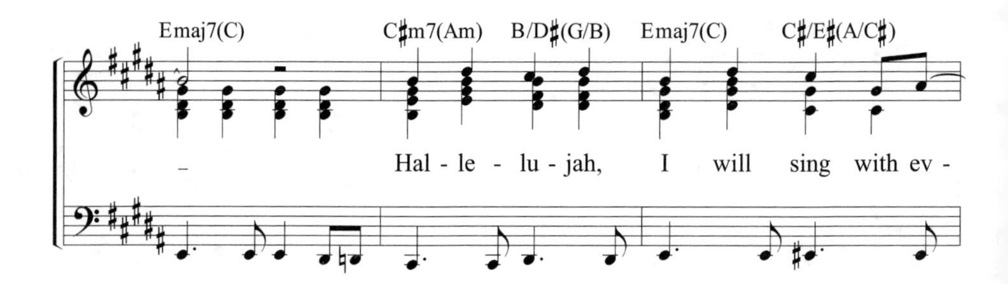

2. When I'm stained with guilt and sin,
He is there to lift me,
Heal me and forgive me;
Gives me strength to stand again,
Stronger than I was before.

3. All the claims of Satan's curse
Lifted through His offering,
Satisfied through suffering;
All the blessings He deserves
Poured on my unworthy soul.

4. Stars will fade and mountains fall;
Christ will shine forever,
Love's unfading splendour.
Earth and heaven will bow in awe,
Joining in salvation's song.

Set your minds on things above, not on earthly things. For you died, and your life is now hidden with Christ in God.

COLOSSIANS 3:2-3

2435. Love divine, all loves excelling

Lk 1:68; Jn 14:17; 1 Cor 6:19; 2 Cor 3:18; 5:17; Heb 4:11; 12:2; 2 Pet 3:14; Rev 4:10; 22:13

Steadily

Music: Rend Collective Experiment & William Thompson
Words adpt: Rend Collective Experiment

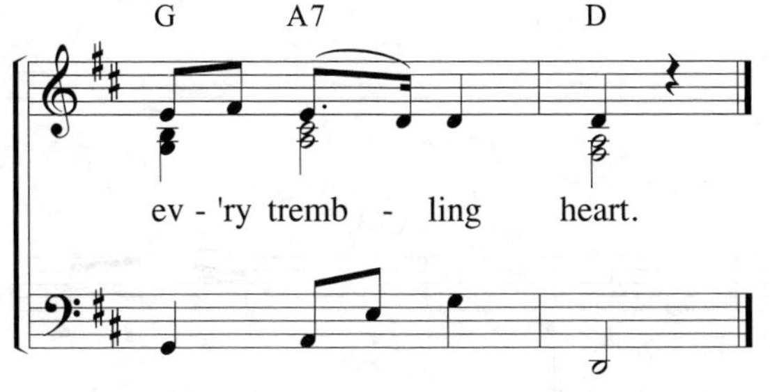

2. Breathe, O breathe Thy loving Spirit
Into every troubled breast!
Let us all in Thee inherit,
Let us find our promised rest.
Take away the love of sinning;
Alpha and Omega be;
End of faith, as its beginning,
Set our hearts at liberty.

3. Come, Almighty, to deliver,
Let us all Thy life receive;
Suddenly return, and never,
Never more Thy temples leave.
May we be a blessing to Thee,
Serve Thee as Thy hosts above,
Pray, and praise Thee without ceasing,
Glory in Thy perfect love.

4. Finish then Thy new creation,
Pure and spotless let us be;
Let us see Thy great salvation
Perfectly restored in Thee!
Changed from glory into glory,
Till in heaven we take our place;
Till we cast our crowns before Thee,
Lost in wonder, love and praise.

Charles Wesley (1707–88)

2436. Love divine, all loves excelling

Lk 1:68; Jn 14:17; 1 Cor 6:19; 2 Cor 3:18; 5:17; 2 Pet 3:14; Rev 4:10

Sensitively

Music: Chris Eaton & John Hartley

2° & 3° to Coda
C
Gm
F
-ceive; sud - den - ly re - turn, and ne - ver, ne - ver
Dm
F/G
G7sus4
C
more Thy tem - ples leave. Thee we would be al - ways
C/E
F
Esus4
E
bles - sing, serve Thee as Thy hosts a - bove, pray and
Am
G
F
Am
C/G
F
C/G
praise Thee with - out cea - sing, glo - ry in Thy per - fect
C
Dm/C
Em/C
Dm/C
D.C. al Coda
love. 3. Fin - ish

Coda

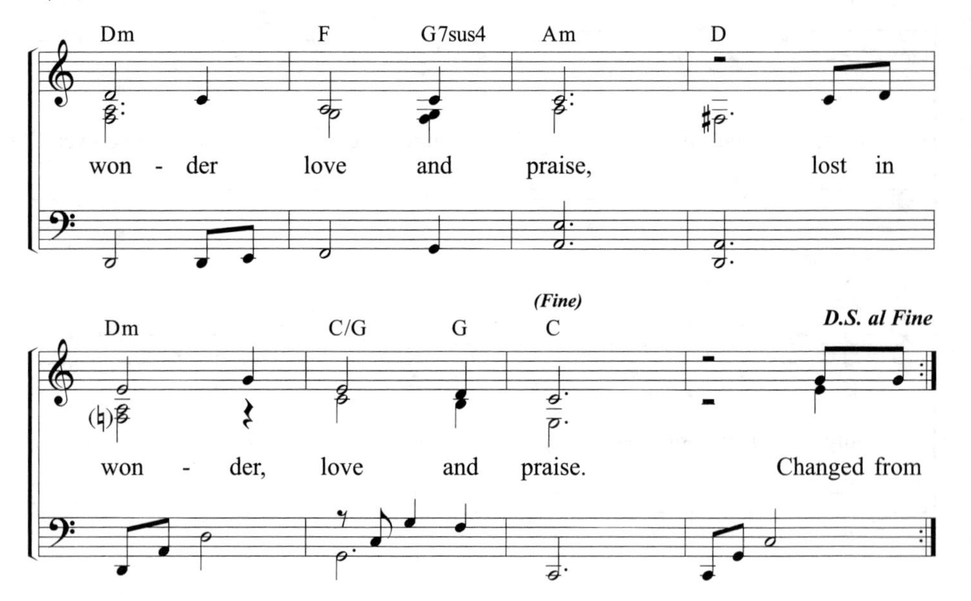

3. Finish then Thy new creation:
   Pure and spotless let us be;
   Let us see Thy great salvation,
   Perfectly restored in Thee:
   Changed from glory into glory,
   Till in heaven we take our place,
   Till we cast our crowns before Thee,
   Lost in wonder, love and praise.

   Changed from glory into glory...

   Charles Wesley (1707–88)

Now the Lord is the Spirit, and where the Spirit of the Lord is, there is freedom. And we, who with unveiled faces all reflect the Lord's glory, are being transformed into his likeness with ever-increasing glory, which comes from the Lord, who is the Spirit.

2 CORINTHIANS 3:18

2437. Love is His word

Mt 26:20; Mk 1:35; 2:15; Jn 13:34; 1 Cor 11:23-25; Gal 5:14

CRESSWELL

Music: Anthony Milner

With strength

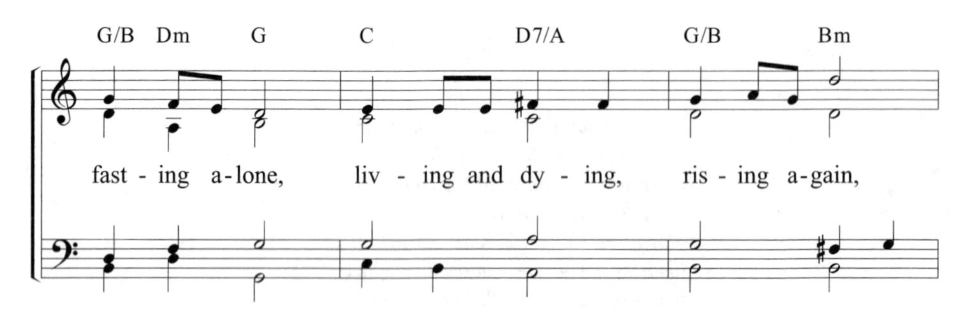

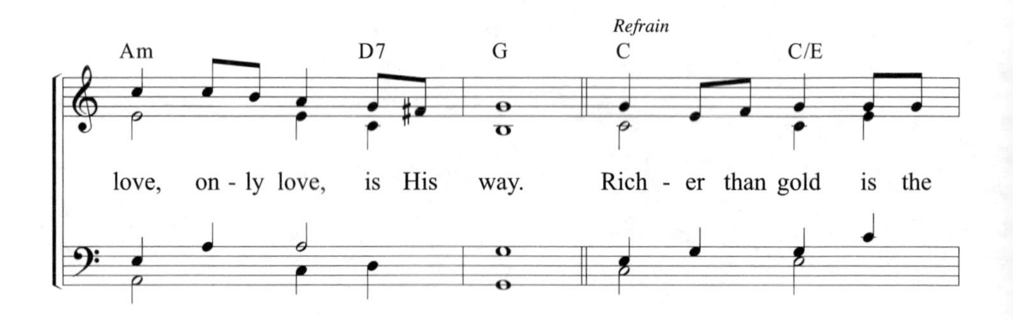

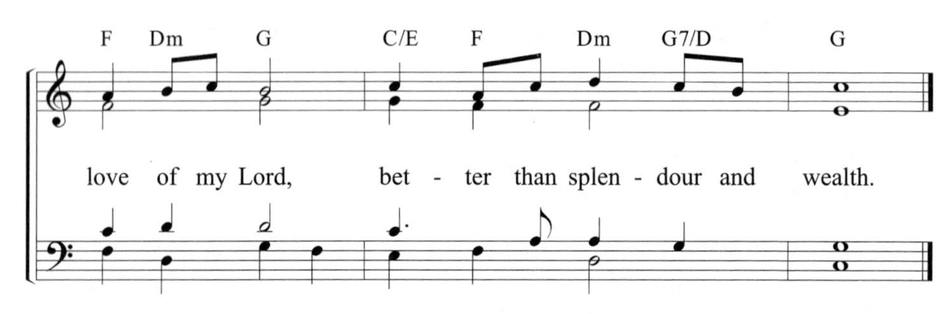

2. Love is His way, love is His mark,
Sharing His last Passover feast,
Christ at His table, host to the Twelve,
Love, only love, is His mark.

3. Love is His mark, love is His sign,
Bread for our strength, wine for our joy,
'This is My body, this is My blood' –
Love, only love, is His sign.

4. Love is His sign, love is His news,
'Do this,' He said, 'lest you forget
All My deep sorrow, all My dear blood.'
Love, only love is His news.

5. Love is His news, love is His name,
We are His own, chosen and called,
Family, brethren, cousins and kin,
Love, only love, is His name.

6. Love is His name, love is His law,
Hear His command, all who are His:
'Love one another as I have loved you' –
Love, only love, is His law.

7. Love is His law, love is His word:
Love of the Lord, Father and Word,
Love of the Spirit, God ever one;
Love, only love, is His word.

Luke Connaughton (1917–79)

2438. Love, shine through

Num 6:25; Mt 5:16; 2 Cor 4:6; 12:10

D/F♯
ev - 'ry - thing is Yours, Lord. All I am,
Am7
hum - bled by Your love. Take Your place:
Csus2
1.
C
Je - sus, be the cen - tre. I am no - thing with - out You.
D.C.(v.2)
2.-4. 2nd time D.S. al Coda
Last time to Coda
C
Mid section
D
Em7
(2°)
You. (And) Cause Your face to
C G D Em7
1. C
shine up - on us. Lord, a - rise and shine.

2.
C
D G/D D7 G/D
shine. Let it shine!
D G/D D7 G/D D/F♯ G Am7 G/B
Let it shine, let it shine,
D/F♯ G Am7 G/B D Em7
let it shine,
C G D Em7 C G D.S.
let it shine! And
Coda D Em7 C G
Tag
(Opt. vocals)
Let it shine, let it shine. Let it shine, let it shine.

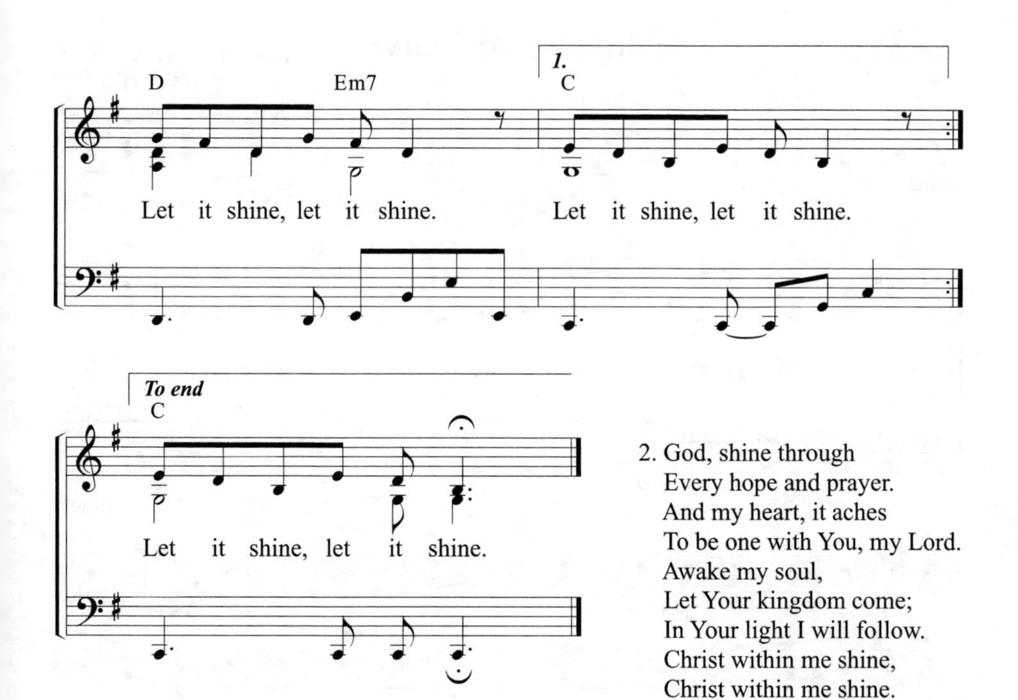

2. God, shine through
Every hope and prayer.
And my heart, it aches
To be one with You, my Lord.
Awake my soul,
Let Your kingdom come;
In Your light I will follow.
Christ within me shine,
Christ within me shine.

2439. Majesty of heaven

Ps 8:1; 40:5; Jn 8:12; Phil 2:9; Col 1:17; Rev 7:9; 11:15

Chris Tomlin, Matt Redman
& Jesse Reeves

Steadily

(v.3)

Verse

D A Asus4 A D

1. Ma - je - sty of hea - ven, Your glo - ry fills

(vv.2,3)

A Asus4 A D F♯m7

the skies; Light of the world, You are

D
Esus4
a - tion cries out: 'Ma - je - sty.'
A
Asus2+4
A
F♯m7
All things You hold to - ge - ther, Your name will
D
Esus4
Last time to Coda
stand for - e - ver; ma - je - sty, You are
D
D/F♯
Esus4
1.
D.C.(v.3)
ma - je - sty.
2.
D
A
E
F♯m7
D
A
E
F♯m7

Mid section
D A E F♯m7 D A
Your name above all others, high and ex -
Esus4 E D A E F♯m7
alt - ed. Your king - dom shall reign for - e - ver,
D A
high and ex -
1.
Esus4 E
alt - ed.
2. D.S. al Coda
N.C.
alt - ed.
Coda
D D/G Esus4 D D/G
ma - je - sty, You are ma - je -
Esus4 D2
- sty.
2. Humbled by Your presence,
Amazed by who You are;
Nothing compares,
You are Lord of all.
3. Merciful and mighty,
My heart is overwhelmed;
You stand alone,
You are Lord of all.

2440. Man of sorrows
(Victory of the cross)

Is 53:3, 5; Lk 4:18; Rom 3:22; 1 Cor 15:55; Phil 2:8-10; Col 1:19; 2:12, 15

Ken Riley & Graham Kendrick

E
F♯m
E
A
took my bro - ken - ness, gave Your righ - teous -
D
A/C♯
D
E
A
D A/C♯
Last time to Coda
ness by the vic - to - ry of the cross,
1.
E
A
D A/C♯
E
D.C.(v.2)
by the vic - t'ry of the cross.
2.
E
Mid section
D
E
F♯m
O death, where is your vic - to - ry? O
D
E
F♯m
A/C♯
death, where is your sting? Christ

D E A F♯m D
died our death at Cal - va-ry; we're raised to life in Him!
Esus4
D.S. al Coda
For the
Coda
Tag
A D A/C♯
Yours is the vic-to-ry,
E A D A/C♯
1.-3.
E
Yours is the vic-to-ry, Yours is the vic-t'ry of the cross.
4.
E F♯m E A
cross. You took my bro-ken - ness, gave Your righ-teous -
D A/C♯ D E A
ness by the vic-to-ry of the cross.

2441. May my prayer
(Like incense/Sometimes by step)

Ps 63:1; 113:3; 119:111-112; Is 25:1; Mt 7:14; 11:30; Lk 1:52; Rev 5:8

Prayerfully

Brooke Ligertwood
David Strasser & Rich Mullins

Like Incense - Brooke Ligertwood

Sometimes By Step – David Strasser and Rich Mullins

Em7
heart is set on keep - ing Your de-crees; be
C
still, my anx - ious urge to-ward re - bel-lion,
Am7
D
Chorus
let love keep my will up - on its knees. O
G
D
C
God, You are my God, and I will e-ver praise
Am7
G
D
You. O God, You are my God, and

Last time to Coda
1. D.C.(v.2)
2. D.S.
C
Am7
Am7
I will e-ver praise You. 2. To You. O
3.
1.-7.
8. D.S. al Coda
Am7
D
Em7
Cmaj7
G
G
You. O
Coda
Am7
Em7
D
You. I will seek You in the mor - ning and I will
C
Am7
Em7
learn to walk in Your ways, and step by step You'll lead
D
C
Am7
me and I will fol-low You all of my days.
rit.
Ped.

Verse
G(D)
2. To all cre - a - tion I can see a lim - it, but
Em7(Bm7)
Your com - mands are bound - less and have none; to
C(G)
Your word is my joy and me - di - ta - tion, from the
Am7(Em)
D(A)
ris - ing to the set - ting of the sun.
G(D)
All Your ways are lov - ing and are faith - ful, the
Em7(Bm7)
road is nar - row but Your bur - den light; be -
C(G)
cause You glad - ly lean to lead the hum - ble,
Am7(Em)
D(A)
I shall glad - ly kneel to leave my pride.

2442. May the God of hope

Rom 15:13

Doug Horley

1.
Em7 Asus4 A G D/F♯ D Dsus4
pow-er of the Ho - ly Spi-rit. May the
2.
D Dsus4 Mid section Em7 A
Fa-ther God, I love You, Fa-ther God, I
D Em7 Asus4 A
trust You, Fa-ther God, I need You ev - 'ry day.
Em7 A
Fill me with Your hope, Lord, fill me with Your
D Em7 Asus4 A D
joy, Lord, fill me with Your peace; let Your love flow.

2443. May the Lord bless you and keep you

Num 6:24-26

(Bless you and keep you)

Marc James

Gently

Verse

D2 A2/C♯ G2

May the Lord bless you and keep you, may the

D2 A2/C♯ G2

Lord be gra - cious to-wards you, may the

D2 A2/C♯ G2 *Last time to Coda*

Lord shine His face up-on you and give you His peace.

1. D2 A2/C♯ G2 2. D2 A2/C♯

May the

G2 D/F♯ G

Chorus

May you al - ways know you're trea -

D
A
- sured, may you al - ways know you're loved.
G
May you trust in God the Fa - ther, may you hope in God the Son.
(hope)
(trust)
G
D
A
May you know your name is writ - ten on the hand of God;
G2
A
A7
God bless you, lit - tle one.
1.
D
G
D
Bless you, lit-tle one;

G
D
al - ways know you're loved.
D.S.
G
D
G
D/F♯
2.
G
A7
D2
A2/C♯
God bless you, lit-tle one.
D.C. al Coda
G2
D2
A2/C♯
G2
May the
Coda
D2
A2/C♯
G2
D
Give you His peace.

The LORD bless you and keep you; the LORD make his face shine upon you and be gracious to you; the LORD turn his face towards you and give you peace.

NUMBERS 6: 24-26

2444. May Your voice be louder

(Full attention)

Ps 123:2; Jn 15:4; Heb 12:2

Jeremy Riddle

2. May Your presence be truer,
May Your presence be nearer
Than all the others,
Than all the others.
May Your light burn brighter,
May Your love go deeper
Than all the others,
Than all the others in my life.

2445. Mercy came

(Fresh mercy)

Is 53:5; Jn 3:3; Rom 5:8-9; Tit 3:4-5; 1 Jn 4:18

Capo 4 (C)

Thoughtfully

Sam Blake, Stephen Gibson, Joel Pridmore & Ian Yates

A2(F)
our hearts re - paired,
we are red - eemed.
B2(G)
Chorus
E(C)
What kind - ness was re - vealed?
Amaj7(F)
E(C)
A(F)
B(G)
C♯m7(Am7)
The Son of God ap-peared: it is Je - sus,
A2(F)
E(C)
1.
D.C.(v.2)
Bsus4(G) B(G)
Je - sus, oh, oh.
2. Mer - cy
2.
Bsus4(G) B(G)
C♯m7(Am7)
A2(F)
it is Je - sus, Je - sus,

2. Mercy won upon the cross,
Christ was judged in place of us.
Our punishment was laid on Him,
One sacrifice for all our sin.

2446. More than gold

Ps 19:10; Is 58:6; Amos 5:24; Mic 6:8; Rom 12:1

Capo 4 (C)

Kieran Metcalfe

Moderately

Verse

G♯m(Em) Amaj7(F) E(C) B(G)

1. More than gold and ex - tra - va-gant rich - es,

G♯m(Em) Amaj7(F) E(C) B(G) G♯m(Em) Amaj7(F)

heart-felt songs of won - der and awe; You have shown by walk-

E(C) B(G) Amaj7(F) Bsus4(G) B(G)

- ing a - mong us what You're long - ing for. 2. A

1. ***D.C.(v.2)***

2.,3. *Chorus*

Bsus4(G) 𝄋 A(F) Bsus4(G) B(G)

Help me to act just - ly, love me - rcy and walk

A(F) E(C) Bsus4(G) B(G)

hum - bly with You. This You re-quire

A(F)
Bsus4(G)
B(G)
A(F)
E(C)
B(G)
of me: my life an of - f'ring to You.
1° D.C.(v.3)
(Fine)
G♯m(Em)
Mid section
Amaj7(F)
This You de - sire, this You re - quire,
E(C)
B(G)
G♯m(Em)
this You de - mand of me;
more than just songs
Amaj7(F)
E(C)
and rich - es a - lone,
but wor - ship through love
B(G)
G♯m(Em)
and me - rcy,
that Your king - dom grows

Amaj7(F)
E(C)
— and jus - tice will flow, — flow like a ne -
G♯7(E)
Amaj7(F)
Amaj7/B(F)
D.S. al fine
- ver - fail - ing stream. — Help me to act —
G♯m(Em) Amaj7(F) E(C) B(G)
2. A voice that — cries — for the rights — of the — bro - ken, a
G♯m(Em) Amaj7(F) E(C) B(G) G♯m(Em) Amaj7(F)
heart that — burns — to em - brace — and for - give, — a spi - rit — free — from self -
E(C) B(G) Amaj7(F) Bsus4(G)
- ish am - bi - tion; You ask — this — of — me. —
G♯m(Em) Amaj7(F) E(C) B(G) G♯m(Em) Amaj7(F)
3. Put these — hands — to work — for Your — jus - tice, melt my — heart — with mer -

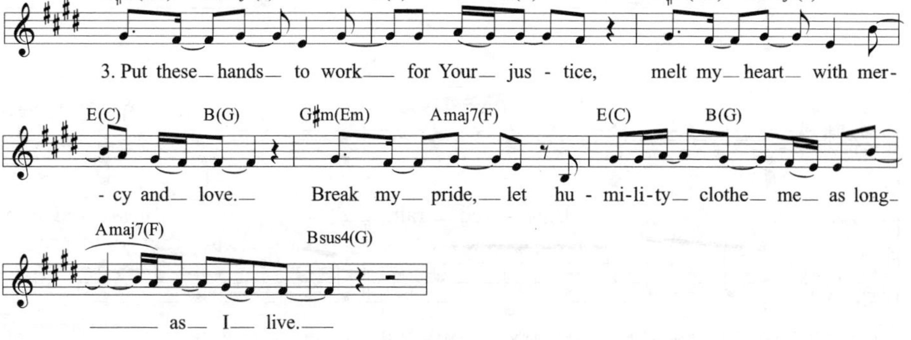

E(C) B(G) G♯m(Em) Amaj7(F) E(C) B(G)
- cy and — love. — Break my — pride, — let hu - mi - li - ty — clothe — me — as long —
Amaj7(F) Bsus4(G)
——— as — I — live. —

2447.
My heart is crying out
(Blessèd rain)
2 Chron 7:13-14; Hos 6:3; Mal 3:10; Jn 7:37
Capo 2 (D)
Marc James
Prayerfully
Verse
E(D) Esus4(D) E(D) B(A) A(G)
1. My heart is cry - ing out for Your heal - ing rain.
This thir - sty soul longs for You a - gain.
I'm cry - ing out for the Fa - ther's grace.
I thirst for You, I long for Your em-brace.
Chorus
Bles - sèd rain, bles - sèd rain

E(D)
A(G)
from the high - est heights to the low - est place.
C♯m7(Bm)
A(G)
Bles - sèd rain,
for the bles - sèd rain;
C♯m7(Bm)
A(G)
this wound - ed heart is cry - ing
(2°-4°) (this cur - sèd land)
1.,4.
B(A)
E(D)
out for the bless - ing.
R.H.
Last time to Coda
B(A)
A(G)
E(D)
Esus4
(D)
E(D)
Oh, for the bles - sèd rain.

D.C.(v.2)
3.
D.S. al Coda
B(A)
A(G)
B(A)
E(D)
E/G♯(D/F♯)
2. My out. Oh, bles - sèd rain,
2.
B(A)
E(D)
out for the bless - ing,
R.H.
Esus4(D)
E(D)
for Your bless - ing.
Esus4(D)
Mid section
E(D)
We are cry - ing out to You, we are cry -
Esus4(D)
E(D)
- ing out to You. We are cry - ing out for You, hear us cry -

Esus4(D)
C♯m7(Bm)
C♯m/B(Bm/A)
- ing out to You. We are cry - ing out for You, we are cry-
A♯m7(♭5)(G♯)
E/G♯(D/F♯)
A(G)
- ing out for You. Hear us cry - ing out for You, we are cry-
B(A)
E(D)
E/G♯(D/F♯) D.S.
- ing out for You. Oh, bles - sèd rain,
Coda
B(A)
A(G)
E(D)
For the bles - sèd rain.
Verse
E(D) Esus4(D) E(D) B(A) A(G)
2. My heart is cry - ing out for this or - phaned land,
E(D) Esus4(D) E(D) B(A) A(G) E(D) Esus4(D) E(D)
for the wound - ed souls that search for love in vain. I'm cry-ing out
B(A) A(G) E(D) Esus4(D) E(D)
for the Fa - ther's love. To flood these streets
B(A) A(G) E(D)
with bless-ing from a - bove.

2448. **My heart is restless**

(Wait for You)

Ps 27:14; 46:10; 146:1

Nikki Fletcher, Tim Hughes
& Luke Hellebronth

2. You know my longing,
You listen to my fears.
I'm not forgotten;
Your goodness draws me near.

F♯m
D
A
Let my heart be still, for You are God.
1.,3.
(Fine)
Esus4
E
D
A
F♯m
D.C.(v.2)
2.
E
E
D
A
You are al - ways good, Lord, for - e-
E
F♯m
D
- ver kind. I will trust and know
A
Esus4
E
D
A/C♯
D
F♯m
that You are God.

Mid section
D
A/C♯
D
F♯m
Praise the Lord, O my soul, praise the Lord.
D
E
A/C♯
D
E
Praise the Lord, O my soul, praise the Lord.
F♯m
D
E
A/C♯
Praise the Lord, O my soul,
D
E
1.-3.
F♯m
4.
F♯m
praise the Lord.
D.S. al fine
I will wait

Wait for the LORD; be strong and take heart and wait for the LORD.

PSALM 27:14

2449. My hope is built on nothing less

(My hope)

Is 43:2; Heb 6:19; 12:28

Chorus & new music: Tim Wanstall, Matt Redman & Robert Marvin

With expression

2. When darkness seems to hide Your face,
I rest on Your unchanging grace.
In every high and stormy gale,
My anchor holds within the veil.

Edward Mote (1797–1874)

2450. My life is built on Your promises
(Alive!)
Jn 3:3; Acts 2:24;
1 Cor 10:4; Col 2:14; 2 Pet 1:4
Ken Riley
& Tim Hughes
Driving
Verse
G
Em7
My life is built on Your pro - mi - ses,
You took my sin and You cleared the debt,
D
D/A
up - on Your love and Your ho - li - ness;
You gave me life when You con-quered death;
1.
G
Em7
D
D/A
You're the so-lid rock on which I stand.
2.
G
Em7
D
Bridge
ri - sen One, in You I'm born a - gain.
And now
C
D
Em
D/F♯
death has lost its hold on me.

Chorus
G
D
I'm a-live 'cause You're a-live,
I'm a-live 'cause You're a-live;
Em7
D/F♯
Csus2
breath-ing life,
breath-ing life through me.
G
D
Ev-'ry-thing You chose to give,
You gave it all so I can live.
Em7
D/F♯
1.,3.
Csus2
Be the life,
be the life in me:
Je-sus, You're a-
(Fine)
G
Dadd4
Em7
C6
G/B
Dadd4
live,
You're a-live.

D.C.
2.
Em7
C6
Am9
Csus2
Mid section
Am
G/B
C
G
D
(3 times)
Je - sus Christ, come a-live in me.
Am
G/B
C
G
D/F#
Je - sus Christ, come a - live in me, in
G(no3rd)
Gmaj7(no3rd)
G6(no3rd)
C/G
me. You're a -
G(no3rd)
Gmaj7(no3rd)
G6(no3rd)
C/G
D.S. al fine
live.

His divine power has given us everything we need for life and godliness through our knowledge of him who called us by his own glory and goodness. Through these he has given us his very great and precious promises, so that through them you may participate in the divine nature and escape the corruption in the world caused by evil desires.

2 PETER 1:3-4

2451. My Lord, You wore no royal crown

Is 53:4; Mk 10:45; Lk 19:10; Jn 8:12, 32

O WALY WALY

English traditional melody
Arr. Paul Hughes

With expression

G2 D/G C2 Bm7 Em Am7 D7sus4 D♯dim7

1. My Lord, You wore no roy-al crown; You did not

Em Am7 G/C Dsus4 Dsus2 D/C

wield the pow'rs of state, nor did You

Bm7 G/B C Bm/D D♯dim7 Em Am7♭5/E♭ Em7

need a scho-lar's gown or priest-ly

Am7 G2/B C2 C/D Gsus4 Gsus2 *(Fine)* G D9sus4

robe, to make You great. 2. You ne - ver

2. You never used a killer's sword
To end an unjust tyranny;
Your only weapon was Your word,
For truth alone could set us free.

3. You did not live a world away
In hermit's cell or desert cave,
But felt our pain and shared each day
With those You came to seek and save.

4. You made no mean or cunning move,
Chose no unworthy compromise,
But carved a track of burning love
Through tangles of deceit and lies.

5. You came unequalled, undeserved,
To be what we were meant to be;
To serve instead of being served,
To pay for our perversity.

6. So when I stumble, set me right,
Command my life as You require;
Let all Your gifts be my delight
And You, my Lord, my one desire.

Christopher Idle

2452. My name is written on Your hands

(Counting on Your name)

Is 43:1; Jn 14:6; Rom 3:3; 4:3; 8:39

Capo 3 (G)

Tim Hughes, Nick Herbert & Ben Cantelon

Gradually building

Verse

Bb(G) F(D) Gm(Em) Ebmaj7(C)

1. My name is writ-ten on Your hands; You've called me Your own, — You've called me Your own. —
Now I am Yours no earth-ly pow'r could tear us a-part, — could tear us a-part. —

Chorus

F(D) Gm(Em) Ebmaj7(C) Bb(G)

I'm count-ing on Your — name, I'm count-ing on Your name,

F(D) Gm(Em) Ebmaj7(C) Bb(G)

I'm count-ing on Your — name to save — me. —

F(D) Gm(Em) Ebmaj7(C) Bb(G)

I'm trust-ing You're the way, I'm trust-ing You're the way,

Last time to Coda
1.
D.C.(v.2)
2.
D.S.
F(D)
Gm(Em)
E♭maj7(C)
B♭(G)
E♭maj7(C)
B♭(G)
trust-ing You're the way, my Sa - viour. - viour. I'm
3.
Mid section
E♭maj7(C)
B♭(G)
E♭maj7(C)
Gm(Em)
- viour. I be - lieve, I be - lieve, I be -
E♭maj7(C)
Gm(Em)
(G/B)
B♭maj7/D
E♭(C)
Gm(Em)
lieve You are the way. I be - lieve, I be -
Dm7(Bm)
E♭(C)
Gm(Em)
Dm7(Bm)
E♭(C)
lieve, I be - lieve You are the way. I be -
Gm(Em)
Dm7(Bm)
E♭(C)
Gm(Em)
lieve, I be - lieve, I be - lieve You are the way.

2. My life is built on nothing less
Than Your faithfulness,
Your faithfulness.
Counting on Christ, and Christ alone,
I'm hoping in You,
Hoping in You.

2453. My praise goes on

Ps 73:1; Jn 17:3; Rom 8:31

Dave Fitzgerald
& Trent Cory

C2
D
C/E
D/F♯
Life with You is e - ver - last - ing!
G
Chorus
Am7
My praise goes on, wor - ship, be strong,
C
G/B
Am7
Dsus4
G
my praise goes on and on and on. Who is a - gainst
Am7
Last time to Coda
C
G/B
me when You are for me? My praise goes on
1.
Am7
Dsus4
G
Gsus4
G
and on and on.

Gsus4
D.S.
2.
Am7
Dsus4
D.S.S.
My praise goes — — and on — and on.
3.
Am7
Dsus4
C
D
Em7
— and on — and on.
1.
G/B
2.
G/B
Mid section
C
You are good, — You are good, — You are good. –
Dsus4
Em
1.
G2/B
— You are good, — You are good, — You are good. — You are good, —
2. D.S.S. al Coda
G2/B
—
Coda
Em7
G/B
C2
— me. My praise goes on. —

2454. My shelter, You shield me from the storm

(Worship forever)

Capo 3 (D)

Ex 15:26; Ps 19:14; 28:7; 118:14; 119:57

Lucy Loo

Last time to Coda
1.
Dm7(Bm7) B♭2(G) Gm7(Em)
In Your pre - sence I bow in awe; You a - lone will I a - dore.
(A) (G/A) (A)
Csus4 C(A) B♭/C C7
2.
Gm7(Em) B♭/C(G/A) F2(D)
i. D.C.
lone will I a - dore. My
ii.
Mid section
Dm7(Bm7) A/C♯(F♯/A♯) Cm7(Am) B♭(G)
For - e-ver lov - ing You, for - e-ver trust - ing You, for-
D.S. al Coda
Gm7(Em) C(A) B♭(G) C(A) (G/A) B♭/C C(A)
e-ver pleas - ing You, lov - ing You more.
Coda
Gm7(Em) B♭/C(G/A) F2(D)
lone will I a-dore.

2455.

My soul will sing
(Psalm 103)

Ps 77:11; 90:2; 103:5, 10-15, 17, 20; 138:1

With a rock feel

Kristyn Getty
& Stuart Townend

D
Chorus
C
High as the hea-vens reach a - bove the earth is Your un -
Bm7
G
fail - ing love, is Your un - fail - ing love.
D
C
Far as the east is ban-ished from the west You took our
Bm7
G
A
sins from us, re-moved our sins from us. How wide, how
Bm
G
1.,2.
D
C2
high is Your un-fail-ing love.

2. Our King delights to show compassion to the weak;
   Their deepest needs He loves to satisfy.
   Throughout the earth His justice and His mercy speak,
   And He will run to meet the victim's cry.
   From everlasting to everlasting
   Our youth renewed with every step we take.

3. Though we are dust, a moment in eternity,
   As flowers bloom today and then are gone,
   He crowns our lives with beauty and with dignity;
   His patience smiles on all who turn to Him.
   From generation to generation
   We'll tell the story of His faithfulness!

Praise the LORD, you his angels, you mighty ones who do his bidding, who obey his word.

PSALM 103:20

2456. My theme song is God's love

Ps 104:3; 148:1-4; Rev 7:12

With a celtic lilt

Godfrey Birtill

3. All praise Him from the heavens
And from the mountain tops.
All you, His angels in the heights,
You, His warriors.

4. Praise Him, the sun and moon,
Praise Him, you shining stars,
Praise Him, you thunder, rain and clouds,
His glorious orchestra.

2457. No more night

Nick J. & Becky Drake

(v.2)
G
D
A/C♯
in the ci - ty of our God, when He comes.
Gmaj7
Bridge
Em7
No more sha - dow, no more shame,
A
D
A/C♯
Bm7
we will see You face to face; the for-mer things
G
A
Gmaj7
will fade a-way when You come.
Chorus
D
A/C♯
Je-sus is com - ing, Je-sus is com - ing; hal-le-lu-
- ing, Je-sus is com - ing; hal-le-lu-

2. Crystal clear, the river flows,
Pouring life down from His throne,
Bringing joy we've never known,
When He comes.
Till that day, by Your grace,
Breathe Your presence in this place;
Give us hope, give us faith
Till You come.

Now we see but a poor reflection as in a mirror; then we shall see face to face. Now I know in part; then I shall know fully, even as I am fully known.

1 CORINTHIANS 13:12

2458. No mountain, no valley

(Healing is in Your hands)

Lk 4:40; Rom 8:37-39; Eph 3:18; Heb 13:12

Building steadily

Daniel Carson, Christy & Nathan Nockels, Matt Redman & Chris Tomlin

3. Our present, our future,
Our past is in Your hands;
We're covered by Your blood,
We're covered by Your blood.

F♯m
Gsus2
D/F♯
no mat - ter where I am, heal - ing is in
now by Your grace I stand, heal - ing is in
F♯m
1.
Gsus2
2.
Gsus2
Your hands. How deep,
Your hands.
D.C.(v.3)
(Fine)
Mid section
D
A/C♯
Bm7
In all things, we know that we are more than
A
Em7
1.
A
con - que - rors; You keep us by Your love.
2.
A
Em7
A
D.S. (with rpt) al fine
You keep us by Your love. How high

2459. No reputation, no stately bearing

Capo 2 (D)

(Born that we may have life)

Mt 2:2; Lk 1:32; 34-35; 2:7; Jn 6:27; Phil 2:7; Col 2:2-3; Rev 17:14

Accented

Chris Tomlin, Matt Maher & Ed Cash

Verse

E2(D) E2/G♯(D/F♯)

1. No re-pu-ta - tion, no state-ly bear - ing, no pa-lace bed

(v.2)

Amaj9(G) B(A)

for ro - yal - ty; but a star in the hea -

E2(D) E2/G♯(D/F♯)

- vens, a sign full of won - der an-nounc-ing the com -

Amaj9(G) Bsus4(A) B(A) *Chorus*

- ing of the King of kings. Re -

A(G) E/G♯(D/F♯) F♯m7(Em) Bsus4(A)
joice, O world! Your Sa - viour has come
E(D) E/G♯(D/F♯) Asus2(G) Bsus4(A) A(G) E/G♯(D/F♯)
through the love of a vir - gin's womb. Son of God,
F♯m7(Em) G♯(F♯) (Bm) (D/A) (G) (D/F♯) C♯m E/B A2 E/G♯ F♯m7(Em) E/G♯(D/F♯)
Son of Man, born that we may have life. You were
3rd time to Coda
A(G) E/G♯(D/F♯) F♯m7(Em) B7sus4(A)
1. Esus2(D) E(D)
born that we may have life.
(D/F♯) Esus2/G♯ E/G♯(D/F♯) A(G) B(A)
D.C.(v.2)
2. A throne in a man -

2.
Esus2(D) E(D) Bm7(Am) Asus2(G)
F♯m7(Em) Esus2(D) E(D) Bm7(Bm)
Asus2(G) F♯m7(Em) E/G♯(D/F♯) N.C.
Re - joice, O world! Your Sa -
- viour has come through the love of a vir -
- gin's womb. Son of God, Son of Man, You were
(Bm) (Bm/A) (G) (D/F♯)
C♯m C♯m/B A2 E/G♯ F♯m7(Em) D.S.
born that we may have life. Re -

2. A throne in a manger, a cross in a cradle,
The hidden revealing this glorious plan
Of the child who would suffer,
The child who would conquer
The sin of every woman,
The sin of every man.

2460.
Not angels nor demons
(I belong)
Rom 8:38-39; 1 Cor 7:23
Capo 3 (D)
Kathryn Scott
& Mildred Rainey
Steadily
Verse
F(D) C/E(A/C♯) B♭/D(G/B) F(D) C/E(A/C♯)
1. Not an - gels nor de - mons, no pow'r on
B♭/D(G/B) C/E(A/C♯) F(D) C/E(A/C♯) B♭/D(G/B) F(D) C/E(A/C♯)
earth or hea-ven; not dis-tance nor dan-ger, no trou-ble
B♭/D(G/B) C/E(A/C♯) Bridge Gm7(Em) F/A(D/F♯)
now or ev - er; no - thing can take me from Your
B♭2(G) Gm7(Em) F/A(D/F♯) Csus4(A) C(A)
Chorus
great love. For - e-ver this truth re-mains. I be-long,
Last time to Coda
F(D) C/E(A/C♯) B♭/D(G/B) C/E(A/C♯) F(D) C/E(A/C♯)
I be-long to You. I be-long, I be-long

2. Not hardship nor hunger,
No pain or depth of sorrow,
Not weakness nor failure,
No broken dream or promise.

2461. Nothing can separate

(Your love never fails)

Ps 30:5; 89:9; 90:2; 118:1; Lam 3:22-23; Mt 8:26; Rom 8:28, 39; 1 Cor 13:8

Gently building

Chris McClarney & Anthony Skinner

Em
C
G
D
love ne - ver fails.
Chorus
C
G
D/F♯
You stay the same through the a - ges; Your
Am
G/B
C
love ne - ver chan - ges. There may be
G
D/F♯
Am
pain in the night, but joy comes with the morn - ing.
C
G
D/F♯
And when the o - ceans rage, I don't have

2. The wind is strong and the water's deep,
But I'm not alone here in these open seas,
'Cause Your love never fails.
The chasm was far too wide;
I never thought I'd reach the other side,
But Your love never fails.

2462. Nothing was hidden

(God knows my name)

Ps 23:6; 139:7, 15; Lam 3:22

Capo 3 (G)

Matt & Beth Redman

Chorus
E♭2(C)
B♭/D(G/B)
God knows my name, and Your kind - ness al - ways is with
F/A(D/F♯)
F(D)
E♭2(C)
me. (And) You know my name; in Your pro -
B♭/D(G/B)
F/A(D/F♯)
F(D)
E♭2(C)
- mise I am se-cure. When I a - wake, sure-ly all
B♭/D(G/B)
F/A(D/F♯)
Gm7(Em)
Your good - ness and mer - cies still re - main.
Last time to Coda
1.
E♭2(C)
F(D)
B♭/D(G/B)
E♭2(C)
I rest in this: that God knows my name.

2. Where can I go, Lord; where could I flee?
Your eyes are watching over me.
Your healing mercies
Restore my life;
In You I rise and I am free,
And You are with me every moment.

2463. Notice the nations
(O my soul)

Ps 57:8; 86:8; Mk 10:45; Lk 4:18; 24:2; Rom 8:19; 1 Cor 15:54; Phil 2:10-11; 1 Jn 1:7; Rev 7:9, 11; 21:5; 22:16

Capo 3 (G)

Aaron Keyes, Matt McMichael & Stuart Garrard

Moderately

has won the day, the sin of man
Gm(Em)
Fsus4(D)
(G/B)
B♭(G) B♭/D
E♭(C)
rise and sing high-est praise
is washed a-way.
1.,3.,6.
D.C.(v.2,3.)
(Fine)
2.,4.
D.S. (ch. 2)
Fsus4(D)
B♭(G)
to hea-ven's King.
Bound-less
5.
Mid section
F(D)
Gm(Em)
Ev-'ry tongue con-fes-sing, ev-'ry knee
E♭(C)
B♭(G)
F(D)
will bow; ev-'ry tribe will wor-

Gm(Em) E♭(C) B♭(G)
- ship e-ver be-fore You now. Ev-'ry hope
F(D) Gm(Em) E♭(C)
is re-a-lised, ev-'ry-thing is made new;
B♭(G) F(D) Gm(Em)
e-ve-ry-one in all of cre-a - tion for-e-ver in
(G) (Em) (D) (Em) (D)
E♭(C) F(D) B♭ Gm F E♭(C) Gm F Dm(Bm)
love with You.
Gm(Em) F(D) E♭(C) F(D) B♭(G)
D.S. al fine
O my

Verse
E♭(C)
B♭(G)
2. Bind - ing the bro - ken, You fa - ther the or - phan, You're the lo - ver of the lone -
E♭(C)
ly, the one and on - ly King e - ver - last - ing, star of the morn - ing.
F(D)
Who in the skies com - pares to You?
Verse
E♭(C)
B♭(G)
3. You came as a ser - vant, self - less and per - fect, death was de - feat - ed
E♭(C)
and the stone was rolled a - way. Now an - gels ac - claim You,
F(D)
cre - a - tion a - waits You; hea - ven and earth have been re - deemed.

2464. Now I will gaze into Your eyes

(Even as I look upon Your face)

Ps 27:8; Mal 3:3; 2 Cor 3:18

Gareth Robinson, John Hartley & Steve Hindalong

Tenderly

Gmaj7
Cmaj7
Chorus
G
grace.
Christ, be with me,
D
F
C
Christ be - fore me, Christ be - hind me, Christ, be in me.
Am
D
Em
E - ven as I look up - on Your face.
Last time to Coda
A
Cmaj7
D
Cmaj7
Je - sus, e - ven as I look up - on Your face.
1.
D.C.(v.2)
2.
Mid section
Gmaj7
2. And as I
Lord, trans -

2. And as I see the glory of
Your perfect sacrifice,
The deepest love,
My precious Saviour, I offer up my life.
Renew my heart, restore my spirit
And purify my mind.

2465. Now may the peace of the Lord

(The peace)

Num 6:24-26; Jn 20:19

Capo 3 (C)

Graham Kendrick

Flowing

Fm7+4(Dm)
Eb/G(C/E)
you and may God's face shine up - on you
Ab2(F)
2° D.S.
Ab2/Bb(F/G)
1.
Eb2(C)
al - ways, and give you peace,
Ab2(F)
Cm7(Am)
Ab2(F)
and give you
Eb2(C)
D.C.
2.
Ab2(F)
peace.
peace,
Fm7/Bb(Dm)
And may God's

Fm7+4(Dm)
Eb/G(C/E)
Ab2(F)
face shine up - on you al - ways,
Ab2/Bb(F/G)
Eb2(C)
Ab2(F)
and give you peace,
1.
2.
Cm7(Am)
Ab2(F)
Bbsus4(G)
Ab2(F)
Ab2/Bb(F/G)
and give you

Eb(C)
peace.

2466. Now unto the King who reigns over all

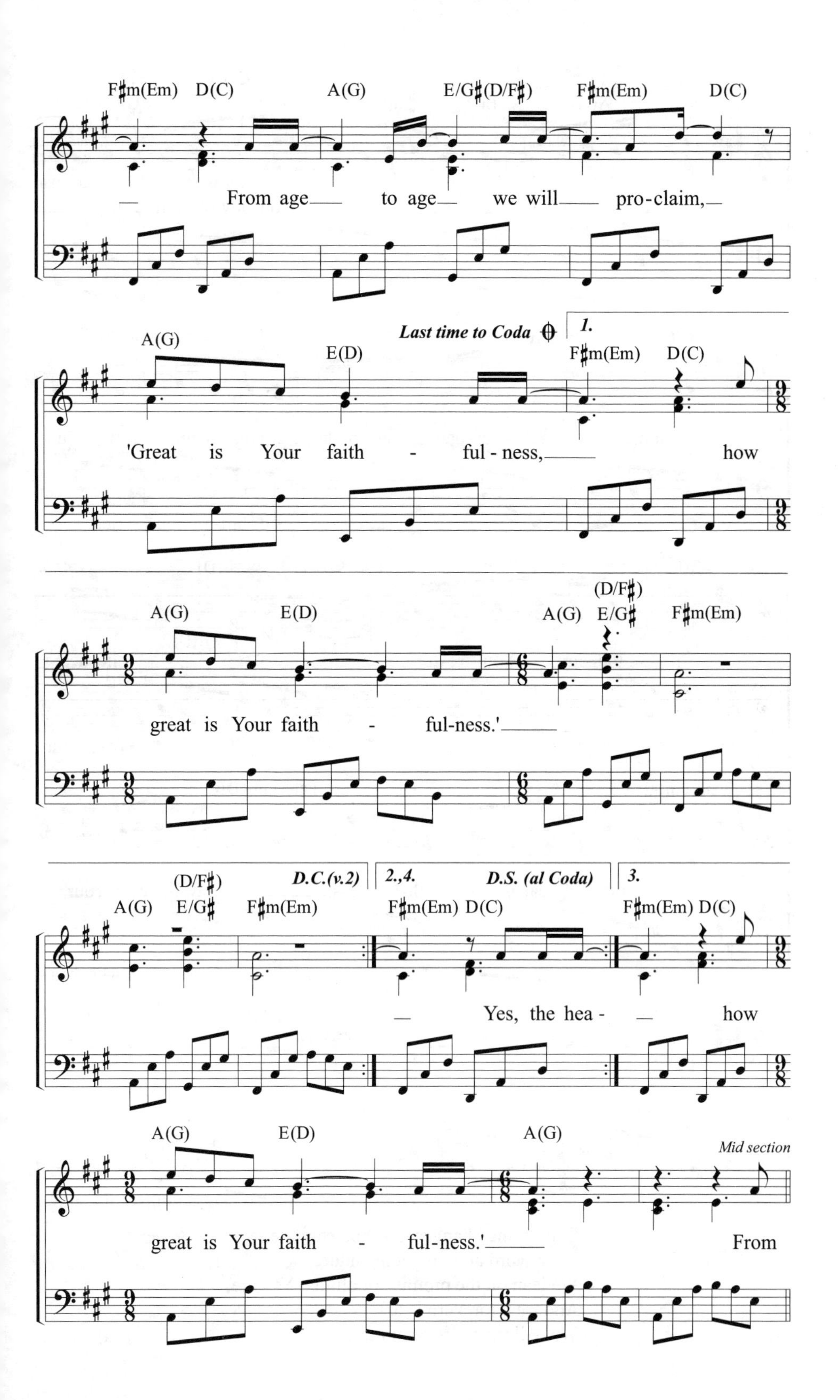
F♯m(Em) D(C) A(G) E/G♯(D/F♯) F♯m(Em) D(C)
From age to age we will pro-claim,
A(G) E(D)
Last time to Coda
1.
F♯m(Em) D(C)
'Great is Your faith - ful - ness, how
A(G) E(D) A(G) E/G♯ (D/F♯) F♯m(Em)
great is Your faith - ful-ness.'
A(G) E/G♯ (D/F♯) F♯m(Em)
D.C.(v.2)
2.,4.
D.S. (al Coda)
3.
F♯m(Em) D(C)
Yes, the hea -
F♯m(Em) D(C)
how
A(G) E(D) A(G)
Mid section
great is Your faith - ful-ness.' From

2. Everything changes, but You stay the same;
Your Word and kingdom endure.
We lean on the promise of all that You are,
And trust forevermore;
We will trust forevermore.

Now to the King eternal, immortal, invisible, the only God, be honour and glory for ever and ever. Amen.

1 TIMOTHY 1:17

2467. Now when peace like a river

(It is well)

Ps 25:13; Is 4:6; 66:12; Jon 2:3; Mt 13:22; 26:28; Heb 10:19, 22

Capo 4 (C)

Words: Horatio Spafford (1828–88)
Adpt. Stuart Townend & Phil Baggaley
Music: Phil Baggaley

Relaxed country rock feel

TYM Sheet Music

C♯m(Am)
A(F)
E(C)
and the cares of this world take their toll.
Bsus4(G)
B(G)
A(F)
In the heat of the day
E(C)
F♯m7(Dm)
C♯m(Am)
there is grace e-nough to say, It is well,
3rd time to Coda
E(C)
A(F)
E(C)
it is well with my soul.
F♯m7(Dm)
A(F)

E(C)
F♯m7(Dm)
A(F)
E(C)
D.C.(v.2)
2. And when Sa -
Coda
F♯(D)
A(F)
It is well, it is well with my soul.
E(C)
F♯(D)
It is well, it is well
A(F)
E(C)
with my soul.

2. And when Satan should tempt me, and trials should come,
Let this blessèd assurance control,
For He sees every weakness and knows every fear,
And has shed His own blood for my soul.

2468. O Christ the same

Lk 7:34; Jn 1:1, 3; 10:28; Acts 7:56; Phil 2:8; Heb 7:25; 13:8; 1 Pet 1:24-25

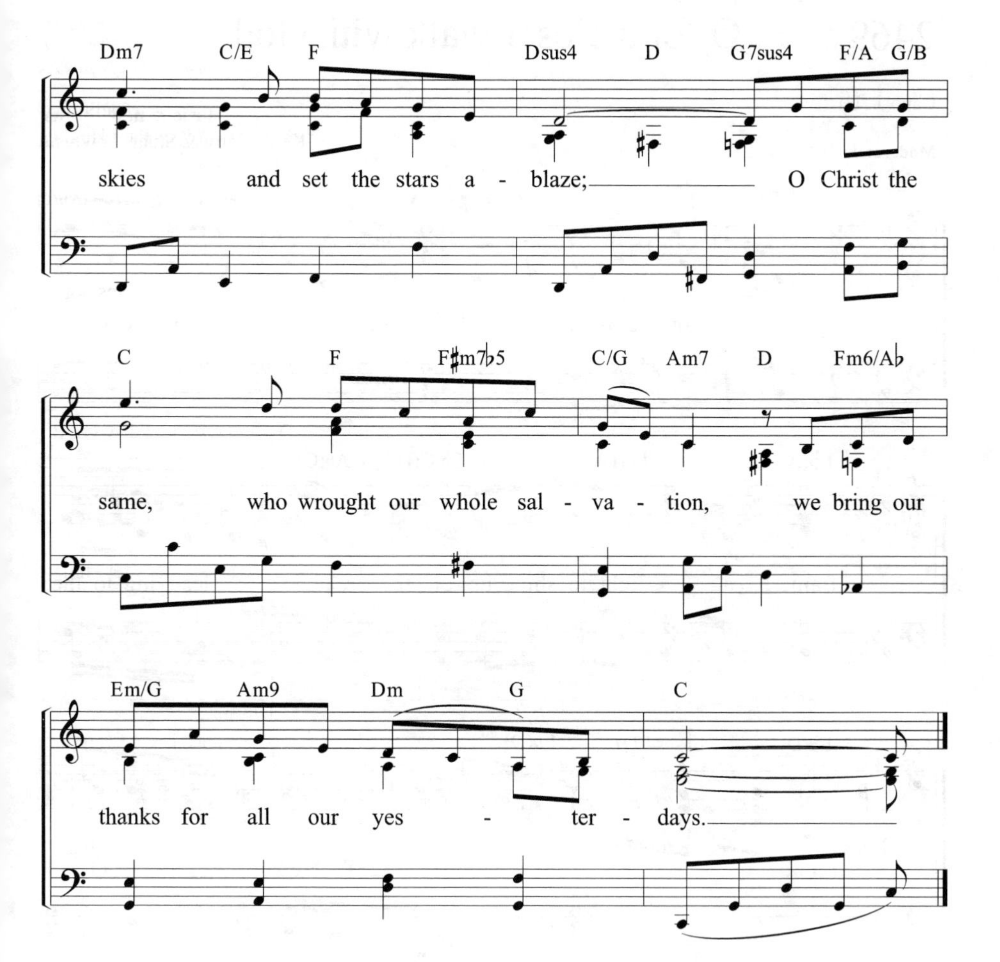

2. O Christ the same, the friend of sinners, sharing
Our inmost thoughts, the secrets none can hide;
Still as of old upon Your body bearing
The marks of love, in triumph glorified:
O Son of man, who stooped for us from heaven -
O Prince of life, in all Your saving power;
O Christ the same, to whom our hearts are given:
We bring our thanks for this the present hour.

3. O Christ the same, secure within whose keeping
Our lives and loves, our days and years remain;
Our work and rest, our waking and our sleeping,
Our calm and storm, our pleasure and our pain:
O Lord of love, for all our joys and sorrows,
For all our hopes, when earth shall fade and flee;
O Christ the same, beyond our brief tomorrows,
We bring our thanks for all that is to be.

Timothy Dudley-Smith

2469. O for a closer walk with God

Ex 20:4-5; 2 Chron 7:1; Jn 4:14; 14:27; Rev 2:4

2. Where is that blessèdness I knew
   When first I saw the Lord?
   Where is that soul-refreshing view
   Of Jesus and His word?

3. What peaceful hours I once enjoyed,
   How sweet the memory still!
   But they have left an aching void
   The world can never fill.

4. The dearest idol I have known,
   Whate'er that idol be,
   Help me to tear it from Thy throne,
   And worship only Thee.

5. So shall my walk be close with God,
   Calm and serene my frame;
   So purer light shall mark the road
   That leads me to the Lamb.

William Cowper (1731–1800)

2470. O God, You're my God

Ps 63:1-2

(To behold You)

Sam Blake, Stephen Gibson,
Joel Pridmore & Ian Yates

Gmaj9
Em
D/A
Gmaj9
You, I look to You: to be-hold
Bm
Gmaj9
D2
You, to a-dore You, to bless Your name.
1.-3.
4.
A
A
Bm
Em
To be-hold
D
A/E
Bm
Em
D/A
A/E
D
D/F♯
Em/G D/A

Bm/D
Gmaj9
D
D/F♯
Em/G D/A
Bm
Gmaj9
Tag
D
O Lord,
Em
D/A
Bm
1.-3.
Gmaj9
send Your pow'r and Your glo - ry.
O Lord,
4.
Gmaj9
D
Em
D/C
O Lord,
send Your pow'r and Your glo-
Bm
1.-3.
Gmaj9
4.
Gmaj9
D
- ry.
O Lord,

2471. Oh, how could it be

(Remembrance)

Lk 22:19-20; 1 Cor 11:23-26; 15:54; 1 Pet 1:3

Matt Redman & Matt Maher
Mid section words: taken from the English translation of the Memorial Acclamation from *The Roman Missal*

Reverently

G D A G D
- brance leads us to wor - ship. And as we wor - ship You,
A G D A
our wor - ship leads to com-mu - nion. We re-spond
Last time to Coda
1.
Em7 D/F♯ G Bm7 A D Dmaj7
to Your in-vi-ta - tion; we re-mem - ber You.
Em7
D.C.(v.2)
2.
D
Mid section
2. See His You. Dy-ing, You de-
G A D G A
stroyed our death. Ris-ing, You re - stored our

Bm
A
life. Lord Je-sus, come in glo-ry, Lord Je-sus, come in
G
1.
D
2.
glo-ry. Dy-ing, You de- Lord Je-sus, come in
D
Dmaj7
Em7
D.S. al Coda
glo-ry. By Your mer-
Coda
G
Em7
D/F♯
-tion, we re-spond to Your in-vi-ta-
G
Bm7
A
D
-tion; we re-mem-ber You.
2. See His body, His blood –
Know that He has overcome
Every trial we will face.
None too lost to be saved,
None too broken or ashamed;
All are welcome in this place.

2472. Oh, how strong the power of Jesus' name

2. Oh, how great the kindness our God has shown;
We were strangers, now we're called His own.
His grace has welcomed the sinner home;
Tender mercies lead us to the throne.

3. Oh, what peace the Spirit of Jesus brings;
Through the trials He will carry me.
One day in heaven our eyes will meet;
Filled with wonder, all the saints will sing.

2473. Oh, Lamb of God

(The praises of the Lamb)

Is 53:4-5; Jn 1:3; 13:14; 19:2, 5; Phil 2:7, 9; Rev 5:12

Kees Kraayenoord

With strength

Dmaj7 *Verse* Bm9

1. Oh, Lamb of God, You once were slain;

R.H.

A7/G D Dmaj7

You took my sin and all my shame. I see the cross,

Bm9 A Em/G

Your sa - cri - fice. You died my death to give me

1.

D F♯m/B Bm7 Gmaj7 G6

life.

Gmaj7 G6 *D.C.(v.2)* *2.,3.* D *Chorus*

me. Hal - le -

Chorus 2
A A7/G D/F♯ Bm A
lu - jah, Je - sus, You are wor - thy to re-ceive the name a-bove all
G A A7/G D/F♯ D
names. Lord, I love You, You have shown me mer - cy, and
Last time to Coda
F♯m Gmaj7
now my life will ne-ver be the same. And
F♯m
1.
G
I will lift my hands and sing the prai - ses of the

D.C.(v.3)
D D2 Bm9 Bm7 Gmaj7 G7 Gmaj7 G6
Lamb.
2. G
prai - ses, the prai - ses, the prai - ses of the
D.S. (ch.2) al Coda
Coda
G
Lamb. Hal - le -
And I
A Bm A/C♯ G/D A/E
will lift my hands and sing the prai - ses of the Lamb.
D D2 Bm Gmaj7 Em/G

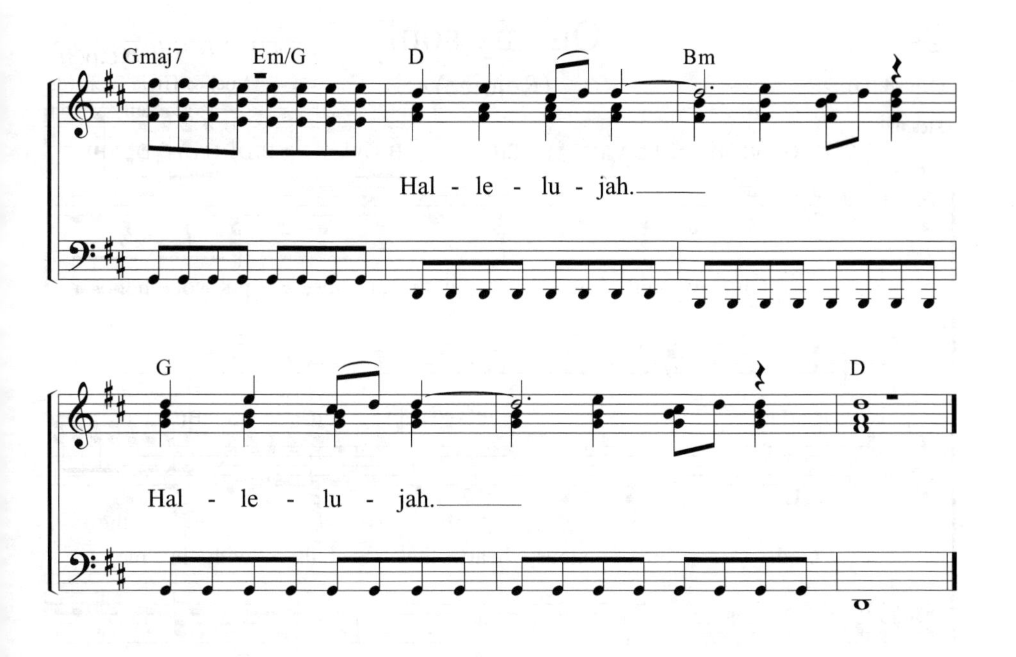

Gmaj7
Em/G
D
Bm
Hal - le - lu - jah.
G
D
Hal - le - lu - jah.

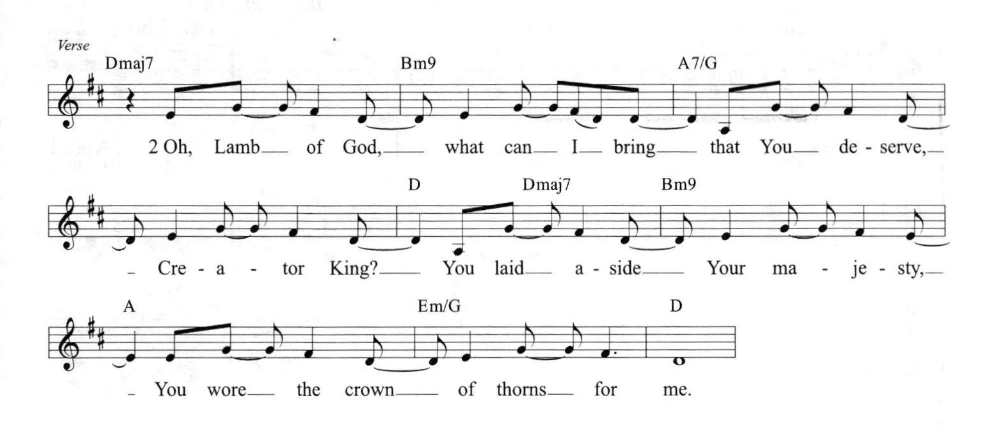

Verse
Dmaj7
Bm9
A7/G
2 Oh, Lamb of God, what can I bring that You de - serve,
Cre - a - tor King? You laid a - side Your ma - je - sty,
D
Dmaj7
Bm9
A
Em/G
D
You wore the crown of thorns for me.

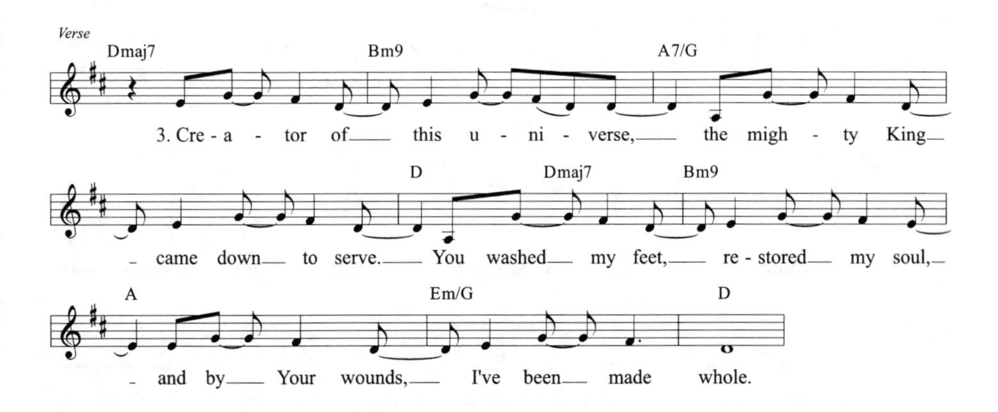

Verse
Dmaj7
Bm9
A7/G
3. Cre - a - tor of this u - ni - verse, the migh - ty King
came down to serve. You washed my feet, re - stored my soul,
D
Dmaj7
Bm9
A
Em/G
D
and by Your wounds, I've been made whole.

2474.
Oh, my soul
(Rejoice)
Deut 33:27; Ps 42:11; Col 1:14, 27
Capo 4 (G)
Noel & Tricia Richards
& Kelly Minter
Steadily
Verse
G♯m(Em) F♯/A♯(D/F♯) E(C) B(G) B/D♯(G/B) D♯7(B)
1. Oh, my soul, down - cast with - in me, put your hope in
G♯m(Em) F♯/A♯(D/F♯) E(C) B(G)
God. An - xious heart that fails with - in me,
1. D.C.(v.2)
2.,3.
D♯m7(Bm) E(C) D♯m7(Bm)
rest now in His arms. all to Him is
E(C) Chorus B(G) C♯m(Am)
light. Re - joice, re - joice, re -
B/D♯(G/B) E(C) F♯sus4(D) B(G) C♯m(Am)
joice, re - joice, my soul, re - joice, re - joice, re -

2. Oh, my soul, awake with worship:
He is your delight.
Do not faint beneath your burden,
All to Him is light;
All to Him is light.

3. For the joy of sin forgiven,
Let our anthem rise.
For the hope of Christ within us,
Everlasting life;
Everlasting life.

2475. Oh, the Lord, our strength and song

(Song of Moses)

Ex 15:2-3, 8; Rev 7:11-12; 11:15

Quite slowly

Chris Moerman, Pat Barrett, Ben Smith, Aaron Keyes & Graham Kendrick

Verse

C2 D Em D/F♯

1. Oh, the Lord, our strength and song; high-est

G C D C2 D

praise to Him be - longs. Christ the Lord, the con-qu'ring

Em D/F♯ G D G *Chorus*

King, Your name we raise, Your triumphs sing. Praise the

D Em C G

Lord, our migh-ty war - ri-or, praise the Lord, the glo-ri-ous

D Dsus4 D D/F♯ Em

One; by His hand we stand in vic - t'ry, by His

Last time to Coda
1.,2.
D.C.
C D C D Em D7/F♯ Cmaj7 D G
name we o-ver-come. 2. Though the
3.,5.
D.S. (al Coda)
4.
Mid section
G Em7 C2 G(no3rd) D
come. Praise the come. The
Em7 C2 G D
Lord shall reign for-e-ver and e-ver. The
(small notes 2°)
Em7 C2 G D
Lord shall reign for-e-ver and e-ver. The
1.
Em7 C2 G D
Lord shall reign for-e-ver and e-ver. The

2.
D.S.
Coda
G
D
G
e - ver and e - ver. Praise the
come.

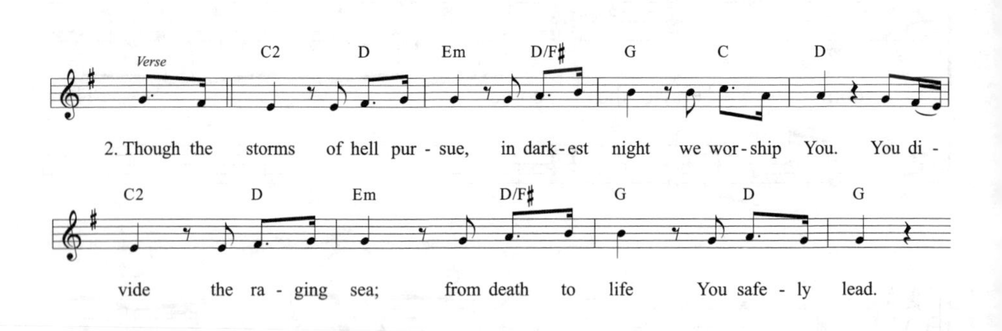
Verse
C2 D Em D/F♯ G C D
2. Though the storms of hell pur - sue, in dark - est night we wor - ship You. You di -
C2 D Em D/F♯ G D G
vide the ra - ging sea; from death to life You safe - ly lead.

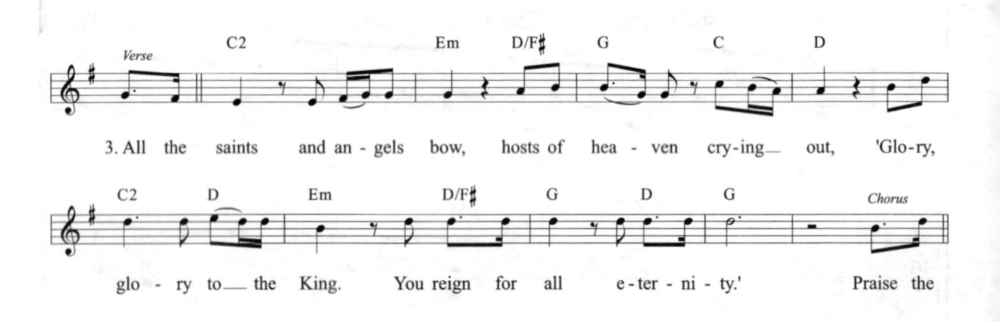
Verse
C2 Em D/F♯ G C D
3. All the saints and an - gels bow, hosts of hea - ven cry - ing out, 'Glo - ry,
C2 D Em D/F♯ G D G
Chorus
glo - ry to the King. You reign for all e - ter - ni - ty.' Praise the

The LORD is my strength and my song; he has become my salvation. He is my God, and I will praise him, my father's God, and I will exalt him. The LORD is a warrior; the LORD is his name.

EXODUS 15:2-3

2476. On a hill far away
(The old rugged cross)

Jn 19:17, 30; Phil 2:7-8; 1 Tim 1:15; 2 Tim 4:8; Heb 13:12-14; Rev 4:10

George Bennard (1873–1958)

2. O that old rugged cross,
   So despised by the world,
   Has a wondrous attraction for me;
   For the dear Lamb of God
   Left His glory above
   To bear it to dark Calvary.

3. In that old rugged cross,
   Stained with blood so divine,
   A wondrous beauty I see,
   For 'twas on that old cross
   Jesus suffered and died
   To pardon and sanctify me.

4. To the old rugged cross
   I will ever be true;
   Its shame and reproach gladly bear;
   Then He'll call me some day
   To my home far away,
   Where His glory forever I'll share.

2477. Once a King went travelling

(Came the light)

Lk 2:7; 5:32; Jn 1:5; Acts 2:24; 2 Cor 4:6; Phil 2:7; 1 Pet 2:24

Steadily

Mark Niedzwiedz

2. Lowly His beginning,
On a bed of straw;
Darkness all around He saw.
But not for the righteous,
In the hush of night;
Come the hour, came the light.

3. Once my Lord did suffer,
So I'd suffer not;
Took our place upon the cross.
But no tomb could hold Him,
In the hush of night;
Come the hour, came the light.

2478. Once I was dead to You

(Promised land)

Is 48:17; 53:5; Lk 4:21; Jn 10:28; 14:3; 1 Cor 6:19-20; Eph 2:13; Phil 1:21; 1 Tim 2:6; Heb 6:19; 9:12

Rhythmically

Lou & Nathan Fellingham & busbee

C
D
un - der - stand. Through Your suff - 'ring I'm for -
not with - stand. His name is Je - sus, sent from
G
Last time to Coda
gi - ven, pres - sing on - ward to the
hea - ven to take us home - ward to the
1.,3.
D.C.
4.
D.S. (Last chorus)
C
D
pro - mised land. 2. Sent from His
3. Now with the
pro - mised land. His name is
2.
C
D
C
Mid section
G
pro - mised land.
You've bought me with a price,
D
A
C
G
D
a per - fect sac - ri - fice; now all I have I give to You.

2. Sent from His Father above,
   Jesus walked this earth,
   Knew His destiny as He read the word.
   Not shrinking back from the task,
   He pursued His goal;
   Came to ransom lives and to make them whole.

3. Now with the Spirit's help I can journey on,
   Knowing peace with God,
   My convictions strong.
   Because of Jesus' blood,
   I am now secure
   And because He lives, my hope is sure.

2479. On Christmas day

Mt 1:23; Lk 2:7, 16; Jn 1:29; 1 Jn 1:1-2

Matt Osgood

Flowing

G A Bm A G D/F♯
Fa - ther made known in Je - sus Christ. This is our
Em7 A D D/F♯
God, wor-thy of praise, the love of the
Last time to Coda
1.
G A D Dsus4 D A/C♯
Fa - ther re - vealed on Christ-mas day. 3.The
2. Mid section
D Em7 A D D/F♯ Em7 A
Im - ma-nu - el, Im - ma-nu - el. Our God is with us
Bm A/C♯ Em7 A D D/F♯
now. Im - ma - nu - el, Im - ma - nu - el. Our

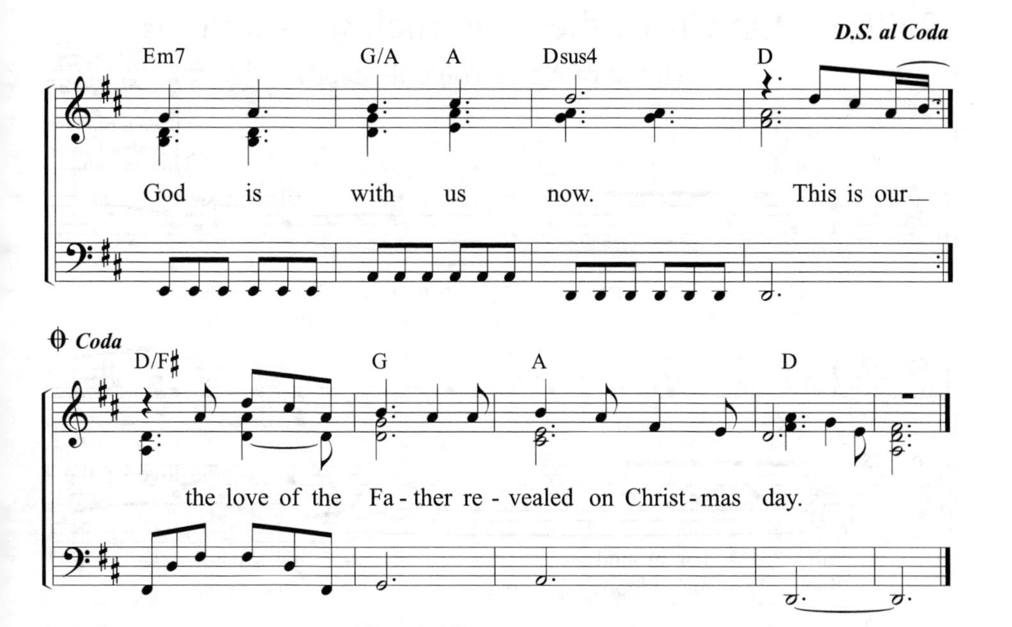

2. The hands that once split night from day
   Now feebly clutch a blade of hay:
   This is Immanuel.
   Majestic King, now small and weak,
   The Word of God must learn to speak:
   This is Immanuel.

3. The shepherds come and bow to Him,
   The Lamb who takes away our sin:
   This is Immanuel.
   For God has entered time and space
   To show the world His endless grace:
   This is Immanuel.

2480. On Christ the solid rock we stand

(Rock of Ages, You will stand)

Lam 3:23; Rom 3:25; 1 Cor 3:11; 10:4; Heb 6:19

Steady rock

Paul Baloche
& Brenton Brown

Verse Amaj7

1. On Christ the solid rock we stand; all other ground is sinking sand:
Our hope is built on nothing less than Jesus' blood and righteousness:

F♯m7 E D2

great is Your faithfulness, great is Your love, O God.

Last time to Coda

1. Amaj7 2. Amaj7 *Chorus*

Rock of A-

D2 A

-ges, You will stand,

D2
F♯m7
our foun-da - tion till the end.
E
D2
F♯m7
Ne-ver fail - ing, God un-chang - ing:
D2
Esus4
1.,3.
Amaj7
Rock of A - ges, You will stand.
F♯m7
Last time D.C. al Coda
2.
Amaj7
D.S.
Oh, Rock of A -

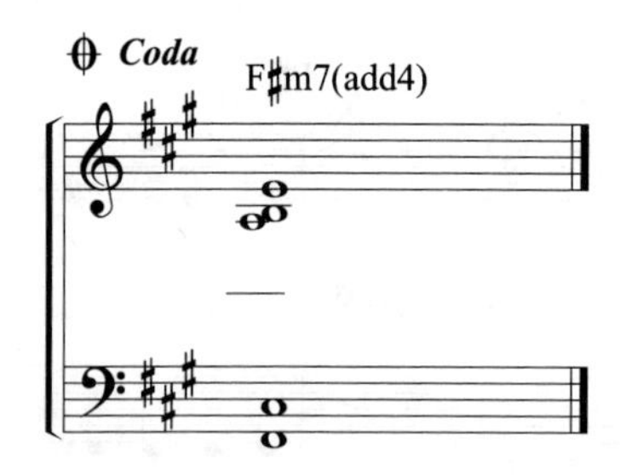

2. When darkness seems to hide Your face,
   I rest on Your unchanging grace:
   Great is Your faithfulness,
   Great is Your love, O God.
   In every high and stormy gale,
   My anchor holds within the veil:
   Great is Your faithfulness,
   Great is Your love, O God.

3. On Christ the solid rock we stand;
   All other ground is sinking sand:
   Great is Your faithfulness,
   Great is Your love, O God.

Edward Mote (1797–1874)
Adpt. Paul Baloche & Brenton Brown

By the grace God has given me, I laid a foundation as an expert builder, and someone else is building on it. But each one should be careful how he builds. For no-one can lay any foundation other than the one already laid, which is Jesus Christ.

1 CORINTHIANS 3:10-11

2481. One day every voice will sing

(Join the song)

Ps 148:1-2; Rev 4:10; 5:11; 7:9

Vicky Beeching & Ed Cash

Capo 3 (D)

Moderately

C/E(A/C♯)
Dm7(Bm)
Him, all crea - tures here be - low: to Him all the glo - ry be -
B♭2(G)
F(D)
longs. Praise Him a - bove, you heav'n - ly host, praise
Last time to Coda
C/E(A/C♯)
Dm7(Bm)
Fa - ther, Son and Ho - ly Ghost, let all the earth sing a - long;
1.
B♭2(G)
F(D)
Gm7(Em)
come join the song.
D.C.(v.2)
Dm7(Bm)
C7(A)
F(D)
Gm7(Em)
Dm7(Bm)
C7(A)

2.
Mid section
B♭2(G)
Gm7(Em)
F/A(D/F♯)
Come join the song that fills e - ter - ni - ty, sung
B♭2(G)
C7(A)
Gm7(Em)
through - out all his - to - ry; as an - gels shout and kings
F/A(D/F♯)
B♭2(G)
B♭m(Gm)
lay down their crowns, we bow down. Praise
F/A(D/F♯)
C/E(A/C♯)
God from whom all bless - ings flow, praise
Cm/E♭(Am/C)
B♭2/D(G/B)
Him, all crea - tures here be - low. Praise

F(D)
C/E(A/C♯)
Him a-bove, you heav'n - ly host, praise
Cm/E♭(Am/C)
B♭2/D(G/B)
D.S.
Fa - ther, Son and Ho - ly Ghost. Praise
Coda
B♭2(G)
F(D)
Gm7(Em)
Come join the song (sing a-long).
Dm7(Bm)
C7(A)
F(D)
Gm7(Em)
Come join the song.
Dm7(Bm)
C(A)
F(D)
2. Gathered round the throne above,
We'll be swept up in the melody;
Hearts will overflow with love,
We'll be singing out a symphony.

2482. One day when heaven

(Glorious day)

Is 53:3-4; Mt 1:23; Lk 23:33; 24:2; Jn 1:14; 17:5; Acts 1:11; 2:24; Rom 5:9; 6:4; 1 Thess 4:16

Unhurried

Michael Bleecker & Mark Hall

C/E
F
me, bu-ried, He car - ried my sins far a-way.
Dm
C/E
Ris-ing, He jus - ti-fied, free - ly for - e -
F
G
- ver: one day He's com - ing, O glo - ri - ous day!
C
F
C/E
O glo - ri - ous day!
1.
D.C.(v.2)
2.,3.
F
F
Dm
O glo - ri - ous day!

2. One day they led Him up Calvary's mountain,
One day they nailed Him to die on the tree;
Suffering anguish, despised and rejected:
Bearing our sins, my Redeemer is He.

3. One day the grave could conceal Him no longer,
One day the stone rolled away from the door.
Then He arose, o'er death He had conquered;
Now is ascended, my Lord evermore.

4. One day the trumpet will sound for His coming,
One day the skies with His glories will shine.
Wonderful day, my beloved ones bringing;
Glorious Saviour, this Jesus is mine.

2483.
One with the Father
(Every knee will bow down)
Jn 13:15-16; 1 Cor 1:23; Phil 2:6-11
Capo 2 (D)
Paul Oakley & Aaron Keyes
Steadily
F♯m(Em) Verse B(A) E(D)
1. One with the Fa - ther, be-ing in ve -
A(G) E/G♯(D/F♯) F♯m(Em)
- ry na - ture God, You made Your-self no -
B(A) E(D)
- thing, just like us.
F♯m(Em) B(A) E(D)
Ho-ly and hum - ble, o-be-di-ent to
A(G) F♯m(Em) E/G♯(D/F♯)
death on a bit-ter cross, there-fore the Fa - ther has ex-alt-

A(G)
B(A)
-ed You on high.
Chorus
E(D)
Ev-'ry knee will bow down, ev-'ry heart will pro-claim:
C♯m7(Bm7)
wor-thy are You, O God, name a-bove ev-'ry name.
A2(G)
Bsus4(A)
E(D)
1.,5. D.C.(v.2)
(Fine)
We will sing: Je-sus is Lord.
2.,4. D.S. (al Fine)
3.
E(D)
Mid section
A(G)
To the glo-ry of God the Fa-ther,

E/G♯(D/F♯)
to the glo - ry of God the Fa - ther,
F♯m7+4(Em)
B(A)
(2°)
to the glo-ri-ous God, the Fa - ther, glo-ry, ho-nour and praise.
to the glo-ri-ous God, our Fa - ther, be ho-nour and praise.
1.
E(D)
2.
E(D)
D.S.S.
To the glo-ry of God
Ev-'ry knee will bow down,
Verse
F♯m(Em)
B(A)
E(D)
A(G)
E/G♯(D/F♯)
2. Suf-fer-ing Sa - viour, free-ly You gave Your life for us;
F♯m(Em)
B(A)
E(D)
make me a ser - vant, as You are.
F♯m(Em)
B(A)
E(D)
A(G)
All of cre-a - tion, the hea-vens and the earth, will tes-ti - fy:
F♯m(Em)
E/G♯(D/F♯)
A(G)
B(A)
You are the Christ, cru - ci - fied! Lord of all!

2484.
Only You carry away
(Good)
Ps 100:5; Is 53:4; Dan 7:9; Rev 7:9
Capo 4 (G)
Dave Fitzgerald
Moderately
Verse
E2(C)
1. On - ly You car - ry a-way
G♯m7(Em)
re - grets and con - fu - sion.
B(G)
E2(C)
On - ly You sweep a - way
G♯m7(Em)
ev - 'ry pain, e - ve - ry sor - row.
B(G)
Bridge
F♯/A♯(D/F♯)
Ho - ly, An - cient of Days.
E2(C)

F♯(D)
E2(C)
Ev - 'ry na - tion, ev - 'ry tongue pro-claim:
Chorus
G♯m7(Em)
E(C)
B(G)
F♯(D)
You are good, You are good, Your love en-dures.
G♯m7(Em)
E(C)
B(G)
F♯(D)
You are good, You are good, Your love en-dures.
G♯m7(Em)
E(C)
B(G)
F♯(D)
You are good, You are good, Your love en-dures for-
1.
D.C.(v.2)
2.-5.
1°&3° D.S. (al Coda)
Last time to Coda
E2/G♯ (C/E)
E(C)
ev - er.
ev-er.

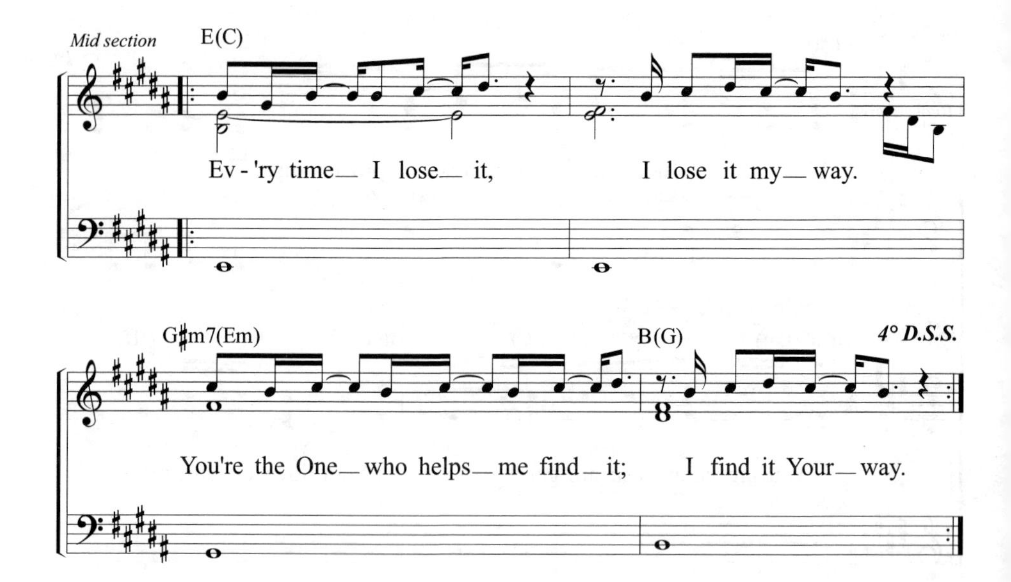

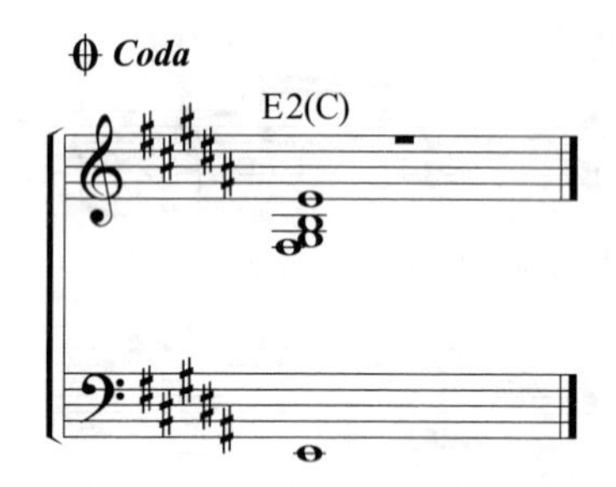

2. Only You take away
Shame, hurt, misunderstanding.
Only You wash away
All the darkness that surrounds me.

2485. On that dark night

(Emmanuel)

Is 1:18; 53:4; Mt 1:23; Rom 5:8; 1 Cor 11:23-25; Phil 2:7-8; Rev 7:14

Reflectively

Vicky Beeching

Bm7
A2/C♯
D
Chorus
love is this? Em-man - u - el,
E/G♯
F♯m7
You're God with us, and we re-mem - ber You
D
A/C♯
E/G♯
through Your bo-dy and Your blood. Em-man-u - el,
F♯m7
You gave Your life, our hearts cry 'thank
1.
D
E/G♯
F♯m7
D2
A2
You' for Your sa-cri - fice.

2. Why would You die for someone like me,
Someone so undeserving?
Why would You leave Heaven's glory
To step down and carry my burdens?
What love is this?

2486. On that day

Mt 6:10, 33; 1 Cor 7:23; Rev 21:4

B♭(G) Cm(Am) B♭/D(G/B) E♭(C) F7(D)
price You paid to bring Your hea-ven to to-day.
B♭(G) (Am) Cm B♭/D(G/B) B♭(G) F7(D)
At great cost You brought Your world in-
B♭(G) F7/A(D/F♯) B♭(G) B♭/D(G/B) C(A) C/E(A)
to our world; we live to know Your pre-sence
1.
D.C.
F(D) F/E♭(D/C) Dm7(Bm) E♭(C) Fsus4(A) F(D)
now, to see Your king-dom come. 3. On that day,
2.
B♭/D(G/B) C/E (A/C♯) F(D) F/E♭(D/C)
come, to know Your pre-sence now, to see Your king-dom

2. On that day, there will be no more sickness.
   On that day, there will be no more death.
   So today I will love,
   I will live, I will work,
   I will join in to see Your kingdom come.

3. On that day, there'll be no hesitation.
   On that day, everyone will worship You.
   So today I will love,
   I will live, I will work,
   I will join in to see Your kingdom come.

2487. On the darkest day of all

Capo 1 (G)

Mk 15:34; 16:4; Jn 11:25; 19:2, 18; Rom 6:8-9; 1 Cor 15:54; 2 Cor 5:21; 1 Thess 4:17; 2 Pet 3:10

Moderately

Matt Osgood

E♭(D) D♭(C) A♭(G) E♭sus4(D)
Son; the grave could not con - tain His ra - diant light.
E♭(D) D♭(C) A♭(G) D♭(C)
The stone was rolled a - way, death's vic - to - ry re -
E♭(D) D♭(C) A♭/C(G/B) B♭m(Am)
versed, in Christ, the re - sur - rec - tion and the life.
E♭(D) Chorus A♭(G) D♭(C) B♭m(Am)
Christ was raised, ne - ver to die a -
E♭(D) A♭/C(G/B) D♭(C) E♭sus4(D)
gain, and He reigns in e - ver - last - ing light.

3. In the darkness of this world,
The hope of glory shines,
The shadows of this age will pass away.
His triumph is assured,
Our future is secure,
For Jesus rose to life on Easter day.

2488. On the day I called

(You are more)

Ps 123:1; 138:3; Heb 12:2; 1 Jn 1:7

With drive

Harrison Wood

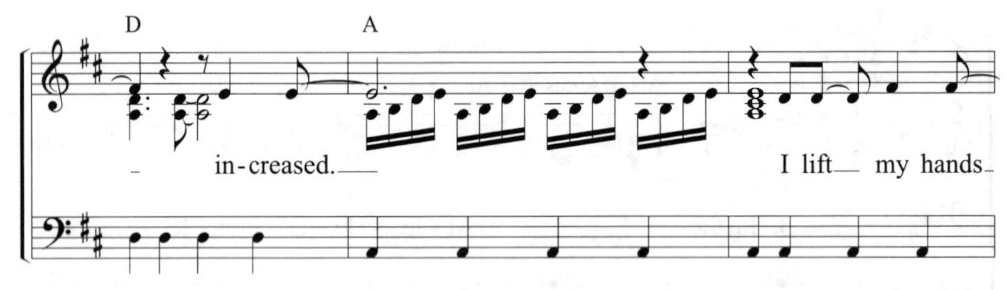

A
(A)
Chorus
Em7
You are more than
Bm
D
my words could e-ver say.
You are Lord
G
D
A
o - ver all, o-ver all of my days.
I will see
Em7
Bm
D
this sea - son through,
I will fix my eyes on You,
A
G
on - ly You,
on - ly You.

3° D.S. al Coda
Last time to Coda
1.
A
Bm7
D
D.C.(v.2)
2. D
2. I wor - ship You
A
Bm7
G
A
Mid section
D
A
'Hal - le - lu - jah,' the earth will sing; may Your name
Bm7
G
2° D.S.
A
be glo - ri - fied.

Coda
D
(4 times)
Dsus2

Verse
Bm7
D
2. I wor - ship You and lift You high; God, for - e -
G
D
A
Bm7
- ver let Your name be glo - ri - fied. I will lift my voice
D
G
and sing Your name, for You gave Your life to cleanse my sin
D
A
and took a - way my shame.

2489. Open my eyes and see

(My soul sings)

Stuart Garrard, Martin Smith & Jonathan Thatcher

Am
G/B
C
Chorus
feel the breath of hea - ven o - ver me.
My soul sings,
G
Am
F
my soul sings, my soul sings how I love You:
C
G/D
C/E
My soul sings, my soul sings, my soul sings:
2nd time D.S.
1.
F
C
Dm7
how I love You.
2.
C/E
F
C
2. Turn the page and see
The wonderful history of love.
I start and end with You,
I'm pulled to the gravity of love.

2490. Open up the skies

(Hope is dawning)

Joel 2:23

Capo 2 (D)

Matt Maher, Michael Gungor, Aaron Keyes & Johnny Parks

Moderately

Verse E(D) A(G) E(D)

1. O - pen up the skies and rain the hea - vens down, the

B(A) E(D) A(G)

hea - vens down. Fa - ther, o - pen up the skies and rain the

E(D) B(A) *1.* A(G) B(A) ***D.C.(v.2)*** *2.,3.* E(D)

hea - vens down on us. round.

Chorus A(G) B(A) E(D) A(G) B(A)

We are long - ing, hope is dawn - ing,

E(D) A(G) B(A) C♯m7(Bm7) B(A)

hea - ven's fall - ing; come, Lord Je -

Last time to Coda
1.
D.C.(v.3)
2.
D.S.
A(G) B(A) E(D)
- sus.
R.H.
Coda
E(D) E(no3rd)(D)
R.H.
Verse
E(D) A(G) E(D) B(A)
2. O - pen up our eyes to see Your glo - ry found, all a-round. Je-sus,
E(D) A(G) E(D) B(A) E(D)
o - pen up our eyes to see Your glo - ry's all a - round.
Verse
E(D) A(G) E(D) B(A)
3. O - pen up our hearts to say, 'Have Your way, have Your way.' Spi-rit,
E(D) A(G) E(D) B(A) E(D)
o - pen up our hearts to say, 'Won't You come and have Your way.'

2491. # O sovereign God

(Praise the Father, praise the Son)

Ps 91:4; Is 66:12; 2 Cor 4:17; Phil 2:9; Rev 7:11

Ed Cash & Chris Tomlin

Last time to Coda
1.
Bm7 D/F# G2 A D Em7 Asus4
one; clothed in pow - er and in grace, the name a - bove all o-ther
D.C.(v.3)
2.
D.S.
D G/D Em7 Asus4 D D/F#
names. 3. To the - bove all o-ther names. O praise the
3.
Mid section
Em7 Asus4 D G Asus4 D
-bove all o - ther names. Yours is the
A Bm7 G2 D
king - dom, Yours is the pow - er, Yours is the
1.
2.
A G2 A Asus4
glo - ry for ev - er. - er

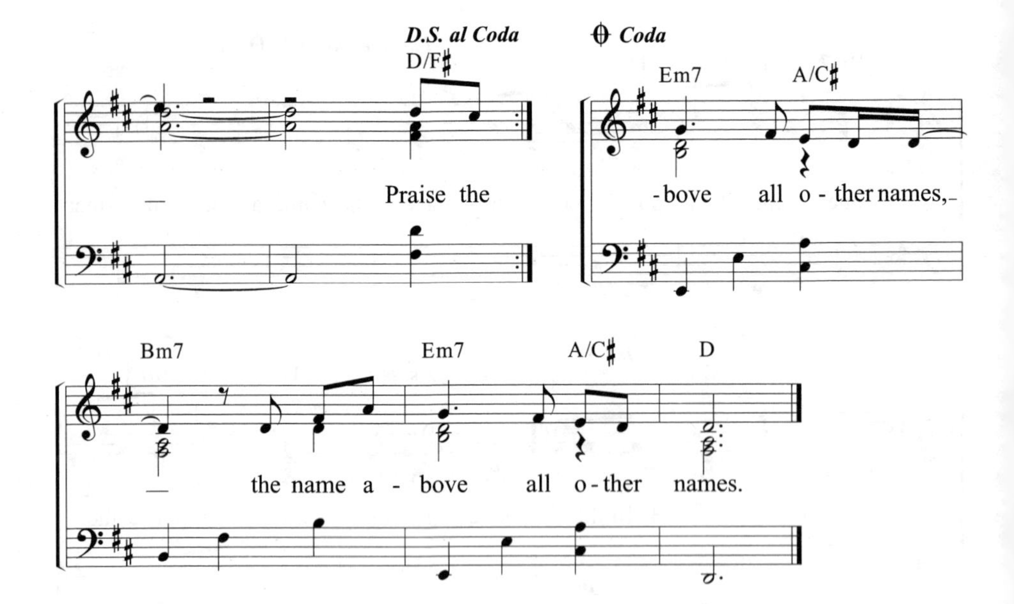

2. These sufferings, this passing tide,
   Under Your wings I will abide,
   And every enemy shall flee;
   You are my hope and victory!

3. To the valley, for my soul;
   Thy great descent has made me whole!
   Your word my heart has welcomed home;
   Now peace like water ever flows.

Though outwardly we are wasting away, yet inwardly we are being renewed day by day. For our light and momentary troubles are achieving for us an eternal glory that far outweighs them all.

2 CORINTHIANS 4:16-17

2492.
Our Father in heaven
(We pray)
Is 55:8-9; Mt 6:9-10; Jn 1:14
Neil Bennetts
& Eoghan Heaslip
Capo 1 (G)
Steadily
(v.2)
(v.3)
Verse
A♭(G)
D♭2(C)
1. Our Fa-ther in hea - ven, hal-lowed be Your name.
A♭/C(G/B)
Our Fa-ther in hea - ven,
hal-lowed be Your name,
1.
Your ho - ly name.
D.C.(v.2)
2. Your

2.,3.
D♭2(C)
Bridge
F m(Em)
And we're fall - ing on our knees,
B♭m(Am)
D♭(C)
Chorus
just to see Your pre - sence here.
(And) we pray,
A♭(G)
E♭/G(D/F♯)
B♭m(Am)
we pray
that Your glo - ry, O God, would be seen
D♭(C)
A♭(G)
E♭/G(D/F♯)
on earth. We pray,
we pray,
in Your mer-
Last time to Coda
B♭m(Am)
D♭(C)
- cy, O God, would You come and dwell here.

1.
A♭(G)
D♭2(C)
A♭/C(G/B)
D.C.(v.3)
3.
D.S. al Coda
D♭2(C)
D♭2(C)
E♭7(D)
3. And and dwell here. We pray,
Mid section
(2°)
here.
2.
D♭(C)
B♭m(Am)
and dwell here.
(2°)
Lord, we need You;
Fm(Em)
A♭(G)
E♭/G(D/F♯)
Lord, we need You;

2. Your ways are not our ways,
And Your thoughts high above;
With wonders unfailing
And a heart full of love.

3. And Your truth shines its wonder,
Bringing light to this day;
The treasure of heaven:
Full of hope, full of grace.

2493.
Our God forever
(God of miracles)
Capo 4 (G)
Jer 32:17; Lk 1:37; 1 Cor 10:13; 1 Thess 5:24
Nick Herbert & Eoghan Heaslip
Moderately
Verse
B(G) E(C) B(G)
1. Our God for - e - ver, we re - mem-
E(C) B(G) E(C)
- ber all You've done; ev - 'ry vic - t'ry
B(G) E(C) G♯m(Em)
when You came through for us. You're in
F♯/A♯(D/F♯) B(G) E(C) G♯m(Em) F♯/A♯(D/F♯)
our hi - sto - ry, You know our ev-
E(C)
1.
Bsus4(G) B(G) G♯m(Em)
- 'ry need.

Bsus4(G) B(G) G♯m(Em)
D.C.(v.2)
2.
F♯(D)
We be-lieve that You're the
Chorus
B(G)
God of mi-ra-cles, the God of mi-ra-cles,
E2(C)
You hear ev - 'ry pray'r;
G♯m(Em)
God of pro-mi-ses, the God of pro-mi-ses, You're

E(C) E2(C) F♯(D) Last time to Coda B(G)
faith-ful to the end: we trust You.
Mid section
G♯m(Em) F♯/A♯(D/F♯)
And You brought us safe
E2(C) G♯m(Em) F♯/A♯(D/F♯) B(G)
this far, and You'll lead us all the
G♯m(Em) F♯/A♯(D/F♯) E2(C)
way; You brought us safe this far,
G♯m(Em) F♯/A♯(D/F♯) B(G) F♯/A♯(D/F♯)
You'll lead us all the way,

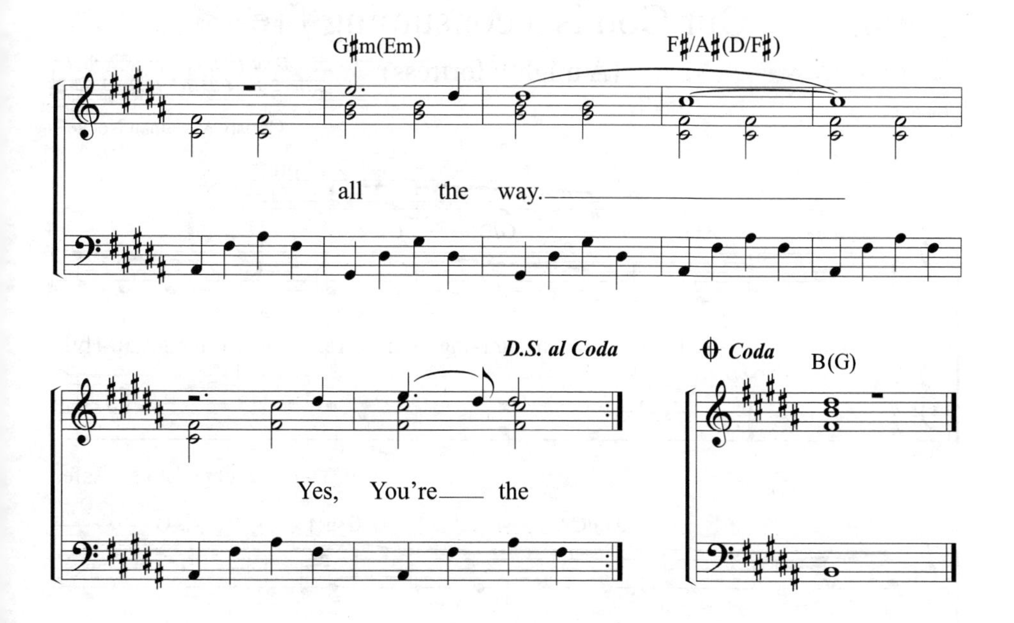

2. You're strong and faithful,
And You inspire songs of praise.
Always working,
You are moving in this place.
There's nothing You can't do,
No heart too far from You.
We believe that You're the...

2494. Our God is a consuming fire

(A mighty fortress)

Deut 4:24; Ps 8:1; 18:2; 91:14; 2 Tim 2:12; 4:8; Heb 12:2, 23, 28-29

Building

Christy & Nathan Nockels

(2°)
C2/E
F
Dm7
eyes on You, we will keep our eyes on You.
Gsus4
G
Chorus
C
F
A migh-ty for-tress is our God.
Dm
C
Gsus4
G
A sa - cred re - fuge is Your name.
C
F
Your king - dom is un - shake - a - ble
1.
Dm
C
Gsus4
G
and with You for - ev - er we will reign.
2. Our

3.,4.
D.S. al Coda
Last time to Coda
2.
Gsus4 G
Gsus4 G
C/E
reign.
reign.
F
B♭
1.
2.
Mid section
C2/E
F
We will keep our eyes on You, we will keep our
Dm7
Gsus4 G
C2/E
eyes on You. So we can set our hearts on You,
F
Dm7
Gsus4 G
D.S.
Lord, we will set our hearts on You.

2. Our God is jealous for His own.
None could comprehend His love and His mercy.
Our God is exalted on His throne,
High above the heavens, forever He is worthy.

2495. Our God is mercy

Ps 46:1; 123:1; Is 55:1; Mt 5:3; Rom 9:16; 13:11; Rev 22:17

3rd time to Mid section
Last time to Coda
1.
2.
E(D)
F♯m(Em)
D(C)
D(C)
Verse
our God is near.
Our God is
The
A(G)
Asus4(G)
king-dom of our God is near, lift your eyes, lift your eyes. The
F♯m(Em)
D(C)
hope of hea-ven's draw-ing near, lift your eyes,
A(G)
lift your eyes. You're blessed if you've been torn a-part, you're
D(C)
F♯m(Em)
blessed if you've a bro-ken heart, for hope is wait-ing

D(C)
D.S. al Mid section
at the door; sal - va - tion's near. 'Cause our God is
Mid section
D(C)
A(G)
Lift up your eyes, lift up your eyes,
D/A(C/G)
A(G)
lift up your eyes and sing. Lift up your eyes, lift
E(D)
F♯m(Em)
D(C)
up your eyes, lift up your eyes and sing.
A/C♯(G/B)
E(D)
Lift up your eyes, lift up your eyes,

F♯m(Em)
D(C)
D.S. al Coda
lift up your eyes and sing.
'Cause our God is
Coda
D(C)
A(G)
E(D)
Our God is near,
our God is
F♯m(Em)
D(C)
A(G)
near,
our God is near.

2496. Our God of heaven, Lord of earth

Gen 2:7; 1 Chron 29:11; Ps 8:3; Mt 1:23; Gal 5:22; Rev 7:12; 11:15

Capo 3 (G)

Peter Simpson

2. We lift the name of Jesus high,
   The One on whom we all rely.
   The Lord of power, God of might,
   We give You praise both day and night.
   Our hearts are glad to hear Your voice,
   We long to worship and rejoice.
   Proclaiming You Creator King,
   Our worship, praise and love we bring.

3. Lord of the ages, You are here,
   The One we love and hold so dear.
   The breath of heaven here on earth,
   Our God who gave the virgin birth.
   Exalt the King in majesty,
   Dominion, power, authority;
   Redeeming love, humility
   Rest on Your crown eternally.

2497. Our God will reign forever

(My Saviour lives)

Capo 4 (G)

Rock feel

Job 19:25; Jn 14:6; Rom 5:2; Rev 11:15; 14:3

Jon Egan & Glenn Packiam

Verse B(G) G♯m(Em) E(C) B(G) G♯m(Em) E(C) B(G) G♯m(Em) E(C) B(G) G♯m(Em) E(C) C♯m(Am)

1. Our God will reign __ for - e - ver, and all the world __ will __ know His name. Ev - 'ry - one __ to - ge - ther sing the song __ of the re - deemed. __

Chorus B(G) G♯m(Em) E(C)

I know that my __ Re - deem - er lives, and now I stand __ on __ what __ He did. My Sa - viour,

B(G)
my Sa - viour lives.
Ev-'ry day a brand
G♯m(Em)
new chance to say, 'Je-sus, You are the on - ly way.'
E(C)
B(G)
G♯m(Em) E(C)
My Sa - viour, my Sa - viour lives.
1° D.C.(v.2)
Last time to Coda
B(G)
G♯m(Em) E(C)
B(G)
G♯m7(Em)
Asus2(F)
C♯m7(Am)

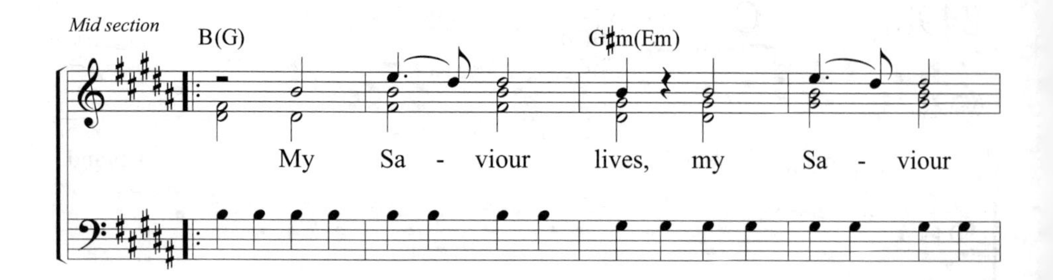

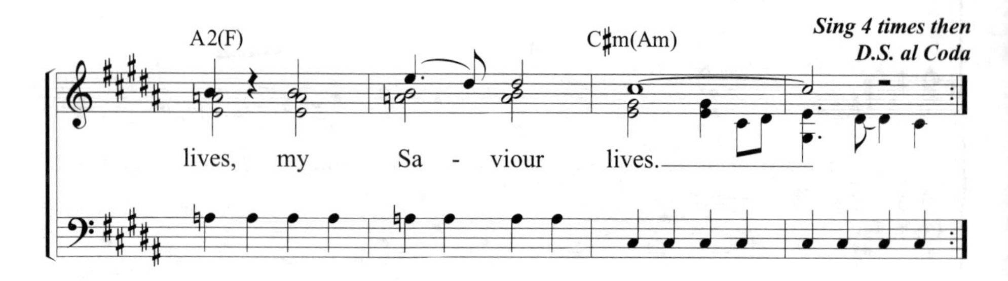

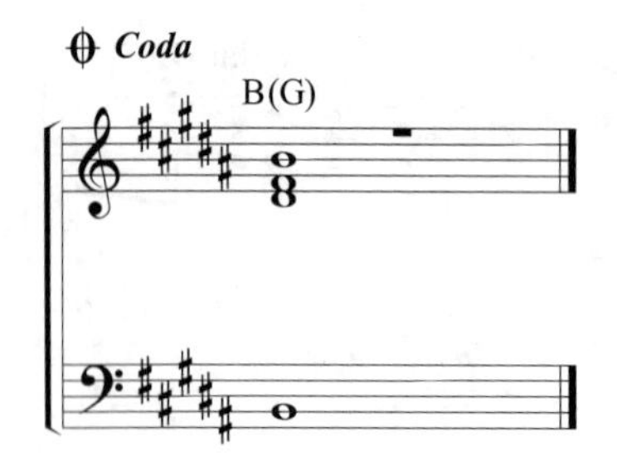

2. The King has come from heaven,
And darkness trembles at His name.
Victory forever
Is the song of the redeemed.

2498. Our hearts are breathing in

(The more we see)

2 Sam 7:22; Ps 19:1; 100:5; Lam 3:22-23

Am7
G6
Dsus4
D
G/B
C2
Your ma - jes - ty sur - rounds us.
In the pow'r of Your life,
G/B
Am7
G6
in the grace of Your cross,
Your mer - cy, Lord, has
1.
D.C.(v.2)
2.
D.S.
Dsus4
D
C2
G/B
Am7(4)
Dsus4
D
found us.
found us, O Lord.
3.
Dsus4
D
Mid section
C
found us. And the more we see, we sing,
C
C6(♭5)
G
Em7
G/B
'Ho - ly is the name of the Lord.'
And the

2. Your power we see displayed
In all that You have made:
In the sky and sea and stars.
And here beneath Your cross,
Your mercy speaks so loud,
Speaking straight into our hearts.

2499. Our hearts will not forget

(Now is the time for us)

Jn 14:6; 17:17; Heb 11:1

Capo 1 (A)

At a medium pace

Luke Hellebronth,
Oliver Snelling & Martyn Layzell

Chorus
B♭(A)
Now is the time for us to sing of Your great love.
Gm(F♯m)
E♭(D)
We worship You, God, forever You, God.
B♭(A)
We hear You calling us to show the world Your love.
Last time to Coda
1.
Gm(F♯m)
E♭(D)
B♭(A)
The sound of freedom will be our anthem.
D.C.(v.2)
Cm(Bm)
Gm(F♯m)
E♭(D)
B♭(A)
Cm(Bm)
Gm(F♯m)

2.
E♭(D)
F/A(E/G♯)
Cm(Bm)
will be our an - them.
E♭(D)
B♭(A)
Mid section
F/A(E/G♯)
We're Yours for - e - ver,
Cm(Bm)
E♭(D)
we stand to - ge-ther,
we trust in You, our God,
B♭(A)
F(E)
we look to You, our God.
We're Yours for - e - ver,
Gm(F♯m)
1.
E♭(D)
we stand to-ge-ther,
we fol-low You, our God.

2. We're daring to believe,
Trusting in what's unseen;
By faith we'll see
You're lighting up the night:
New hope that shines so bright
Eternally.

2500. Over all He reigns

(He reigns)

1 Chron 16:31-33; Lk 3:5; Rev 17:14

Marc James

Steadily

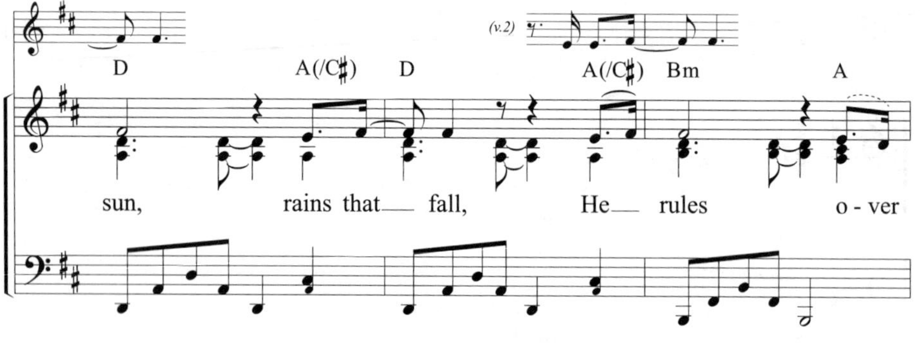

A
G
D
reigns, let all the earth rej-oice. He
A
Bm
G
D
reigns, let ev - 'ry tongue con-fess: with love
Last time to Coda
1.
G
D
A
D
A
and right - eous-ness He reigns.
D.C.(v.2)
2.
Bm
A
D
A
D
He reigns. 2. All who
Mid section
Em
Bm
A
D
Ev-'ry moun-tain be bowed down, ev-'ry val - ley raised,

2. All who live, all who've died,
The sin-sick heart, the sanctified.
Above all thought, every claim,
In war or peace He reigns.

2501. O worship the King

Ps 104:1-3; Is 54:5; Dan 7:9; Lk 1:78; Jn 15:15; Rev 7:11

Capo 1 (G)

New music & additional chorus: Chris Tomlin

With energy

1.,4.
Last time to Coda
2.,3.
2. O
For
Chorus
D♭(C)
Fm7(Em)
B♭m7(Am)
You a - lone are the match-less King, to You a - lone be all
A♭/C(G/B)
D♭(C)
ma - jes - ty. Your glo - ries and won - ders what
Fm7(Em)
B♭m7(Am)
tongue can re-cite? You breathe in the air,
A♭/C(G/B)
D♭(C)
1.
2.
D.S.
You shine in the light.
3. O

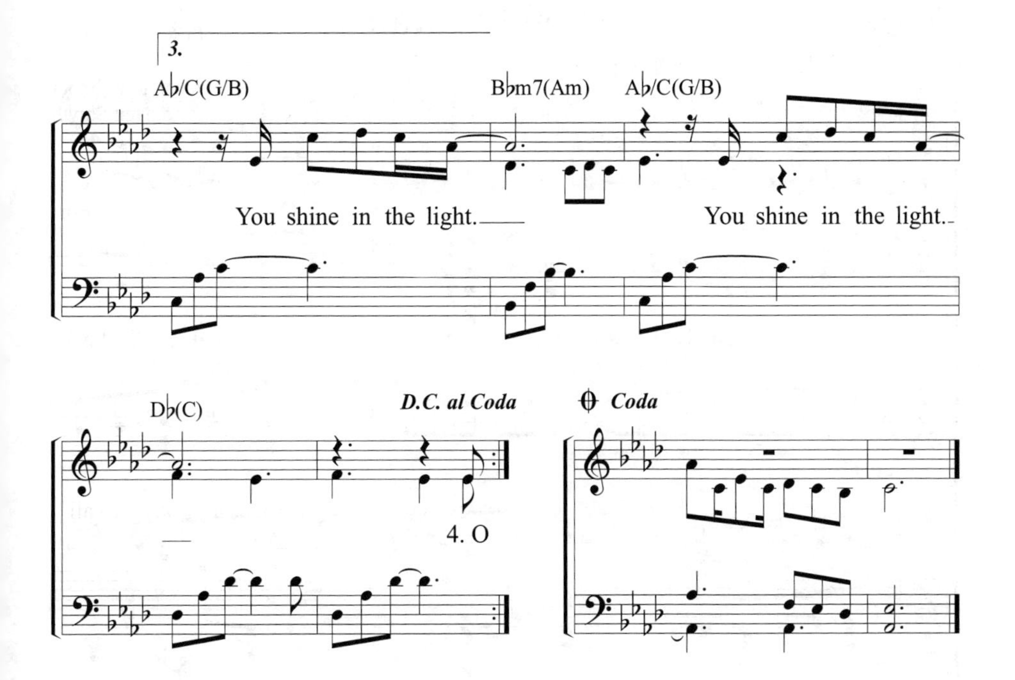

2. O tell of His might, O sing of His grace,
Whose robe is the light, and canopy, space;
His chariots of wrath the deep thunderclouds form,
And dark is His path on the wings of the storm.

3. O measureless might, ineffable love!
While angels delight to worship above,
Thy mercies, how tender, how firm to the end,
Our Maker, defender, Redeemer and friend!

William Kethe (d.1594)
Adpt. Robert Grant (1778–1838)

2502. Patiently I wait

Ps 40:1-3; 1 Cor 2:9

Sarahanne Wilmont
& Neil Smyth

With praise

D
Bm7 D/A G
My legs don't shake, because You've heard my cry.
Chorus
G
You've given me a new song to sing,
D
G
Bm
and my mouth won't stop smiling. You've given me
G
D
A Bm G
someone to trust, and my feet are firm.
D
You've given me more than I can feel, and I

2. The things You've planned,
No one can try recounting;
There are so many wonders
You've done for me.
And Your mercy falls,
It lands on my life;
Your love and truth –
They protect me still.

2503. Praise belongs to You
(Glorified)

Ps 8:1; 111:10; 148:7
Rom 8:19; Rev 4:10; 22:20

Jared Anderson

Moderately

(v.2)
D A F♯m7 Esus4 E
The great-est joy I've found is to lay a crown be-fore my
D2 A F♯m7 E D2 A F♯m7 Esus4 E
King, before my King.
Chorus
D2 A F♯m7 Esus4
I've come to wor - ship, I've come to lift up Your name,
D2 A F♯m7 Esus4
for You de-serve this life laid down like the one that You gave.
D2 A F♯m7 Esus4
I have but one voice, one heart and one sa - cri - fice,

2. Praise belongs to You,
Let songs of children rise;
You silence all Your foes,
You set Your glory in the skies.
Praise belongs to You,
Creation's calling now
For the King to be revealed;
O King of heaven, come down;
King of Heaven, come down.

2504. Praise the Lord who reigns above

Capo 3 (D)

Ps 47:8; 150:6; Mt 6:9-10; Acts 17:28; Rev 5:12

With increasing intensity

New music & chorus: Chris Eaton & John Hartley

Verse

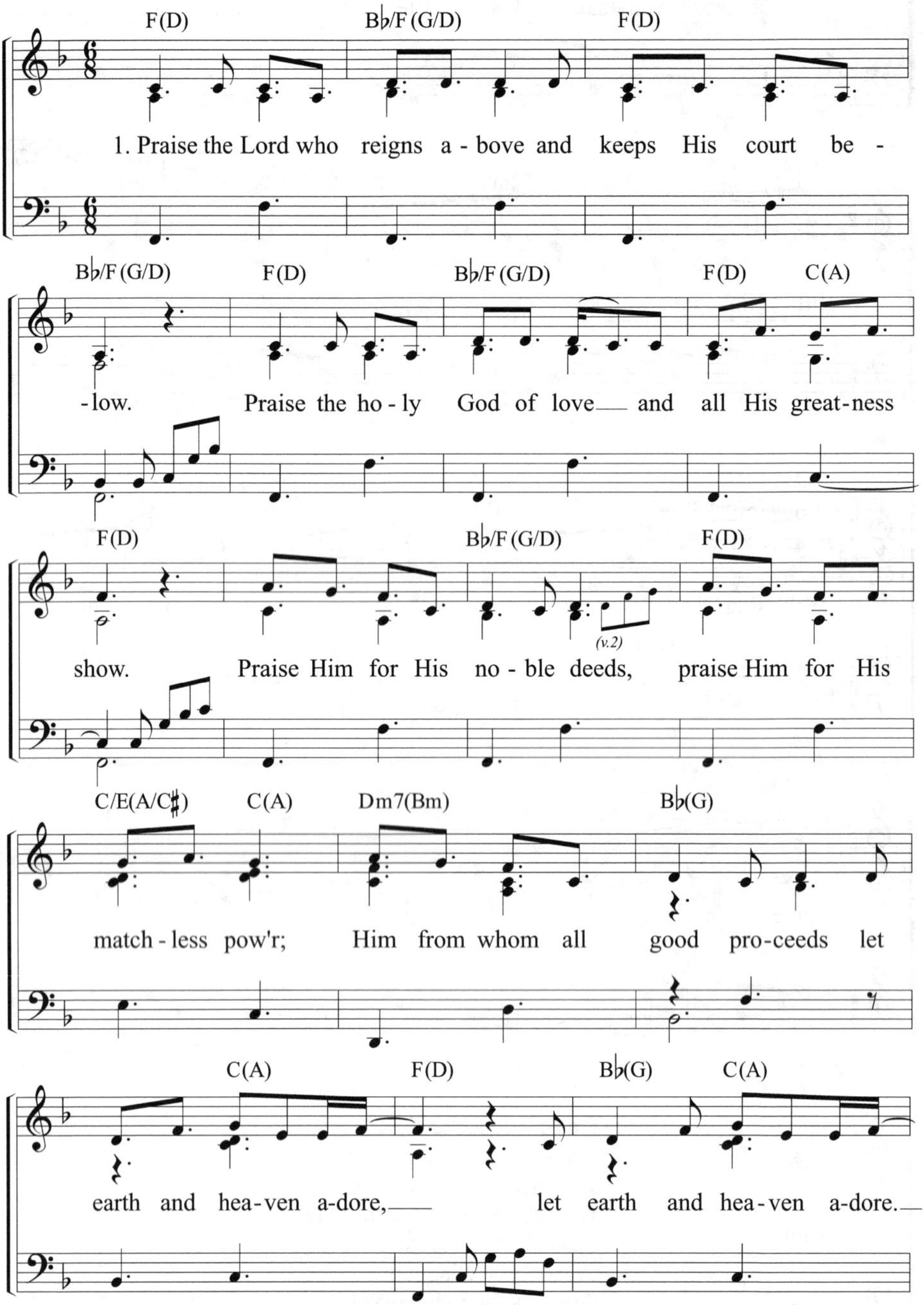

F(D) B♭/F (G/D) F(D)
1. Praise the Lord who reigns a - bove and keeps His court be -

B♭/F (G/D) F(D) B♭/F (G/D) F(D) C(A)
-low. Praise the ho - ly God of love and all His great-ness

F(D) B♭/F (G/D) F(D)
show. Praise Him for His no - ble deeds, (v.2) praise Him for His

C/E(A/C♯) C(A) Dm7(Bm) B♭(G)
match - less pow'r; Him from whom all good pro-ceeds let

C(A) F(D) B♭(G) C(A)
earth and hea-ven a-dore, let earth and hea-ven a-dore.

F(D)
B♭/F (G/D)
Chorus
F(D)
B♭2(G)
F(D)
Praise the name of Christ, ce-le - brate and
C(A)
Dm(Bm) F/C(D/A)
B♭(G)
lift Him up high. Praise the Lord of life.
Last time to Coda
C(A)
B♭/D(G/B)
C/E(A/C♯)
B♭(G)
We'll sing the sto - ry of ho - nour and glo - ry and praise the
1.
D.C.(v.2)
C(A)
F(D)
B♭sus2(G)
F(D)
B♭sus2(G)
name of Christ.
3.
C(A)
D.S. al Coda
2.
C(A)
F(D)
name. Praise the name of Christ.

2. God in whom they move and live,
Let every creature sing.
Glory to their Maker give,
And homage to their King.
Hallowed be Thy name beneath,
As in heav'n on earth adored.
Praise the Lord in every breath;
Let all things praise the Lord,
Let all things praise the Lord.

Charles Wesley (1707–88)

Let everything that has breath praise the LORD.

PSALM 150:6

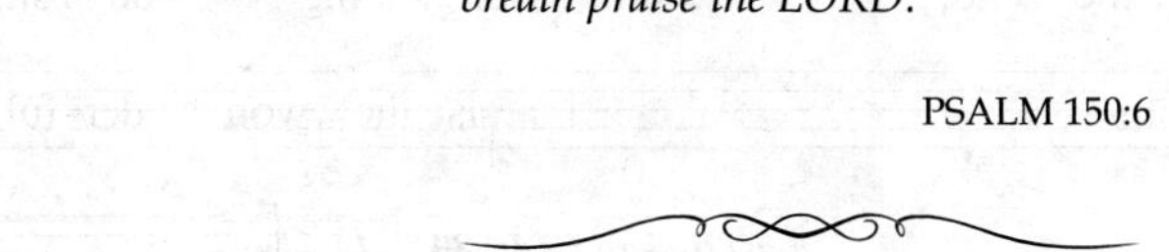

2505. Precious cornerstone

(All to us)

Lk 1:35; 1 Cor 13:12; 2 Cor 1:20; 1 Pet 1:24; 2:6

Chris Tomlin, Matt Maher, Matt Redman & Jesse Reeves

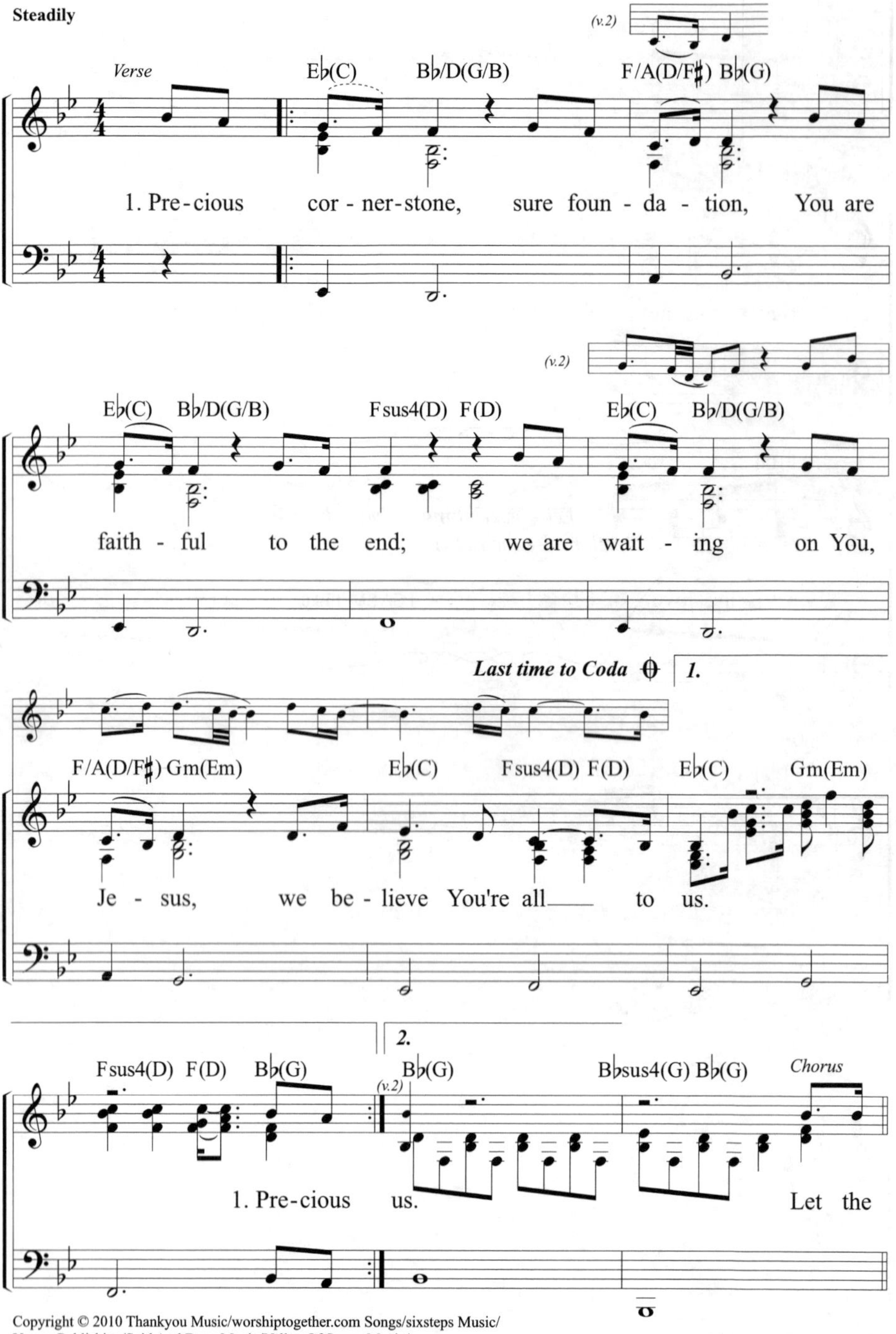

Capo 3 (G)

Steadily

Verse

E♭(C) B♭/D(G/B) F/A(D/F♯) B♭(G)

1. Precious cornerstone, sure foundation, You are

E♭(C) B♭/D(G/B) Fsus4(D) F(D) E♭(C) B♭/D(G/B)

faithful to the end; we are waiting on You,

Last time to Coda 1.

F/A(D/F♯) Gm(Em) E♭(C) Fsus4(D) F(D) E♭(C) Gm(Em)

Jesus, we believe You're all to us.

Fsus4(D) F(D) B♭(G) 2. B♭(G) B♭sus4(G) B♭(G) *Chorus*

1. Precious us. Let the

F(D)
E♭(C)
B♭(G)
glo - ry of Your name be the pas - sion of the church; let the
right - eous - ness of God be a ho - ly flame that burns. Let the
Gm(Em)
sav - ing love of Christ be the mea - sure of our lives; we be -
B♭/F(G)
Fsus4(D)
1.
B♭/D(G/B)
F/A(D/F♯)
lieve You're all to us.
D.C.(v.2)
2.
D.S.
2. On - ly us. Let the

3.
Bb(G)
Bbsus2+4(G) Bb(G)
Mid section
Eb(C)
Gm(Em)
us.
You're all to
F(D)
Bb(G)
Eb(C)
Gm(Em)
F/A(D/F#)
Bb(G)
us, You're all to us, You're
1.
Eb(C)
Gm(Em)
Eb(C)
F(D)
all to us, yes, You are.
Bb(G)
(Optional)
F/A(D/F#)
Bb(G)
(You're all to us, You're all to us.) You're
2.
Cm7(Am)
Bb/D(G/B)
Eb(C)
F(D)
Bb(G)
all to us, You are.

2. Only Son of God sent from Heaven,
Hope and mercy at the cross.
You are everything, You're the promise,
Jesus, You are all to us.

3. When this passing world is over
We will see You face to face,
And forever we will worship;
Jesus, You are all to us.

2506. Prepare the way

Ps 24:7-8; 100:5; Is 6:3; 63:1; Mt 3:3

A A/C♯ D2 Bm7
is full of His glo - ry, cre - a - tion calls: 'Pre-pare
A/E E A A/C♯ D2
the way.' His love en-du - reth for-e - ver, His pow'r
F♯m7 A/C♯ D Esus4 E A A/C♯
is with - out an end, His strength is vic - to-ry's trea-
Last time to Coda
D2 Bm7 Esus4
- sure; let all who call His name pre-pare the way.
1.
A E/A D2 A E/A D
D.C.

2.
Bm7 A E/G♯ A Bm7 D/A A E/G♯ F♯m
Mid section
Let the
Bm A E/G♯ A Bm A
King of glo - ry en - ter in, let the King of glo - ry en-
1.
E/G♯ F♯m
2.
E/G♯ F♯m D2
- ter in. Let the - ter in. Who is this King of glo-
Esus4 E
D.S. al Coda
Coda
Esus4 E
- ry? The Lord,
pre-pare the way.
A E/A D2 A E/A D2 A

2507. Raise up, raise up the standard

Ps 149:8; Jer 51:27; Mt 5:3; Lk 1:79; 4:18; 2 Cor 4:6; Gal 4:4; Heb 13:8

Music & chorus: Godfrey Birtill

D
E
A
Yes - ter - day, to - day, for - e - ver the same.
D
E
A
(Fine)
Yes - ter - day, to - day, for - e - ver the same.
(v.2)
Verse
A
D
1. Hear the glad sound, the Sa-viour comes, the Sa-viour pro-mised long.
A
D
Let ev-'ry heart pre-pare a throne and ev - 'ry voice a song.

2. He comes the broken heart to bind,
The bleeding soul to cure;
And with the riches of His grace,
To bless the humble poor.
He turns the darkness into light
He clears the mental ray,
And on the eye long closed in night
He pours celestial day.

Phillip Doddridge (1702–51)
Adpt. Godfrey Birtill

2508.
Rebuild Your temple
(Kingdom come)
2 Chron 7:1; Mt 6:10; Lk 5:38; Jn 15:2; Acts 15:16
Capo 4 (C)
Andy Flannagan
Steadily, with a strong beat
Verse
E(C) A/E(F/C) B/E(G/C)
1. Re-build Your tem-ple, O mer-ci-ful God,
Re-vive this bo-dy, O Kiss of Life,
re-store this na-tion, please.
re-new our vi-sion, please.
Re-kin-dle em-bers once burn-ing with heat,
Cre-ate new wine-skins to car-ry new blood;
1. 2.
F♯m7(Dm) C♯m7(Am) Bsus4(G) F♯m7(Dm) A(no3rd)(F)
re-turn us to our knees.
would You Your truth re-lease?
B(G) Chorus A(F) E(C) B(G) A(F)
Let Your king-dom come, Your will be done on

F♯m7(Dm)
C♯m7(Am)
Bsus4(G)
B(G)
earth as it is in heav - ven. Let Your
A(F)
E(C)
G♯(E)
(Am) C♯m
(Am/G) C♯m/B
king - dom come, Your will be done on earth
A(F)
G♯7(E)
1.
C♯m(Am)
B/D♯(G/B) E(C)
as it is in heav'n.
B/D♯(G/B) C♯m7(Am)
D.C.(v.2)
B/D♯(G/B)
2.
C♯m(Am)
D.S.
Now let Your
3.
C♯m(Am)
B/D♯(G/B) E(C)
B/D♯(G/B)

2. Reverse this current that's flowing away,
Rebuke our pride, Lord, please.
Remove religion that hides from Your face;
Would You this moment seize?
Reveal the blueprints to where You would lead,
Release dry wood to die.
Redeem Your children as promised of old;
For them, to You we cry.

2509. Redeemed, from the empty way of life

Ps 40:2; Mk 6:48; Jn 10:9; Gal 3:13; 1 Tim 1:19; 1 Pet 1:18-19

Gently, swung 16ths

Godfrey Birtill

G
C2
D
I've got to get to You; re - vive, re - store, re - new me.
Em7
D/F♯
C
D
Chorus
Don't wan-na get my faith ship-wrecked, with-out You I'm a mess. O
G
D/F♯
Em
C
G
D/F♯
Je - sus, I'm cra - zy for You. Je -
Em
C
G
D/F♯
sus, I'm des-p'rate for You. Je - sus, Je - sus,
Em7
C
G
D/F♯
Je - sus, come and get me. O Je - sus, Je - sus,

2. Redeemed from the curse of sin and death,
Redeemed, with the chance to start again.
Oh, how I love the word that breaks us free,
O Jesus, You I need.

3. Redeemed from the pit of messy clay.
Redeemed by the power of God's grace.
Oh, how I love to hear my Saviour's Name,
O Jesus, speak again.

2510. Relentless is Your love for me

Ps 36:5; Song 2:16; Mal 3:3; Heb 12:29

Capo 3 (G)

Liz Clarke

Flowing

Verse

B♭/E♭(G/C) E♭(C) (G/C) B♭7/E♭ E♭(C) (G/C) B♭/E♭ E♭(C) (G/C) B♭/E♭

1. Re - lent - less is Your love for me;

Cm7(Am) A♭maj7(F)

I can't con-ceive the rea - son

B♭sus4(G) B♭7sus4(G)

You should love me so. Con -

B♭/E♭(G/C) E♭(C) (G/C) B♭7/E♭ E♭(C) (G/C) B♭/E♭ E♭(C) (G/C) B♭/E♭ Cm7(Am)

sum - ing, like a fire in my heart,

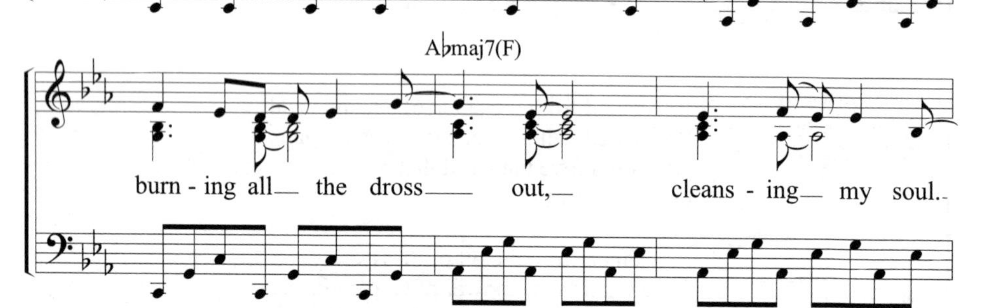

Chorus
B♭sus4(G)
B♭7sus4(G)
B♭/E♭(G/C) E♭(C)
Your love
Cm7(Am)
reach - es to the hea - vens,
reach - es to the val -
A♭(F)
B♭sus4(G)
- leys, reach - es to the sky.
B♭7(G)
B♭/E♭(G/C) E♭(C)
And Your grace and mer - cy o - ver - whelms
Cm7(Am)
A♭(F)
me. I am Yours for - e - ver, for -

2. Pursuing with determination
Your beloved creation,
Never letting go.
Reaching out Your gift of grace
That I might know forgiveness,
Healing my soul.

2511. Resting in Your promise
(Defender)

Ps 17:9; 46:1-2; 91:2; Lk 1:37; 2 Cor 12:9; Phil 4:7; Heb 12:2; 1 Pet 5:7

Steadily

Chris McClarney, John Hartley, Miriam Webster, Michael Tyler, Kees Kraayenoord & Henk Pool

Em7
D
A
Chorus
I will fix my eyes on You. You're my de-fen-
D
Em7
-der, I hide my hope in You; You are the lov-
Bm7
A
Gmaj7
-ing arms my bro-ken heart can run to. And I will re-mem-
Last time to Coda
D
Em7
-ber that there is no-thing You can't do, 'cause You are God
1.,3.
2° D.S.S. al Coda
Bm7
A
Gmaj7
and You are good, and I sur-ren-der: You're my de-fen-

2. You are strong when I am weakest,
You're the peace that passes everything I see:
I put my trust in You.
I'm surrendering completely,
Laying all my cares here at Your feet:
I put my trust in You.

2512. Reveal to us how Your heart beats

(The way)

Lk 15:20; Jn 8:12; 14:6

Unhurried

Cathy Burton

Em
D
C2
- dren who are bro-ken to-day.
Chorus
G
D
C
Je-sus, You are the way to the Fa - ther's arms, a
D
G
D
wel-come em-brace. Je-sus, You are the way to the Fa - ther's heart,
Em
C
G/B
Am
where He lov - ing - ly re - stores; Je-sus,
Last time to Coda
1.
D.C.
C
D
G
C
G/B
Am7
You are the way to the Fa - ther.

2.
G
C2
G/B
Am7
Mid section
- ther.
You are the way,
G
C2
G/B
You are the truth,
You are the light,
Je-
1.-3.
Am7
4.
D.S. al Coda
Am7
- sus.
You are the way
- sus.
Coda
G
C
G/B
Am
- ther.
to the Fa - ther.
G
C
G/B
Am7

2513.
Rising up like a tide
(Victorious)
Heb 12:1
Capo 3 (G)
Johnny Parks
& Matt Redman
Expectantly
Verse
B♭(G) E♭(C) B♭(G)
1. Ri - sing up like a tide, it's a sound we can't
(v.2)
E♭(C) F(D) Gm(Em) E♭(C)
hide: this is it. Who can stop this noise?
B♭(G) E♭(C)
See the church through the world with the
B♭(G) E♭(C) F(D)
saints of the past stand-ing strong. Who can
Gm(Em) E♭(C)
stop this noise?

Bridge
E♭(C)
Break

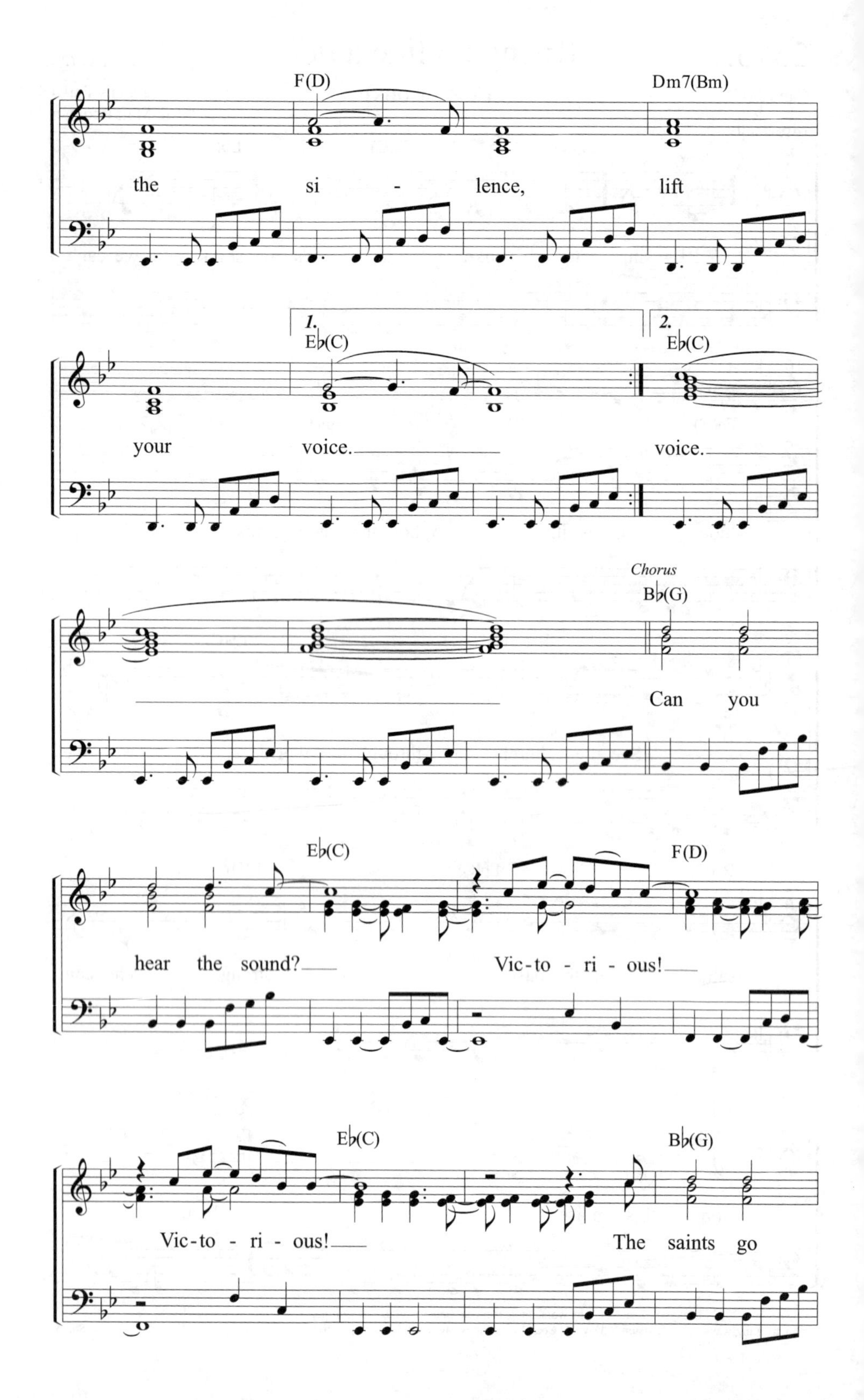
F(D)
Dm7(Bm)
the si - lence, lift
1.
2.
E♭(C)
E♭(C)
your voice.
voice.
Chorus
B♭(G)
Can you
E♭(C)
F(D)
hear the sound?
Vic-to - ri - ous!
E♭(C)
B♭(G)
Vic-to - ri - ous!
The saints go

2. The drums, the dance,
The cry of our hearts rising up;
Who can stop this noise?
Oh, the prayers, the psalms,
The works of our hands are the song.
Who can stop this noise?

2514. Rock of Ages

Ex 17:6; 33:22; Ps 18:2; Is 1:18; Zech 13:1; Jn 13:8; 19:34; 1 Cor 10:4; 13:12; Heb 10:22; 1 Jn 1:7; Rev 19:4

Gently building

Music & additional words: Colin Webster

Verse

C F2 C

1. Rock of A - ges, cleft for me, let me hide my - self in

G/B Am F2 C G/B

Thee; let the wa - ter and the blood from Your wound - ed side which

C Am G/B C

flow'd be for sin the dou - ble cure, save from
(D.S.) eyes shall see the King and the

F2 C Am G/B

wrath and make me pure; cleanse from guilt and cleanse from
glo - ries of His heav'n, there be - hold You face to

C F2 G *Chorus*

sin, white as snow and pure with - in. Rock of
face, saved for e - ver by Your grace.

2. Nothing in my hand I bring,
   Simply to the cross I cling;
   Naked, come to You for dress;
   Helpless, look to You for grace;
   Foul, I to the fountain fly:
   Wash me, Saviour, or I die.
   All my works could not atone,
   You must save, and You alone.

3. While I draw this fleeting breath,
   When my eyes shall close in death,
   When I soar to worlds unknown,
   See You on Your judgment throne;
   Then my eyes shall see the King
   And the glories of His heaven,
   There behold You face to face,
   Saved forever by Your grace.

Augustus Toplady (1740–78)

2515. Search my heart

Ps 139:23; Jn 15:5; Heb 12:2

Joel Houston
& Matt Crocker

Driving rock feel

1.
G
G/D Em9 C
D.C.(v.2)
2.,3.
G
D
You took the cross, You
Last time to Coda
Em7
took my shame, re - stored my life;
Mid section
C
G
C
now I live to wor - ship You.
Em7
D
C
G
With-out You I am no - thing.

Em7
D
C
G
With-out You I am no - thing.
Em7
D
C
With-out You I am no - thing, with-out You
D.S. al Coda
I am no - thing, with-out You I am no - thing.
Coda
C
Tag
G
Lord, I will fol - low You. With-out You
D
I am no - thing. With-out You I am no - thing.

2. Hear my cry and hear my prayer,
Draw me close – I know You're near.
Give me strength and give me grace
To walk with You, Lord, all my days.

2516. See Him high upon the cross

Job 19:25; Ps 22:3; Lk 23:33; 24:6; Phil 2:9

Last time to Coda
G C Dm7+4 C/E
deem - er lives. He lives! He lives! I know that my Re -
1.,3.,5.
2.,4.
G G C Dm7+4
deem - er lives. He deem - er lives to - day.
1. D.C.(v.3)
2.
C/E F2 F2 C
Beau -
1.-3.
4.
D.S. al Coda
Dm7 C/E F2 Fsus4 F
ti - ful Je - sus. He
Coda
G C
deem - er lives. He lives!
2. Buried in the tomb He lay,
All hope – it seemed to fade.
But then upon that glorious day
He rose up from the grave.
3. Now You are exalted above,
Enthroned upon our praise.
The triumph of the cross will resound
Through heaven's endless days.

2517. See Martha weeping at a tomb

(God of compassion)

Ps 23:4; Jn 11:17, 19, 25, 32-33, 35; 2 Cor 1:3-4; Eph 2:4-5

Simon Brading & Graham Kendrick

Capo 6 (C)

Steadily

(v.3)
(v.3)
B(F)
D♯m(Am)
C♯(G)
deep de-spair, pours out her pain, and His heart breaks. Then His
(v.3)
G♯m(Dm)
B(F)
F♯/C♯(C)
an-ger burns in the face of death: Je-sus weeps, Je-sus
C♯(G)
Chorus
G♯m7(Dm)
B/F♯(F)
B(F)
weeps. God of com-pas-sion, God of com-
F♯(C)
C♯(G)
G♯m7(Dm)
pas-sion is here. God of all com-fort
Last time to Coda
B/F♯(F)
B(F)
F♯(C)
is here with us, has come to us;

1.
C♯(G)
D♯m(Am)
C♯(G) D♯m(Am)
C♯(G)
God of com - pas-sion.
B(F)
F♯/A♯(C/E) B(F)
F♯/A♯(C/E)
D.C.(v.3)
2.
C♯(G)
F♯/A♯(C/E)
And
Mid section
B(F)
F♯/A♯(C/E)
B(F)
F♯/C♯(C/G)
now He lives, He is the life, He is the life.
A♯m(Em)
B(F)
F♯/A♯(C/E)
B(F)
A - live in Him, we'll ne-ver die,
F♯/C♯(C/G)
1.
A♯m(Em)
F♯/A♯(C/E)
2.
A♯m(Em)
D.S. al Coda
ne-ver die. And God of com -

2. See Mary stumbling through her tears,
To meet the One who could have saved him.
Why did it have to end this way?
Did He not care her heart was breaking?
And she falls facedown,
In her deep despair;
Pours out her pain,
And His heart breaks.
Then His anger burns
In the face of death:
Jesus weeps, Jesus weeps.

3. There is no pain He does not know,
No road of bitterness or sadness,
No depths of sorrow we can go;
He walks the valley there beside us.
Let us lift our eyes,
Look into the face
Of a God who knows,
A God who weeps.
And His voice cries out
In the darkest place:
'I am the life, I am the life.'

2518. See the stricken boat

(The man who calmed the sea)

Mt 27:45, 51; Mk 4:37-39, 41; 5:22-23, 36, 41; 8:34; 24:2; Acts 2:24; 2 Cor 12:9

Stuart Townend
& Gary Sadler

Steadily

Verse D(no3rd) Bm7 Asus4 Em7 Gsus2 Asus4

(Small notes v.1)

1. See the stric - ken boat as it is tossed up-on the sea;

D(no3rd) Bm7 Asus4 (Small notes v.1) D(no3rd) D/F♯

hear the fear - ful cries that wake the man from Ga - li - lee. He

(Small notes vv.2 - 4.)

G D(no3rd) D/F♯ G A(add4)

stands be-fore the rag - ing, speaks peace and har - mo - ny:

D(no3rd) Bm7 Asus4 D(no3rd)

winds and waves o - bey, He is the man who calmed the sea.

(Small notes vv.2 - 4.)

1. D A7 D A7 D.C.(v.2) 2.,3.,4. *Chorus*

And

Em7
D/F♯
G
A(add4)
as she stands be - fore them, what joy from a - go - ny! He's the
Em7
D/F♯
A7 D/A A
1.,2.
D13
Mas - ter and the Ma - ker, He's the man who calmed the sea.
D.C.(v.3.,4.)
3.
D
A7
D
A7
D13
Tag
sea. I'll
Cmaj7
Bm7
Am7
Bm7
trust You for to - mor - row and seek You for to - day, for You're the
Em7
F
G
Am7
C
Mas - ter and the Ma - ker, You're the man who calms the

2. Hear among the crowds
   A desperate father's anguished plea:
   'Heal my dying child,'
   He begs the man from Galilee.
   With words that banish sorrow:
   'Don't fear, but just believe...
   Daughter - live again!'
   Commands the man who calmed the sea.

3. Feel the bitter pall
   That shrouds the hill of Calvary;
   High upon the cross
   There hangs the man from Galilee.
   The earth it quakes with sorrow,
   The sky grows dark with grief;
   All creation mourns
   To lose the man who calmed the sea.

   (Chorus 2)
   But no, death could not hold Him,
   The stone is rolled away!
   For He's the Master and the Maker,
   He's the man who calmed the sea.

4. Now I hear the call
   That echoes down through history:
   'Come, deny yourself,
   Take up your cross and follow Me.
   Through every joy and sorrow
   My grace is all you'll need.
   Trust Me in the storm,
   For I'm the man who calms the sea.'

   (Chorus 3)
   No fear shall overwhelm me,
   For, Lord, I do believe
   You're the Master and the Maker,
   You're the man who calms the sea.

2519.
Servant and King
(Love come down)
Mt 1:23; 12:21; Mk 10:45; Lk 1:35; Jn 8:12; 15:15; 1 Cor 10:4; Rev 22:13
Capo 3 (G)
Eghan Heaslip & David Ruis
Steadily
Verse
(v.2)
B♭(G)
1. Ser - vant and King, Sa - viour and Friend, the
E♭(C)
Gm(Em)
Son of God, the Son of man. Je - sus, Im - ma -
(v.2)
F/A(D)
E♭(C)
F(D)
- nu - el, the Light of the World re - vealed.
B♭(G)
Chorus
E♭(C)
We will tell the sto - ry, we will sing the

Gm(Em)
Dm(Bm)
Gm(Em)
song: the pro-mise of sal - va-tion, jus-tice for all; the
Last time to Coda
1.
Eb(C)
Bb(G)
Fsus4(D)
reign of our God, love come down.
F(D)
Bb(G)
C7sus4(A)
Gm(Em)
Eb2(C)
D.C.(v.2)
2.
Bb/D(G)
Eb2(C)
Fsus4(D)
F(D)
Mid section
Let the peo -
Eb(C)
Bb(G)
Gm(Em)
- ple of God sing, let the peo - ple of God

2. Rock of Ages, beginning and end,
The hope of all nations is coming again.
Jesus, Immanuel,
The Light of the World to come.

2520. Shall I take from Your hand Your blessings?

(As long as You are glorified)

Job 2:10; Ps 131:2; Mt 6:10; Jn 15:10; Phil 4:11-12

Mark Altrogge

Am G/B C2
trust when I reap a har - vest, but when
G/B D
Chorus
G Am7
win - ter winds blow, then doubt? Oh, let Your will be
G/B C2 G Am7 Dsus4 D
done in me; in Your love I will a - bide. Oh, I
Last time to Coda
G Am7 G/B C2 G D
long for no - thing else, as long as You are glo - ri -
1.
D.C.(v.2)
G Am7 Em7 C2 G D G Gsus4 G
fied. 2. Are You

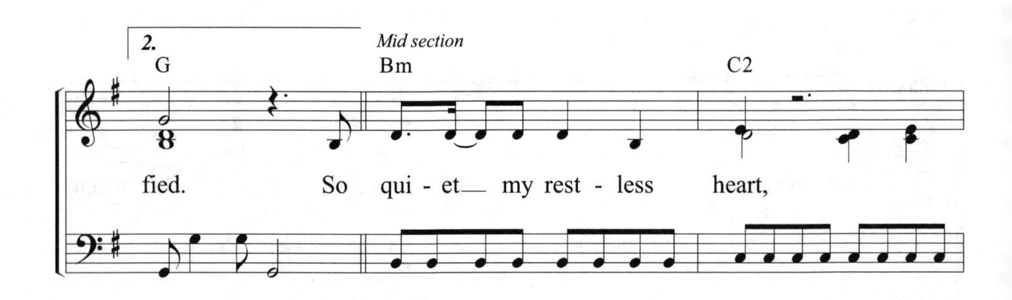

2. Are You good only when I prosper,
And true only when I'm filled?
Are You King only when I'm carefree,
And God only when I'm well?
You are good when I'm poor and needy,
You are true when I'm parched and dry.
You still reign in the deepest valley,
You're still God in the darkest night.

2521. Shining wonders, fields of splendour

Ps 33:8; 150:6; Rev 7:9, 11

(Symphony)

Chris Tomlin, Matt Redman, Jason Ingram, Louie Giglio & Matt Maher

1.
D.C.(v.2)
2.
B/E
A/E
E
stand in awe.
2. My
In
F♯m7
E/G♯
B
sym - pho - ny with all cre - a - ted things,
sing the song that we were made to sing:
we stand in awe,
we stand in awe.
Mid section
A
C♯m7
All the an - gels, all the hea - vens,
In the skies and in the o - ceans,

2. My heart's ovation, Yours forever.
I will sing, sing Your praise.
Let every nation under heaven
Shout Your name, sing Your praise.

2522. Shout the news that God is here

(Shout it!)

Ps 70:4; 96:10-11; Mt 1:23

Geraldine Latty

Latin feel

Verse

Dm A7 Dm A7 Dm A7

1. Shout the news that God is here; let them know, let

Dm A7 Dm A7

ev-'ry-one know. The si-lenced voice can sing a-gain;

Dm A7 Dm

let them know, let ev-'ry-one know.

Chorus

A7 Dm A7

Shout it – let the sky give voice. Shout it – let the earth ap-plaud.

Dm A7 C7 B7(♭5) B♭7 A7

Shout it – let the sea make noise. For our God is

2. Shout the news that God is here;
Let them know, let everyone know.
The ones abandoned found again;
Let them know, let everyone know.

3. Shout the news that God is here;
Let them know, let everyone know.
The hopeless can believe again;
Let them know, let everyone know.

2523.
Spirit, break out
Lk 11:2; Eph 2:14
Capo 4 (G)
Luke Hellebronth, Myles Dhillon,
Tim Hughes & Ben Bryant
Quite slow
(5th time)
Chorus
E(C)
F♯(D)
(3° sing 8va)
Spi - rit, break out,
break our walls down.
Spi - rit, break out,
G♯m(Em)
B2/D♯(G/B)
break our walls down.
E(C)
F♯(D)
Spi - rit, break out,
Spi - rit, break out,
hea - ven come down.
Last time to Coda
G♯m(Em)
B2/D♯(G/B)
1°, 4° & 5° D.C.
hea - ven come down.

E(C)
Verse
F♯(D)
1. Our Fa - ther, all of hea - ven roars Your
G♯m(Em)
B/D♯(G/B)
name; sing loud - er, let this place e - rupt with
E(C)
F♯(D)
praise. Can you hear it? The sound of hea - ven touch - ing
G♯m(Em)
earth, the sound of hea - ven touch - ing
1.
E(C)
earth. Our Fa - ther,
2.,3.
E(C)
D.S. al (Coda)
earth. Spi - rit, break out,

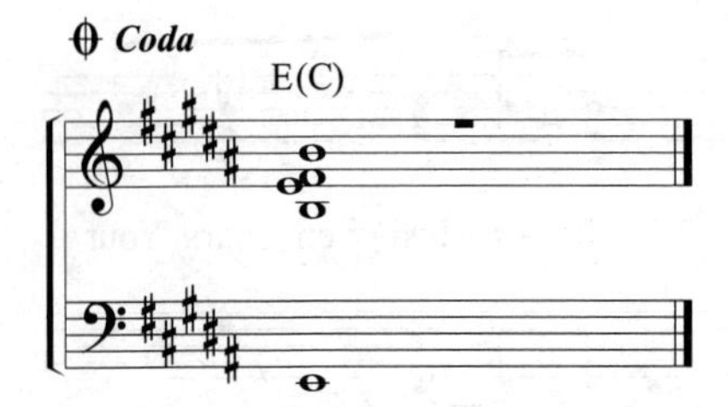

2. King Jesus, You're the name we're lifting high.
Your glory – shaking up the earth and skies.
Revival – we want to see Your kingdom here,
We want to see Your kingdom here.

2524. Spirit, come

Ezek 37:5; Lk 3:16

Nick J. & Becky Drake

Am
G
Am
F
D.C.
guide us through the night;
Spi - rit of the Lord.
Dm
Am
C
G
(1° omit L.H.)
Dm
Am
C
1.
G
Breathe on us, Spi-rit of God.
2.
Mid section
F
Come like a fire, burn like a flame,
Am7
G
o - pen our hearts for more of You a - gain.

Am7
F
Come like a fire,
burn like a flame,
(2° Am7)
C
G
o - pen our hearts
for more of You
a - gain.
(small notes 2°)
1.
Am7
Come like a fire,
2.
Am
C F G
C F G C F G Am C F G

2525. Spirit, fall

Ezek 37:5; Jn 15:26; Acts 2:2; 1 Jn 4:14

Capo 3 (G)

Jason Ingram, Louie Giglio, Kristian Stanfill & Daniel Carson

Worshipfully

Cm7(Am)
Gm(Em)
B♭(G)
1.-3.
F(D)
Oh, oh, oh.
4.
Mid section
F(D)
Cm7(Am)
Gm(Em)
F(D)
Oh, come, mag-ni-fy the Son, Sa-viour of the
E♭(C)
B♭(G)
1.,3.,5.
Gm(Em)
F(D)
2.
D.S.
Gm(Em)
F(D)
world, the hope for ev - 'ry-one. Oh, ev - 'ry-one.
4.
D.C.
Gm(Em)
F(D)
ev - 'ry - one. Spi - rit,
6.
Gm(Em)
F(D)
E♭2(C)
B♭(G)
ev - 'ry - one.

2526. Spirit of God

(Wait for You)

Ps 130:5; Ezek 37:5

Eoghan Heaslip
& David Ruis

With intensity

Verse

Dmaj7

1. Spi - rit of God, fall in this place;

F♯m7

move in our hearts, come have Your way. We will

Dmaj7

wait for You, Spi-rit,

F♯m7 E/G♯ *1st time D.C.(v.2)*

wait for You.

Chorus A E/G♯ D2

Come, O come and breathe on us.

Esus4 E7 A E/G♯
Come, we're hun-
D2 E 1. D2
gry for Your touch a-gain.
D.C.(v.1) 2.,3.
F♯m7 G6(9) Bm7
1st time D.S.
F♯m7 G
A
2. Open our eyes,
Help us to see,
We need Your voice;
O Spirit, speak.
We will wait for You,
Spirit, wait for You.

2527. Spirit of heaven

(Christ in me)

Rom 3:22; 1 Cor 3:15; Gal 4:19; Col 1:27; Heb 4:16

Keith Getty & Stuart Townend

With a lilting feel

2. Spirit of beauty and holiness,
Come refine with fire from above,
Till I am cast in Your righteousness,
And I love the things that You love.

3. Breathe Your forgiveness when darkness falls
And my heart is heavy with sin;
Fill me with faith for the higher cause
Of the ceaseless praise of the king.

2528. Standing on this mountain top

(Never once)

1 Sam 7:12; 1 Cor 1:9

Capo 3 (G)

Matt Redman, Jason Ingram & Tim Wanstall

Moderately

Gm(Em)
e - ver walk a - lone, ne - ver once did You
breath - ing in Your grace, e - ver - more we'll be
E♭(C)
B♭(G)
leave us on our own. You are faith - ful,
breath - ing out Your praise. You are faith - ful,
1.
Gm(Em)
F(D)
D.C.(v.2)
God, You are faith - ful.
2.-4.
2nd time D.S. (chor 2) al Coda
Gm(Em)
F(D)
E♭(C)
B♭(G)
God, You are faith - ful. You are faith - ful,
Last time to Coda
Gm(Em)
F(D)
God, You are faith - ful.

Mid section
E♭(C)
F(D)
Scars and strug-gles on the way,
but with joy our hearts can say,
Gm(Em)
F(D)
ne-ver once did we e-ver walk a-lone.
E♭(C)
F(D)
Car-ried by Your con-stant grace,
held with-in Your per-fect peace,
Gm(Em)
F/A(D/F♯)
ne-ver once, no, we ne-ver walk a-lone.
D.S. al Coda
Coda
F(D)
faith - ful.

God, who has called you into fellowship with his Son Jesus Christ our Lord, is faithful.

1 CORINTHIANS 1:9

2529. Stand up, come on, stand your ground

Capo 2 (Em)

Neh 4:14; Ps 57:8; Is 63:1; Rom 8:31; Eph 6:13

Moderately

Graham Kendrick

F♯m7(Em)

1. Stand up, come on, stand your ground.

(Gtr)

Stand up, come on,

don't back down.

(v.2) 𝄋𝄋 F♯m7(Em)

Rise up,

come on, side by side.

(v.2)

(v.2) (v.3)

D/F♯(C/E)

Wake up,

B/F♯(A/E)
Bridge
come on, don't stand by. For our God is
3° to Coda 1
E(D)
D(C)
D2(C)
strong to save; why should we be a - fraid?
Chorus
A(G)
E2/G♯(D/F♯)
Stand up and fight for your sis-ters, fight for your bro-thers,
Last time to Coda 2
F♯m7(Em)
E(D)
D2(C)
fight for your homes, your sons and your daugh-ters. Stand up, come on,
1.
D.C.(v.2)
F♯m7(Em)
let's take some ground.

2.,4.
D.S. (Ch. 2)
3.
F♯m7(Em)
Stand up and fight __ let's take some ground. __
3. Hands up, come on
F♯m/E(Em/D)
Dmaj9(C)
ho - ly hands, join up, pray - ing
B/D♯(A/C♯)
D.S.S. al Coda 1
Coda 1
D2(C)
'cross the land.
Ev - 'ry - bo - dy stand up,
ev - 'ry - bo - dy stand up,
ev - 'ry - bo - dy stand up,

2. Speak up, come on, make some noise.
Cry out where they have no voice;
For justice, come on, fight to win.
For mercy, come on, muscle in.

(Chorus 2)
Stand up and fight
For the orphans,
Fight for the widows,
Fight for the truth
To shine in the shadows.
Stand up, come on,
Let's take some ground.

3. Hands up, come on, holy hands;
Join up, praying 'cross the land.
Lift up, honour Jesus' name;
Look up, never be ashamed.

2530. Still, my soul, be still

Ps 31:14; 51:10; 62:1-2, 5; Eph 6:16; 1 Jn 2:24

Keith & Kristyn Getty
& Stuart Townend

Quietly & unrushed

2. Still, my soul, be still;
Do not be moved
By lesser lights and fleeting shadows.
Hold on to His ways,
With shield of faith
Against temptation's flaming arrows.

3. Still, my soul, be still;
Do not forsake
The truth you learned in the beginning.
Wait upon the Lord,
And hope will rise
As stars appear when day is dimming.

2531. Still You speak

1 Sam 3:10; Is 26:3; 1 Cor 13:12; Heb 12:2; Jas 1:22

2. Still You speak,
   If only we would listen,
   Through the wars and conflicts of our time.
   Lord, if each day,
   We'd kneel and pray to You,
   What wisdom we could find.

3. Still You speak,
   If only we would listen,
   Through the creeds and doctrines that divide.
   Lord, teach us still,
   To seek Your will and let
   Your voice speak through our lives.

4. Still You speak,
   If only we would listen,
   Through the years that come and go so fast.
   Lord, may Your ways
   Shape all our days until
   We see Your face at last.

2532. Surrounded by forces too strong

(Greater is He)

Capo 4 (C)

Rock

Is 43:2; 2 Cor 4:7-8; Phil 2:9; Col 1:27; 1 Jn 4:4

Seth Mosley & Peter Furler

E(C)
Asus2(F)
and we don't fear what is to come, 'cause the bat -
B(G)
Chorus
E(C)
- tle's al - rea - dy been won.
Great - er is He that is in
A(F)
C♯m(Am)
B(G)
us than he that is in the world.
A(F)
1.
E(C)
Christ in us, the hope of glo - ry.
A(F)
D.S. (v.2)
2.
A(F)
Oh, Christ in us, the

E(C)
A(F)
E(C)
hope of glo - ry,
the hope of glo - ry,
A(F)
C♯m(Am)
A(F)
the hope of glo - ry,
the hope of glo -
E(C)
A(F)
E(C)
- ry.
the hope of glo - ry.
E(C)
Verse
Asus2(F)
E(C)
Asus2(F)
2. His name is love,
His name is po - wer-ful.
E(C)
Asus2(F)
B(G)
He is stron - ger than death,
His name is a-bove ev-'ry o - ther.

When you pass through the waters, I will be with you; and when you pass through the rivers, they will not sweep over you. When you walk through the fire, you will not be burned; the flames will not set you ablaze.

ISAIAH 43:2

2533. Take me to that secret place

(Draw me unto You)

1 Kings 19:12; Ps 63:1, 5; Song 1:4

Prayerfully

Paul Oakley, Andy Ferrett
& Marc James

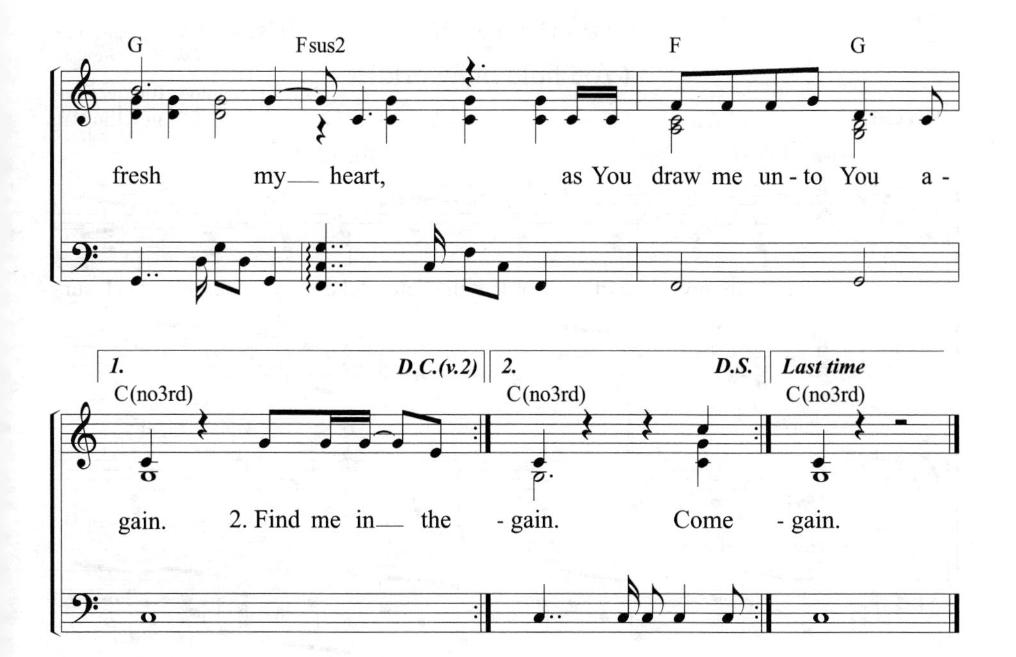

2. Find me in the secret place,
Waiting for Your presence here.
Come nourish me and make me whole;
Draw me unto You again.

2534. Take my heart
(You hold my world)

Ps 46:10; Mt 6:14; Jn 10:28; Rom 12:1; 1 Pet 5:7

Israel Houghton, Tommy Sims & Aaron Lindsay

Emaj7/G♯ E F♯ G♯m7 B F♯/A♯ B/D♯
God, and know that You are
Chorus
E F♯/E E B B/D♯
God. You hold my world in Your hands,
E F♯ G♯m7
You hold my world in Your hands, and I am a-mazed at Your
B/D♯ E G♯m7 F♯/A♯
love; I am a-mazed that You love me.
B B/D♯
You hold my world in Your hands,

E
Gdim7
G♯m7
F♯ E
You hold my world in Your hands, and I'm not a-fraid:
B/D♯
E
F♯sus4
F♯
my world is safe in Your hands, oh, in Your
1.
D.C.(v.2)
E
B
G♯m7
F♯
Emaj7/G♯
B2/D♯
F♯maj7/A♯
hands.
2
E
B
G♯m7
F♯
E
B/D♯
F♯maj7/A♯
hands.
E
B
G♯m7
F♯
Emaj7/G♯
B/D♯
F♯maj7/A♯

Mid section
B
E/B
You won't let go of me,
You won't let go of me,
B
A2
You won't let go of me,
You won't let go,
1.
2.
F♯/A♯
F♯/A♯
B
ne-ver let go.
ne-ver let go.
You won't let go of me,
Emaj7
Gdim7
You won't let go of me,
G♯m7
B/D♯
Amaj9
You won't let go of me,
You won't let go,

2. Take my life,
Lord, will You take my life.
You are the reason that I live.
I believe You have forgiven me,
And by Your grace I will forgive,
And know that You are God,
And know that You are God.

'I give them eternal life, and they shall never perish; no-one can snatch them out of my hand.'

JOHN 10:28

2535. Teach me, Lord Jesus

Graham & Alyson Tucker

2. Help me to love, Lord, the way that You do:
Pure and unselfish, humbled anew.
Lord, I pray, show me Your way,
So that I may be more like You.

2536. Thank You

Eph 1:7

Capo 1 (C)

Mark Beswick
& Howard Francis

2. For all the times I thought to complain,
Prayers unanswered again;
Remind me of the blood that You gave
To erase all of my mistakes,
And for all the reasons why
I forget to tell You I thank You.

2537. Thank You, Father, for Your unending grace

(Keep me close)

Capo 1 (D)

Is 53:5; Eph 1:7

Gareth Scott

Simply

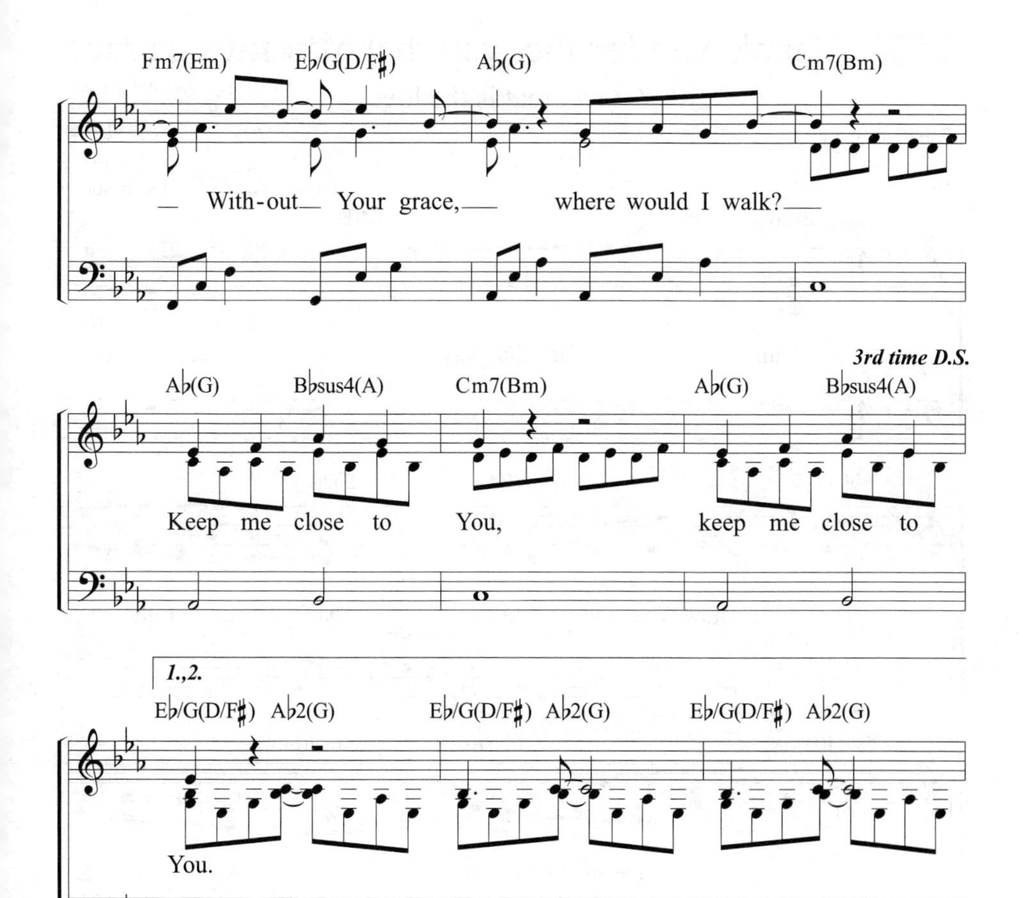

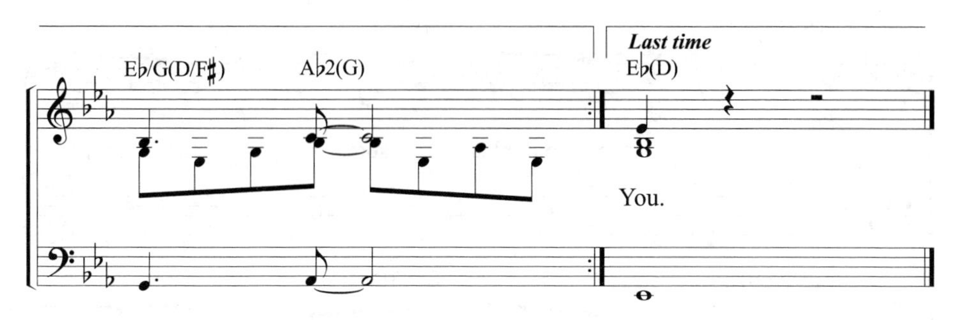

2. You are holy,
Yet You reached out to us.
Through love You showed
Forgiveness at the cross.

3. Thank You, Saviour,
For taking my sin's place.
With arms wide You shouldered
The weight of all my shame.

2538. Thank You for the way that You love us

(How great is the love)

Is 53:4; Jn 1:3; 19:17; Acts 2:24; 1 Cor 7:23; Eph 2:5; 1 Pet 1:18; 1 Jn 3:1

Capo 3 (G)

Paul Baloche, Meredith Andrew & Jacob Sooter

Steadily

E♭2(C)
Fsus4(D)
F(D)
B♭(G)
B♭sus2(G)
(small notes v.2)
Thank You for the way that You love us.
B♭sus4(G)
Chorus
B♭(G)
F(D)
Je - sus, faith - ful King, Lord, with grate -
Gm7(Em)
E♭(C)
- ful hearts we sing, how great is the love,
B♭/F(G/D)
F(D)
Gm7(Em)
E♭2(C)
how great is the love of our Sa - viour.
Fsus4(D)
B♭(G)
The weight of the cross, the curse of our shame;

F(D)
Gm7(Em)
You car-ried it all and rose from the grave.
Eb2(C)
Bb/F(G/D)
Fsus4(D)
How great is the love, how great is the love of our Sa-
Last time to Coda
1° D.C.(v.2)
Gm7(Em) Eb2(C) Fsus4(D) F(D) Gm7(Em) Eb2(C) Fsus4(D) F(D)
- viour, of our Sa - viour.
Mid section
Eb2(C)
F(D)
Thank You for the way that You love
1.
Gm7(Em)
Bb/D(G/B)
Eb2(C)
us, how You love us. Thank You for the way

2. Thank You for the grace
That has saved us;
You forgave us.
Thank You for the way
You have freed us.
We have been ransomed,
We've been rescued,
We've been purchased
With the price of Your own life.
Thank You for the way
That You love us.

2539.
The air is filled with angels
(Blessing and honour)
1 Cor 13:12; Col 1:16-17; Rev 1:8, 16-17; 4:10-11
Capo 3 (D)
Vicky Beeching & Jonny & Sarah MacIntosh
Moderately, building
Verse
F(D)
1. The air is filled with an - gels who
Dm7(Bm)
speak and shout Your name. The
Gm7(Em)
at-mos-phere is chan-ging
C(A)
as e - ter-ni-ty in-vades, and
F(D)
sud-den-ly a-bove us
Dm7(Bm)
the floor of hea - ven breaks.
Gm7(Em)
As Your Spi-rit falls down, we will
C2(A) C(A) Csus4(A)
Chorus
say: bless-ing and

Fsus4(D)
F(D)
Dm7(Bm)
ho - nour, glo-ry and pow - er
G7(E)
B♭(G)
be to Your name, be to Your name. All of the
Fsus4(D)
F(D)
Dm7(Bm)
prai - ses through-out the ag - es
G7(E)
B♭2(G)
C(A)
be to Your name, be to Your name, for-e-ver
F(D)
Dm(Bm)
C(A)
more.

2. One day we will see You shining like the sun,
Face to face with beauty, eye to eye with Love.
Standing with the elders, we will throw our crowns
At the feet of Jesus as we shout:

I am the Alpha and the Omega, says the Lord God, who is, and who was, and who is to come, the Almighty.

REVELATION 1:8

2540. The Alpha, Omega, beginning and end

(All things made new)

1 Pet 2:9; Rev 21:4-6, 18, 23; 22:1, 12-13, 16

Rhythmic

Paul Field
& Jonathan Veira

Verse

E A/E E

1. The Al - pha,— O - me - ga,— be - gin - ning— and end; He'll make
God will— be faith - ful,— on Him we— de - pend;

B E

all things— new, He'll make all things— new. Our

1. *2.*

B E D A E

all things— new. All things made— new,

Chorus

D A B E

all things made— new. Cre - a - tor— and Sa - viour— re -

A E D A E

turn - ing— a - gain: He'll make all things new, He'll make

2. This beautiful day will put shadows to flight;
He'll make all things new
He'll make all things new.
What wonder will be in that glorious sight;
He'll make all things new,
He'll make all things new.

(Chorus 2)
All things made new,
All things made new.
We'll walk out of the darkness
And into the light;
He'll make all things new,
He'll make all things new.

3. The river of life flowing out of God's love;
He'll make all things new,
He'll make all things new.
A city of gold built in heaven above;
He'll make all things new,
He'll make all things new.

(Chorus 3)
All things made new,
All things made new.
When Jesus, the bright morning star,
Shines on us,
He'll make all things new,
He'll make all things new.

4. No more to suffer, to fight and to die;
He'll make all things new,
He'll make all things new.
No more will pain leave its mark on our lives;
He'll make all things new,
He'll make all things new.

(Chorus 4)
All things made new,
All things made new.
When God wipes away
Every tear from our eyes,
He'll make all things new,
He'll make all things new.

2541. The die has been cast

Lk 9:62; Rev 17:14

F/A(D/F♯)
B♭(G)
C(A)
I've got to get in the purpose of God. I've got to get up,
F(D)
F/A(D/F♯)
B♭(G)
I've got to get out, I've got to get in the purpose of God.
Last time to Coda
1.
D.C.(v.2)
2.
Mid section
Csus4(A)
C(A)
C(A)
F(D)
B♭(G)
2. Low li-ving no more, Our Lamb has
F(D)
C(A)
F(D)
B♭(G)
F(D)
con - quered; let us fol - low Him, let us fol - low Him.
1.
2.
C(A)
C(A)
F(D)
Our I wan-na run, run, run, run, run,

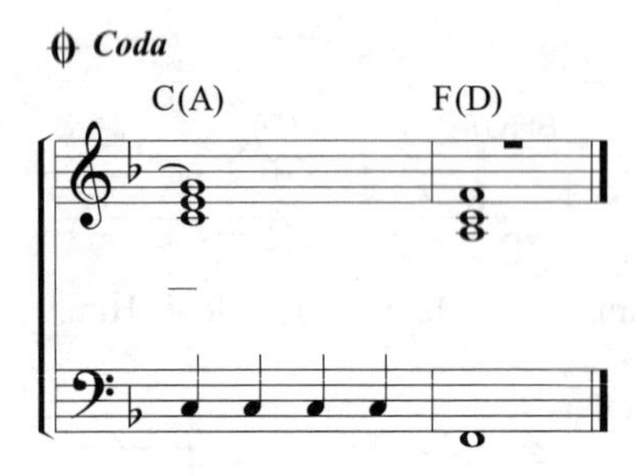

2. Low living no more,
Cheap talk, cheap giving no more.
No colourless dreams;
I'm going forward.
And I don't have to be right,
First, tops or recognised,
And I don't have to lead:
I'm following Jesus.

'No-one who puts his hand to the plough and looks back is fit for service in the kingdom of God.'

LUKE 9:62

2542. The earth cries out

Ps 33:20; 91:2; 115:4; 123:2

Capo 3 (G)

Andy & Wendy Green

Flowing & rhythmic

2. There's pretty things that catch my eye,
Loud voices want attention;
But all we see apart from You
Are feeble imitations.

2543. The Father's Son

(Behold the Lamb)

Mt 1:23; Jn 1:29; 8:12; Eph 1:7; Heb 10:20; Rev 5:12

Thoughtfully

Lauren Keenan

1.,3.,5.,6.
Dmaj7
takes a-way the sin of the world. Be-hold the Lamb
2.
E F♯m7 E/G♯ F♯m7
sin of the world.
D.C.(v.2)
4.,7.
E/G♯
E D
2. You came sin of the world.
F♯m E Bm7 A E/G♯ D
F♯m E Bm
1.
A E/G♯
D.C.(v.3)
3. Most wor -

2. You came to make a way for us,
   Transforming love, eternal grace;
   Upon the cross, redemption's cost:
   Now I am free, Jesus.

3. Most worthy One, upon the throne,
   All power, wealth, wisdom and strength;
   Eternal King, our praise we bring:
   All honour to our God.

2544. The God of time and eternity

(Our God, He reigns)

Mt 28:18; Acts 17:24; 2 Cor 5:21; Col 1:27; 1 Pet 1:24-25; Rev 11:15; 19:6

Capo 2 (Bm)

Rocky

Simon Brading
& Matt Redman

(v.3)

Verse

C♯m(Bm)

1. The God of time and e - ter - ni - ty

(v.3)

A(G)

or - ches - trates all his - to - ry; our God, He reigns for - ev -

(v.3)

B(A) C♯m(Bm)

- er. At His com - mand the whole world was made,

in His love, He came down to save;

A(G)
B(A)
A(G)
our God, He reigns for-ev - er. Our God, He reigns for - e -
F♯(E)
Chorus
B(A)
C♯m(Bm)
- ver. Our God, He reigns, our God, He reigns,
A(G)
E(D)
now and for - ev - er, o- ver all things;
B(A)
C♯m(Bm)
A(G)
the first and last word will al-ways be His.
F♯(E)
A(G)
1.-3.
C♯m(Bm)
Hal - le - lu - jah, praise the God who reigns!

2. The Father's plan of amazing grace,
Pierced hands for a sinful race;
Our God, He reigns forever.
And we exchange through His life and death
Guilty stains for His righteousness;
Our God, He reigns forever.
Our God, He reigns forever.

3. He's seated high in authority
Yet lives inside of you and me;
Our God, He reigns forever.
Earthly power will fade away,
But Jesus' rule – it will never end;
Our God, He reigns forever.
Our God, He reigns forever.

2545. The heavens, horizons of this earth
(Far greater)
1 Kings 8:27; Jer 10:6-7
Capo 3 (C)
Rich White
Positively
Verse
Cm(Am) A♭(F) E♭(C)
The heavens, horizons of this earth
nature, the science of this world
B♭/D(G/B) Fm7(Dm) Cm(Am) B♭(G)
cannot contain You, my God.
cannot restrain You, my God.
1. 2.
A♭(F) Bridge (G/F) B♭/A♭ (F) A♭maj7 B♭(G)
All
Unrivalled, beyond
E♭/G(C/E) A♭(F) (G/F) B♭/A♭ (F) A♭maj7 B♭(G)
equal, You are matchless, God.
Chorus
E♭(C) E♭/D(C/B)
You are far greater, You will forever

Last time to Coda
A♭(F)
Cm(Am)
A♭(F)
B♭(G)
reign o - ver all,
reign o - ver all.
1.
D.C.
2.
Cm(Am)
A♭(F)
E♭(C)
B♭/D(G/B)
A♭(F)
The
E♭(C)
B♭(G)
E♭/G(C/E)
Mid section
A♭(F)
E♭(C)
There is no one like You,
B♭(G)
E♭/G(C/E)
1.-3.
4. D.S. al Coda
God.
There is
Coda
Cm(Am)
A♭(F)
E♭(C)
B♭/D(G/B)
Cm(Am)

2546. The Light of the World

Gen 2:7; Mt 5:14; Lk 19:10; Jn 1:3, 14; 3:3; 8:12; Phil 2:8; 1 Pet 2:9

2. The Light of the World
Now shone as a man,
And walked through the valleys
He'd carved with His hands.
A servant to those
He'd breathed into life,
He felt our injustice
And shared in our strife.

3. The Light of the World
Preached justice for all,
Defying the proud
And defending the poor;
Then humbled Himself
To death on a cross,
To crush the oppressor
And rescue the lost.

4. The Light of the World
Still shines on the earth,
With gifts of forgiveness,
The hope of new birth.
So open your heart,
Don't hide in the night;
Step out of the darkness
And into His light.

2547. The Lord bless and keep you

Num 6:24-26

Noel Richards
& Wayne Drain

1.
2.
D.C.
C
F2
C
F2
C
F
C
G
you.
The
you,
God be
with
Am
F
C
G
C
F2
C
F2
C
you,
God be
with
you.

2548. The Lord is gracious and compassionate

Ps 103:12; 145:8-9

Building in intensity

Graham Ord

Verse

G D
The Lord is gra - cious and com - pas - sion - ate, —

C 1. G Gsus4 2. G D/F♯
slow to an - ger and — rich in love. rich in love.

Em C
The Lord is good to all; — He has com -

G D
pas - sion on all that He has made.

Chorus

G D G/B
As far as the east — is from the west, — that's how

C
G
Gsus4
far He has re-moved our trans - gres-sions from us.

Tag
(Fine)
G
D
G/B
C
G
Gsus4
Praise the Lord, O my soul, praise the Lord.

2549. The Lord is here among us

Ps 18:2-3; 84:5; Is 25:4

(My refuge)

Capo 4 (G)

Claire Hamilton
& David Østby

Gently

B/D♯(G/B)
E(C)
strength is found in You, our strength is found in You a-lone.
F♯sus4(D)
Chorus
E(C)
You are our re - fuge, You are our home,
B/D♯(G/B)
G♯m7(Em)
You are as close as the men-tion of Your
F♯sus4(D)
B/D♯(G/B)
E(C)
name. You are our re - fuge, You are our home,
B/D♯(G/B)
G♯m7(Em)
You are as close as the men-tion of Your

2. The Lord is here among us,
Our fortress and our shield;
A God who gives us courage in the fight.
The Lord is here among us,
Available and true;
A God whose name is worthy to be praised.

The LORD is my rock, my fortress and my deliverer; my God is my rock, in whom I take refuge. He is my shield and the horn of my salvation, my stronghold. I call to the LORD, who is worthy of praise, and I am saved from my enemies.

PSALM 18:2-3

2550. The Lord is our rock

Ps 18:46; 48:1; 139:2; 1 Cor 10:4

2. King of the lost, Lord of the broken,
You know every thought.
You laugh with the joyful and cry with the hurting;
We lift up our voice to You.

2551. The Lord's my Shepherd

(Angel of the Lord)

Ps 18:2; 23:1, 4, 6; 91:9-11; Eph 6:10-11; Phil 4:7; 1 Tim 2:6; 2 Tim 1:7

Miriam Webster

Steadily

Though I walk through the dark val-ley of death, I will

2. The Lord's my refuge,
No evil can come near me,
Dwelling in His secret place.
I put my trust in Him,
He is my shield;
I will let His peace rule in my heart.

3. He ransomed me,
He gave me all authority,
Power, love and a sound mind.
Strong in the Lord
And the power of His might,
I will put on His armour and stand.

(2°)
Chorus
G
Am7
D7sus4
Sure - ly, the an - gel of the Lord is a - round
I am my Fa - ther's child, no e - ne-my can touch
G
Am7
me. I have no cause to fear, my God
me. I will not die, but live to tell
D7sus4
1.,3.
G
2.
G
D.C.(v.3)
will not for - sake me.
what He has done.
4.
G

2552. The love of God

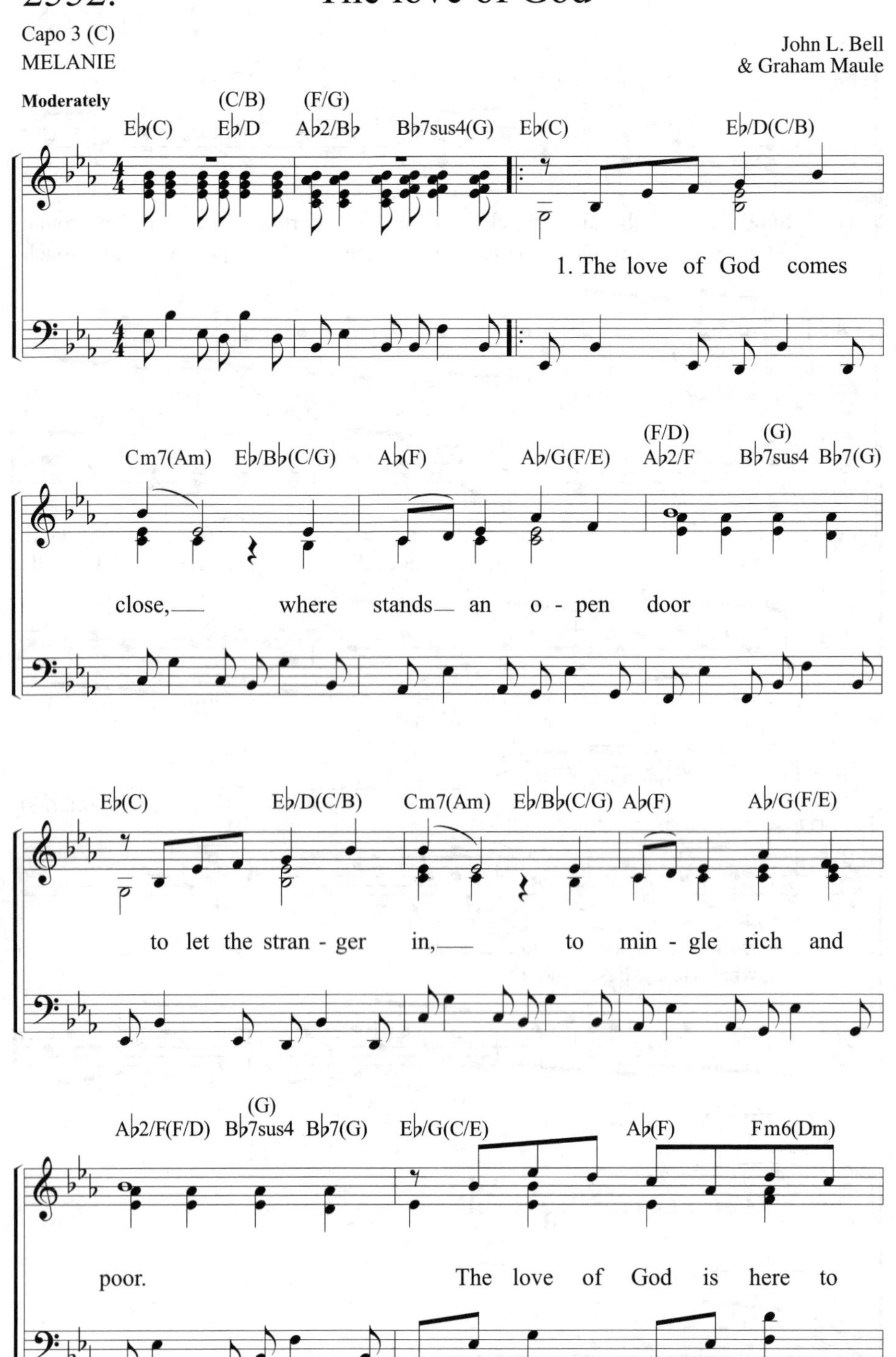

From Enemy of Apathy (Wild Goose Publications, 1988)

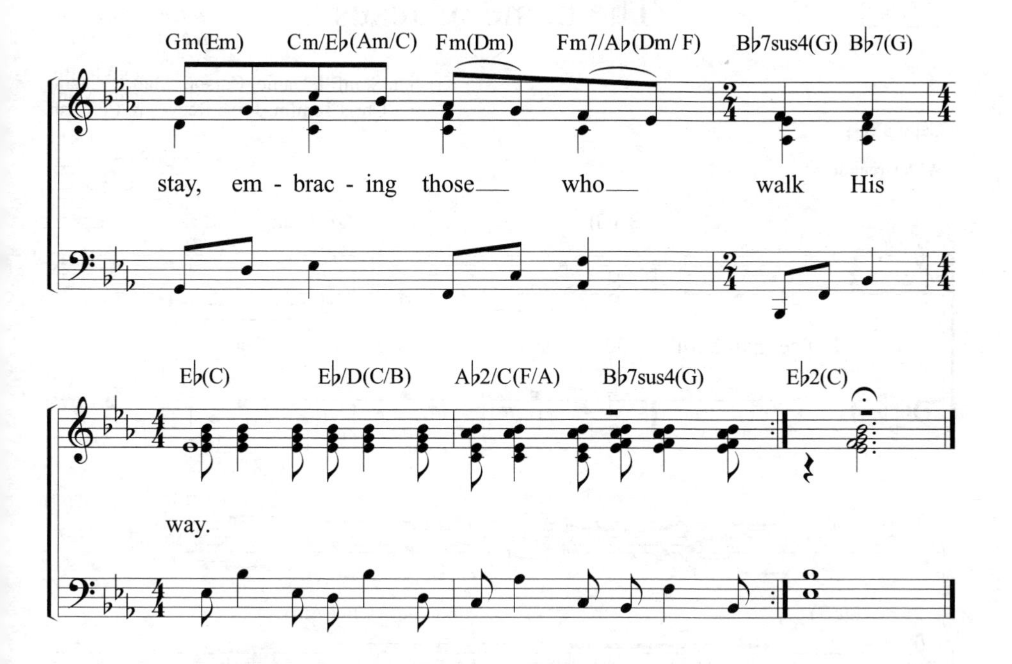

2. The peace of God comes close to those caught in the storm,
   Forgoing lives of ease to ease the lives forlorn.
   The peace of God is here to stay,
   Embracing those who walk His way.

3. The joy of God comes close, where faith encounters fears,
   Where heights and depths of life are found through smiles and tears.
   The joy of God is here to stay,
   Embracing those who walk His way.

4. The grace of God comes close to those whose grace is spent,
   When hearts are tired or sore and hope is bruised or bent.
   The grace of God is here to stay,
   Embracing those who walk His way.

5. The Son of God comes close, where people praise His name,
   Where bread and wine are blest and shared, as when He came.
   The Son of God is here to stay,
   Embracing those who walk His way.

2553. The name of Jesus

Ps 150:6; Prov 18:10; Is 25:4; Lk 4:18; 11:2

Kristian Stanfill, Daniel Carson, Matt Redman, Chris Tomlin, Jesse Reeves & Ed Cash

E♭(C)
po - wer in Your name, there is
Fsus4(D)
1.,2.
F(D)
Chorus
3.
F(D)
po - wer in Your name. In the There is
Gm7(Em)
po - wer in Your name, there is
F/C(D/A)
Chorus
B♭(G)
po - wer in Your name. In the name of Je -
Gm7(Em)
E♭(C)
- sus there is life and healing, chains are bro -

2. The name of Jesus
Is a fortress,
A saving place to run,
A hope unshakeable.

3. Bring salvation,
Bring Your kingdom,
Let all that You have made
Bring glory to Your name.

The name of the LORD is a strong tower; the righteous run to it and are safe.

PROVERBS 18:10

2554. The perfect wisdom of our God

Ps 119:105; Mt 5:45; 26:39; Jn 1:3; Rom 1:20; 12:2; 1 Cor 1:27, 31; Heb 1:3

Capo 3 (G)

Moderately

Stuart Townend
& Keith Getty

2. The matchless wisdom of His ways
That mark the path of righteousness;
His word a lamp unto my feet,
His Spirit teaching and guiding me.
And oh the mystery of the cross,
That God should suffer for the lost,
So that the fool might shame the wise
And all the glory might go to Christ!

3. O grant me wisdom from above,
To pray for peace and cling to love,
And teach me humbly to receive
The sun and rain of Your sovereignty.
Each strand of sorrow has a place
Within this tapestry of grace;
So through the trials I choose to say:
'Your perfect will in Your perfect way.'

2555. There at the cross

Jn 15:13; 17:1; Phil 2:7

Capo 4 (G)

Nick Herbert
& John Peters

Solid rock style

E(C)
F♯(D)
B(G)
F♯/A♯(D/F♯)
E(C)
B(G)
Je - sus. You're the One I a-dore,
Last time to Coda
1.
E(C)
B(G)
E(C)
F♯(D)
B(G)
E(C)
Sa - viour, Sa - viour.
B/A♯(G/F♯)
E(C)
D.C.(v.2)
2.
Mid section
G♯m(Em)
viour. I see You glo-ri-fied
E(C)
B(G)
G♯m(Em)
in the sac - ri-fice. The grea-test act of love is
E(C)
F♯(D)
G♯m(Em)
lay-ing down Your life. I see You glo-ri-fied

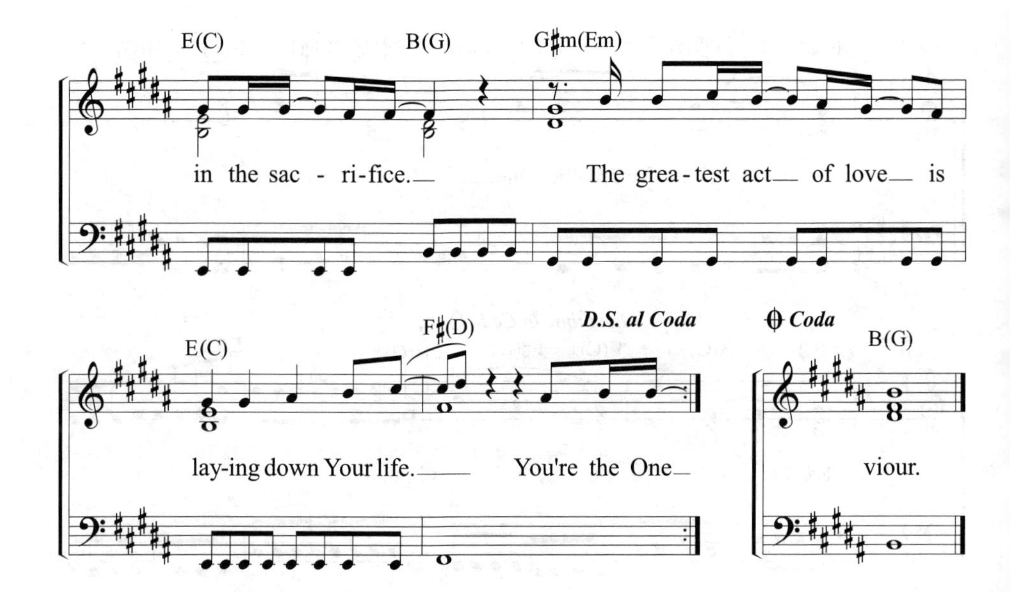

2. Before all time, worshipped in wonder,
Praise of creation and heaven above.
I gaze in awe at Your surrender,
Made Yourself nothing there at the cross.

Jesus... looked towards heaven and prayed: 'Father, the time has come. Glorify your Son, that your Son may glorify you.'

JOHN 17:1

2556.
There is a crimson stream
(Crimson stream)
Is 1:18; 64:6; Lam 3:22-23; Ezek 36:26; Jn 1:4; 8:12; 1 Cor 7:23; 2 Cor 5:21; 1 Jn 1:7
Capo 2 (D)
Reflectively
Paul Oakley
Verse
A2/C♯(G/B) B7sus4(A) E(D) A(G) E(D)
1. There is a crim-son stream that wash-es white as snow,
hope, the light of life, this grace that won't let go,
A2(G) A2/C♯(G/B) B/D♯(A/C♯) C♯m(Bm) A(G)
a love that longs to know me as Your own.
this fire that burns can change a heart of stone.
Bsus4(A)
1. This
2.
A2(G) Chorus
And no-thing can stop this love from reach-ing me.
E(D) Bsus4(A)
A2(G) E(D) A(G) E(D)
No-thing can keep Your blood from clean-sing

2. No shame can keep me bound,
No sin can own the keys;
The price was paid in full to set me free.
No more these filthy rags;
I'm clothed in purity.
My Saviour's righteousness is mine to keep.

2557. There is a day

(His name shall be honoured)

Rom 8:22; Phil 2:10-11; 2 Thess 1:10; I Jn 3:2; Rev 1:7; 7:9

Becky & Nick J. Drake

Steadily

Verse

G/B C(no3rd)

1. There is a day when all will be known,

D G/B C(no3rd)

there is a day when all eyes will see

D Em C

that He is Lord and ru-ler of hea-

D G C

-ven and of earth.

1.

2. Cre-a-tion groans

2.,3.

Chorus

His name shall be ho-

C
D
Em
- noured in all of the world, His name shall be ho -
C
D
Em
- noured in all of the world, His name shall be lift -
G/B
C
D
Em
- ed high and glo - ri - fied, and ho -
1.
C
D
C/G
- noured in all of the world.
D/A
D.C.(v.3 - ch.2)
2.
C
D
3. We join to-day - noured in all of the world.

D.S.
3.
G
C
D
Your name shall be ho - - noured in all of the world.
G
Tag
C
For You are King and You reign
G
D
C
for - e - ver; You are King, the whole world
1.
G
D
2.
G
D
is Yours. You are King, is Yours. You are Je -
Am
G/B
C
D
- sus, and one day all see.

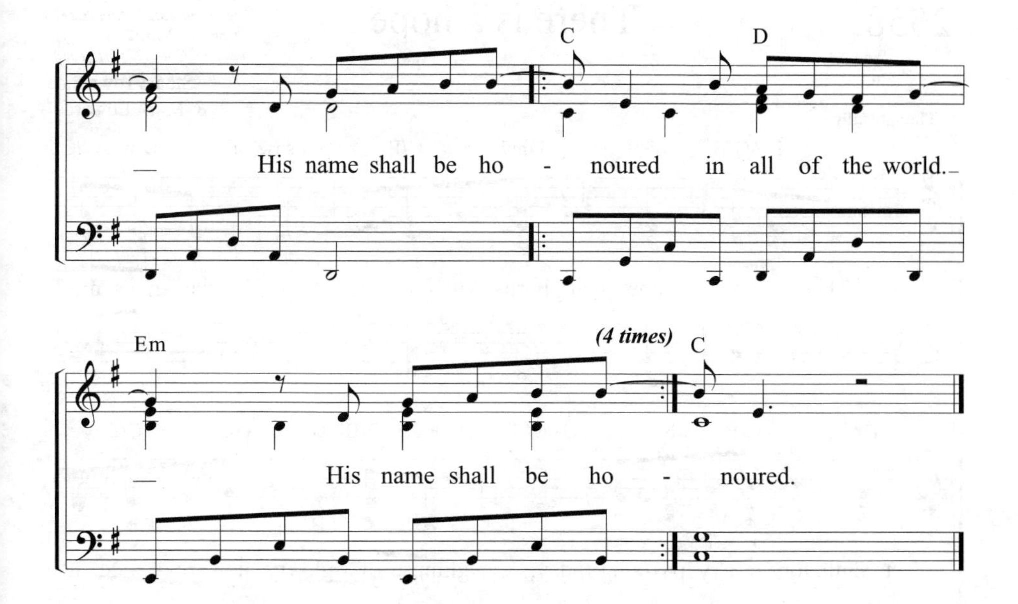

2. Creation groans to see His return,
Our hearts await the glory of God;
He will appear, and we will be like Him when He comes.

3. We join today with nations and saints,
We sing today, declaring: 'You reign!'
Let every voice in unison now confess Your name.

(Chorus 2)
Your name shall be honoured in all of the world,
Your name shall be honoured in all of the world,
Your name shall be lifted high and glorified,
And honoured in all of the world.

2558. There is a hope

Deut 33:27; Rom 8:18; 1 Cor 13:12-13; 2 Cor 1:21; Col 1:27; 1 Pet 1:8

Stuart Townend
& Mark Edwards

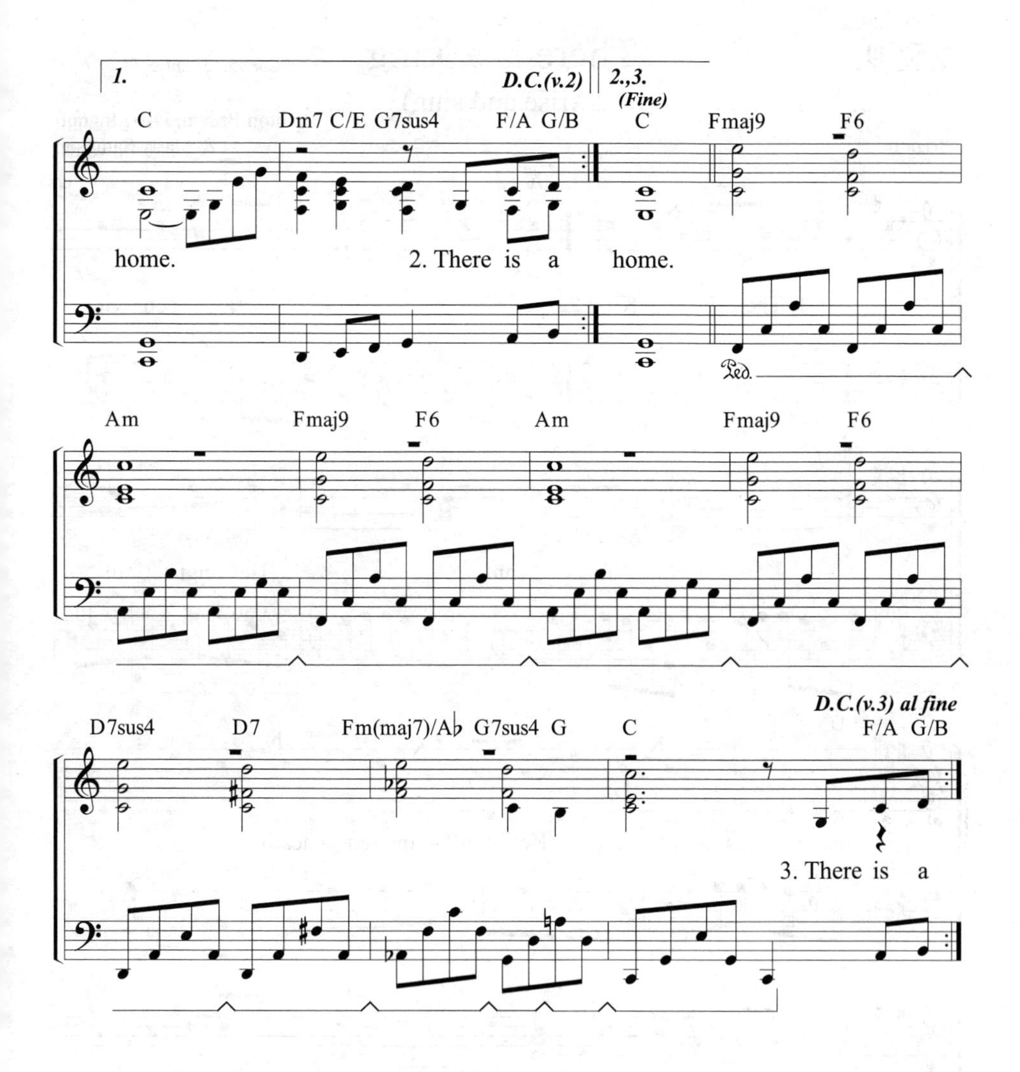

2. There is a hope that lifts my weary head,
   A consolation strong against despair,
   That when the world has plunged me in its deepest pit,
   I find the Saviour there!
   Through present sufferings, future's fear,
   He whispers, 'Courage!' in my ear.
   For I am safe in everlasting arms,
   And they will lead me home.

3. There is a hope that stands the test of time,
   That lifts my eyes beyond the beckoning grave,
   To see the matchless beauty of a day divine
   When I behold His face!
   When sufferings cease and sorrows die,
   And every longing satisfied.
   Then joy unspeakable will flood my soul,
   For I am truly home.

2559. There is a King

(Arise and sing)

1 Cor 15:55; Eph 5:14; Heb 1:3

Brenton Brown, Jason Ingram
& Marty Sampson

A E F♯m7 D
— we will a-rise — and sing. A-rise, -
Last time to Coda
1.
A E F♯m7 D
— we will a-rise — and sing.
D.C.(v.2)
2.,4.
D.S. (al Coda)
3.
D D
2. Come, — a - wake — sing. A-rise, — sing. —
Mid section
A E F♯m7
— Beau - ti-ful, — beau - ti-ful, -
D A E
— there is — not one, — there is — not one — who is — so

1.
F♯m7
D
2.
F♯m7
D
beau - ti-ful,
beau - ti-ful,
D.S.
Coda
D
A-rise,
sing.
A-rise, and sing.
A-rise, and sing.
A-rise, and sing.
A

Verse
(D)
A
F♯m7
2. Come, a - wake, rise from the ground,
E
D
o - pen your eyes and see what you have found.
Bm7
A
F♯m7
Come, a - wake, all you who sleep,
E
D
and search no more, for He is all we need.

2560. There is an everlasting kindness

(The compassion hymn)

Is 25:4; 52:7; 53:4; Mt 8:3; 9:36; Mk 10:14; Lk 23:43; Jn 19:2, 25; Rom 12:1; Eph 1:8; Tit 3:4; Heb 1:3

2. And with compassion for the hurting You reached out Your hand,
As the lame ran to meet You and the dead breathed again.
You saw behind the eyes of sorrow and shared in our tears;
Heard the sigh of the weary, let the children draw near.

3. We stood beneath the cross of Calvary and gazed on Your face,
At the thorns of oppression and and wounds of disgrace;
For surely You have borne our suffering and carried our grief,
As You pardoned the scoffer and showed grace to the thief.

4. How beautiful the feet that carry this gospel of peace
To the fields of injustice and the valleys of need;
To be a voice of hope and healing, to answer the cries
Of the hungry and helpless with the mercy of Christ.

2561. There is a song that must be sung
(Round the earth)

Eph 1:7; Phil 2:10; Rev 5:9; 7:9-10

Tim Hughes
& Eoghan Heaslip

Rock

(v.2, 1°)

A *Verse* D F♯m D **1.** **2.** E *Chorus*

1. There is a song that must be sung,
of how grace and love
have redeemed us.

Our only hope and our only claim
is in Jesus' name
we're forgiven,
forgiven.

(v.2) (v.2)

Let the

(D.S., 1°&3°)
A
D
song go round the earth, sound His prai - ses, tell His worth:
(D.S., 1°&3°) tribe and ev - 'ry tongue join the great and glor - ious song:
Bm
Je - sus is Lord, Je - sus is
D
1.,5.
Asus2 A Asus2 A
Lord!
D.C.(v.2)
Last time to Coda
2.,4.
D.S.
Asus2 A Asus2 A
E
Let ev - 'ry
3.
Mid section
E
F♯m
He is high - er, He is great - er, He is faith-

2. A day will come in history
When all will bow down in worship,
And there with one heart,
There with one voice,
Our song will rise up together, together.

2562. There is Love that came for us

(Stronger)

Lk 19:10; 24:6; Jn 8:32; Phil 2:8; Col 1:27; Heb 7:3

Reuben Morgan & Ben Fielding

With increasing intensity

Am F C
bro - ken, You have saved me. It is writ - ten: 'Christ is
Last time to Coda
1.
G F G Fmaj7 G C/E Cmaj7 Fmaj7 G
ri - sen.' Je - sus, You are Lord of all.
2.
C/E C F Am C/E G/B F
3. No be - all.
Mid section
Am C/E G/B G F
So let Your name be lift - ed high - er,
1.,2.,3.
Am7 G C G
be lift - ed high - er, be lift - ed high - er. So let Your name

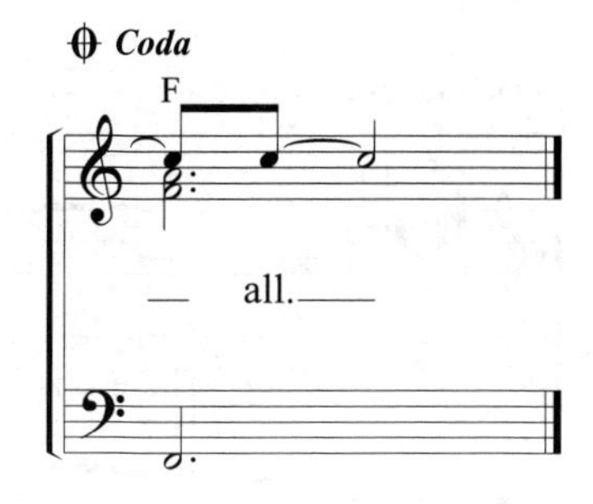

2. Faithfulness none can deny,
Through the storm and through the fire.
There is truth that sets me free:
Jesus Christ, who lives in me.

3. No beginning and no end,
You're my hope and my defence.
You came to seek and save the lost,
You paid it all upon the cross.

2563. There is mercy new today

Ps 131:3; Lk 11:2; Jn 14:6; Gal 5:22; Eph 2:7; Col 1:14; Heb 10:19-20

Moderate rock

Jos Wintermeyer & Nathan & Lou Fellingham

E
A/C♯
You are the God who saves,
D
A/C♯
and You are good. (Yeah) In You our hope
Last time to Coda
1.
D.S. (al Coda)
2.
E
re - mains. You are the Lord
D.C.(v.2)
G
D
3.
Mid section
C
D
Con-fess that Je - sus is the on-

2. There's forgiveness for our sin,
There's acceptance not shame,
There's assurance of new life;
Jesus made the way.
There is hope beyond today,
There is restoration;
There is healing past the grave,
There's eternal life.

2564. There is no greater love than this

(I am redeemed)

Is 51:11; Mt 26:48-49, 67; 27:26, 30; Lk 15:24; Jn 15:13; Rev 5:9

Nathan Jess

Intimately

G2
Bm7
I am re - deemed.
There's none on earth,
C2
Em7
no wealth nor fame,
to which I'll sing,
Last time to Coda
1.
D.C.(v.2)
G2
Bm7
for You're my King.
3.
D.S. (ch. 2) al Coda
2.
Bm7
Bm7
King.
'Cause I've been found
King.
Mid section
C2
G2
Bm7
Hal - le - lu - jah,
hal - le - lu - jah,
I

1.
C2
2.
am re-deemed;
am re-deemed;
C2
D.S.
Coda
Bm7
And I will sing
deemed.
Verse
Em7
C2
G2
Em7
2. On the day You were beat - en
it ne-
ver crossed Your mind
that I was not worth dy-ing
for;
my soul You came to earth to find.
Chorus 2
'Cause I've been found
by ma - je-sty,
I know my King,
and I will sing with all my lungs..
I once was lost,
now ran - somed free;
my soul must sing –
I am re - deemed!

2565.
There is nowhere else
(Running after You)
Capo 4 (G)
Ps 84:2; 91:14; Song 1:4; Lk 15:20; Col 3:24
Ben Cantelon
Rock
Verse
C Em D
1. There is no - where else I'd ra - ther be than
(v.2)
C Em
in Your pre - sence; e - ven in the wil - der - ness I'll seek
D C
for Your di - rec - tion. I'm call - ing, I'm
Em F C
Chorus
long - ing for more of You. I'm
G D(D)
run - ning, I'm run - ning af - ter You, 'cause

Last time to Coda
(Ch. 2)
Em
no one else will e - ver do; my heart is set on You.
1.
D.C.(v.2)
2.,4.
D.S. (Chorus 2)
C2
C
On - ly You. I'm
3.
C
Mid section
C
You are my re -
D
Em
(2nd x)
G
ward, and it's You I'm liv - ing for; take
C
1.
D
G
all that I am, for I am Yours. You

2. King of glory, You're my great reward,
My one desire.
Only You can satisfy my soul;
Please take me higher.

(Chorus 2)
I'm longing, I long to see Your face,
To feel the warmth of Your embrace;
I'm running after You.

My soul yearns, even faints, for the courts of the LORD; my heart and my flesh cry out for the living God.

PSALM 84:2

2566. There is strength within the sorrow

2.
B(G)
Chorus
E(C)
B(G)
Your plans are still to pros - per, You've
(plans)
F♯(D)
G♯m(Em)
E(C)
B/D♯(G/B)
not for-got - ten us; You're with us in the fire and the flood.
F♯(D)
E(C)
B(G)
Faith-ful for - e - ver,
F♯(D)
G♯m(Em)
Last time to Coda
E(C)
F♯(D)
per - fect in love, You are sov - 'reign o - ver us.
1.
D.C.(v.2)
3.
D.S.S. al Coda
B(G)
B(G)

2.
B(G)
B(G)
Mid section
(small note on rpt)
E-ven what the e-ne-my means for e-
E(C)
C♯m7(Am)
-vil, You turn it for our good; You turn it for our
F♯/A♯(D/F♯)
B(G)
good and for Your glo-ry. E-ven in the val-ley You are faith-
E(C)
C♯m7(Am)
-ful; You're work-ing for our good, You're work-ing for our
1.
F♯(D)
2.
F♯/A♯(D/F♯)
D.S.
good and for Your glo-ry. good and for Your glo-ry. Your

Coda
B(G)

Verse
G♯m(Em)
E(C)
F♯(D)
2. You are wis - dom un-i-ma - gined; who could un - der-stand Your ways,
B(G)
G♯m(Em)
E(C)
reign - ing high a - bove the hea - vens,
F♯(D)
B(G)
G♯m(Em)
E(C)
reach-ing down in end-less grace? You're the lift - er of the low - ly,
F♯(D)
B(G)
G♯m(Em)
com-pas - sio-nate and kind; You sur-round and You up-hold
E(C)
F♯(D)
B(G)
me, and Your pro-mi-ses are my de - light.

2567. There on the cross

Jn 19:18; Gal 2:20

Ken Riley

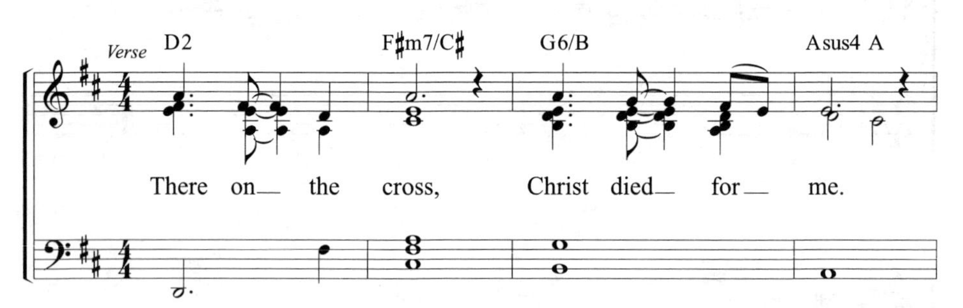

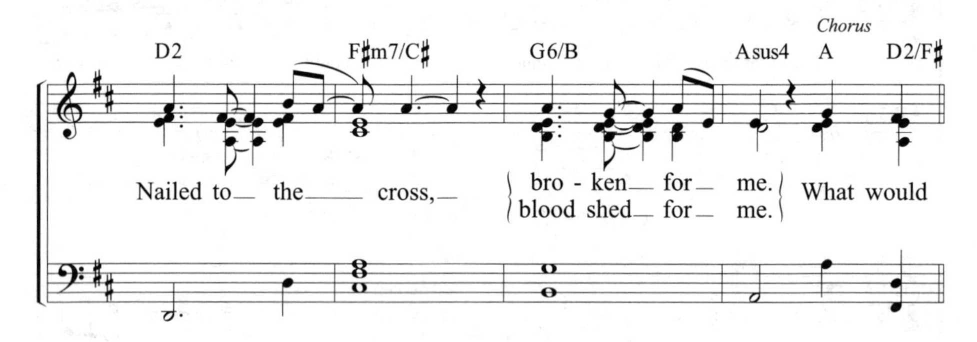

1.,3. D.C.
2.
Mid section
Dsus4 D D/F♯ G G G
(Fine)
Je - sus?
Here I am,
A D/F♯ G
ho - nour - ing the sa - cri - fice You made;
1. A Bm
all I am wor - ship - ping the God who
C/D
2. A Bm
saves.
wor - ship - ping my God!
Bm7 G A2 G/B

A2/C♯
G
A2
Dsus4
D
D/F♯
G2
Dsus4
D
G
D.S. al fine
What would

I have been crucified with Christ and I no longer live, but Christ lives in me. The life I live in the body, I live by faith in the Son of God, who loved me and gave himself for me.

GALATIANS 2:20

2568. There's a song creation's singing

(Praise)

Ps 123:2; 130:5-6; 2 Pet 1:19

Paul Baloche
& Brenton Brown

2. God, our hearts are yearning for You
Like the watchmen waiting for the dawn.
And our eyes are turned towards You,
For that day when You return,
And till that day we'll sing:

2569. There's a sound that comes from heaven

(Restoration song)

Mt 16:16; Mk 10:45; Rom 10:9; 2 Cor 3:18; Heb 12:1

Vibrantly

Lou & Nathan Fellingham
& busbee

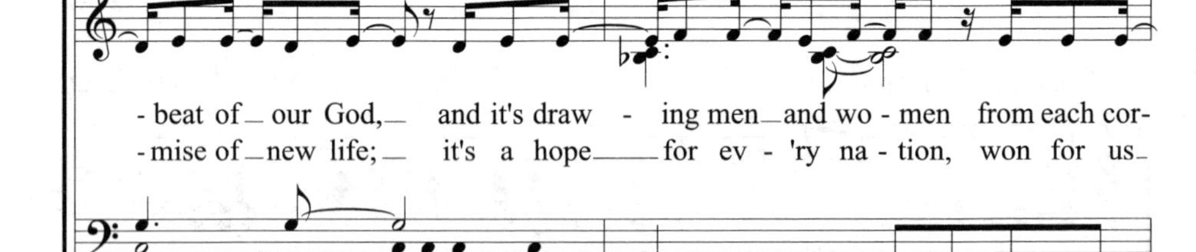

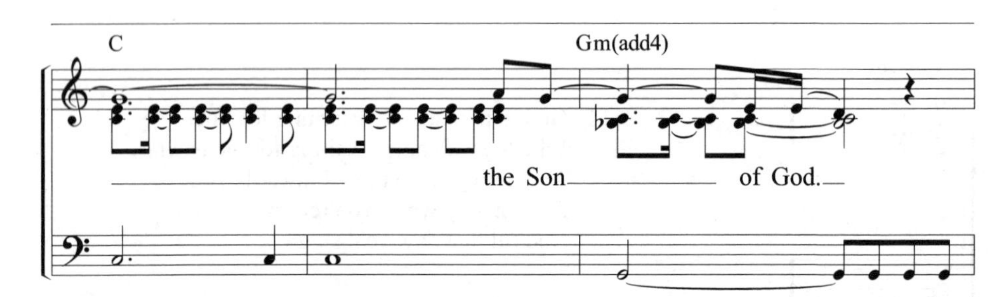

D.C.(v.2)
4.,6.
B♭sus2
B♭sus2
2. It's a sto - - ship on and on. There's life
C
Dm7
C/E
for all who call
that He is Lord.
1.,3.
2.
D.C.(v.3)
4.
F
F
F
and con-fess
3. Liv-ing with
G/B
C
F
Bridge
G/B
C
On and on and on we move,
F
G/B
C
N.C.
walk-ing to-wards the ris - ing sun.

2. It's a story of a nation birthed in promise to one man,
Then delivered from oppression, echoing God's future plan.
Generations guided onward by His faithfulness and love,
Now the promise rests in Jesus whom we'll worship on and on.
There's life for all who call and confess that He is Lord.

3. Living with their hearts submitted to the One who's won their love,
Being changed into His likeness, God's reflection on the earth.
With a passion for His kingdom, for His Spirit and the word,
Who'll be patient, kind and generous, loving those broken and lost.
They serve the risen Christ, who served to give them life.

2570.
There's a time for tears
(Ecclesiastes)
Eccles 3:4-5, 8
Martin Smith
& Tim Hughes
With quiet intensity
Verse
F♯m Bm/F♯ D2
1. There's a time for tears and a time to dance. There's a
F♯m Bm/F♯ D2
time to let go and a time for ro - mance. There's a
F♯m Bm/F♯ D2
(v.2)
time for war and a time for peace. There's a
F♯m Bm/F♯ D2
time to em-brace and a time to re - lease.
Chorus
A/C♯ D Bm A E A/C♯ D
1.
Bm A
Oh, my Lord, I need to find. Take my hand, and I will

D.C.(v.2)
2
D
Bm A D
fol-low.
2. There's a
I will fol-low.
A/C♯ D Bm A E A/C♯ D
Oh, my Lord, I need to find. Take my hand, and
Bm A D
Mid section
D A
I will fol-low.
Now's the time for
1.-3.
Esus4 F♯m7
4.
Esus4 F♯m7
sing-ing
sing-ing.
Your love
D A Esus4 F♯m7
in ev - 'ry breath I take,
in ev - 'ry step I make,

2. There's a time to love and a time to hate
All the evil choices that we make.
It's a time to rise and a time to fall.
It's a time to keep or just throw it all.

2571.
There's no banquet so rich
(Banquet)
Capo 4 (C)
Ps 34:8; Is 55:1-2; Lk 14:17; 1 Cor 11:23-26; Rev 19:9; 21:4
Graham Kendrick
Flowing
Verse
1. There's no ban-quet so rich as the bread and the wine; no ta-ble more ho-ly, no wel-come so kind. There's no mer-cy so wide as the arms of the cross: come and taste, come and see, come find and be found.
(-fice.)
Copyright © 2009 Make Way Music, P.O.Box 320, Tunbridge Wells, Kent, TN2 9DE. www.grahamkendrick.co.uk info@makewaymusic.com International copyright secured. All rights reserved. Used by permission.
SoF 5

D.C.(v.2,4.)
2.,3.,4.
B(G)
A(F)
B(G)
C♯m(Am)
2. There's no
known.
B(G)
Chorus
C♯m(Am)
B/C♯(G/A)
C♯m(Am)
B/C♯(G/A)
Take the bread,
drink the wine,
Last time to Coda
v.3 D.S.
C♯m(Am)
B/C♯(G/A)
B/D♯(G/B)
C♯m(Am)
(not 1°)
and re - mem - ber His sa - cri - fice.
B(G)
C♯m(Am)
B(G)
C♯m(Am)
D.C.(v.3)
3. There's a
Coda
B/D♯(G/B)
C♯m(Am)
B(G)
sa - cri - fice.

2. There's no banquet so rich,
   For what feast could compare
   With the body of Jesus,
   Blessed, broken and shared?
   Here is grace to forgive,
   Here is blood that atoned;
   Come and taste, come and see,
   Come know and be known.

3. There's no banquet so rich
   As the feast we will share
   When God gathers the nations
   And dines with us here.
   When death's shadow is gone,
   Every tear wiped away,
   Come and eat, come and drink,
   Come welcome that day.

4. There's no banquet so rich,
   For our Saviour we find
   Present here in the mystery
   Of these humble signs.
   Cleansed, renewed, reconciled,
   Let us go out as one,
   Live in love, and proclaim
   His death till He comes.

Taste and see that the LORD is good; blessed is the man who takes refuge in him.

PSALM 34:8

2572. There's no greater sacrifice

(Saviour and friend)

Is 53:4; Jn 15:13; 19:18; 2 Cor 5:21; Phil 1:21

Capo 3 (C)

Ken Riley

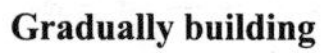

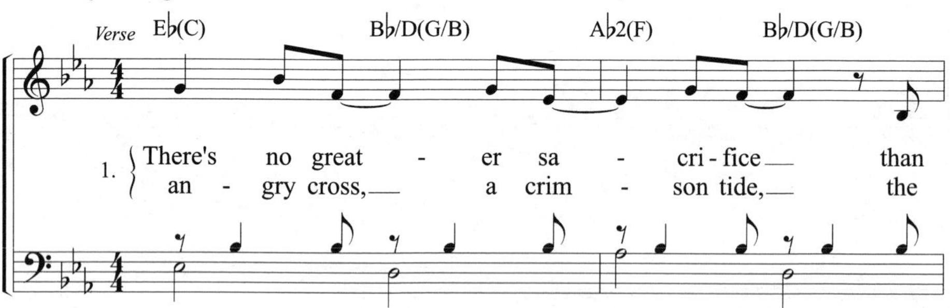

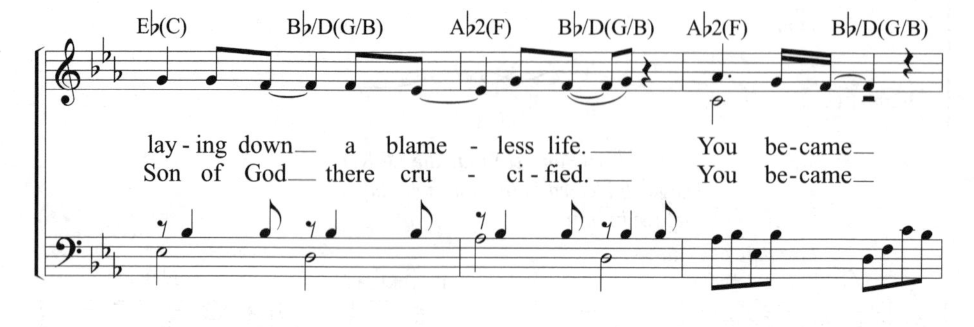

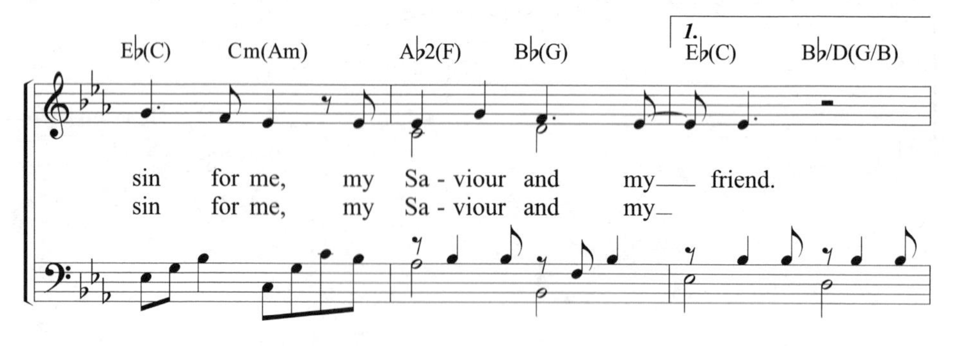

2. Chose to bear my guilt, my shame,
My darkest thoughts, my spear of pain.
You became sin for me,
My Saviour and my friend.
There's no thing that I could give
But live to die and die to live.
You became endless grace
That loves me till the end.

2573. There's no lack in all You've given

(My soul is well)

Ps 23:6; 25:13; 146:1; Lam 3:24; Mk 14:38; Lk 10:42; Eph 1:6; Phil 4:18

Capo 2 (G)

Jordan Dillon & Simon Brading

Moderate rock

F♯m(Em) *Verse* E/G♯(D/F♯) A(G)

1. There's no lack in all You've given,
There's no promise I am missing,

F♯m(Em) E/G♯(D/F♯) A(G)

I am richer than a king;
all I need has been supplied;

F♯m(Em) E/G♯(D/F♯) 1.,3. A(G)

in the gift of Christ our portion, my soul is well.
You're the strong and firm foundation,

B(A) 2.,4. A(G) Bsus2(A)

my soul is well, my soul is well.

D(C) *Chorus* F♯m(Em) E/G♯(D/F♯) A(G) D(C)

Praise the Lord, O my soul, cry out;

F♯m(Em) E/G♯(D/F♯) A(G) D(C) E(D)
praise the Lord, O my soul. Praise the Lord, O my
Last time to Coda
1.
A(G) F♯m(Em) D(C) E(D) A(G)
soul, cry out, for in You my soul is well.
D.C.(v.2)
2.
Asus4(G) D(C) E(D) A(G)
Mid section
my soul is well. To the
Bm7(Am) E(D)
praise of all Your glo - ry and Your grace, to the
A(G) E/G♯(D/F♯) D(C)
praise of all Your glo - ry and Your grace, in the

Bm7(Am)
E(D)
won - der of Your good - ness I will sing, 'Great is the Lord.'
A(G)
1.
2.
D.S.
To the
Coda
D(C)
E(D)
A(G)
Last chorus
D(C)
E(D)
my soul is well.
Praise the Lord, O my
A(G)
F♯m(Em)
D(C)
E(D)
A(G)
soul, cry out;
praise the Lord, O my soul.
D(C)
E(D)
A(G)
F♯m(Em)
Praise the Lord, O my soul, cry out, for in You

2. Though the struggles have been many
And the flesh inside me, weak,
Lord, Your grace and truth have taught me
My soul is well.
Though I've wandered in confusion
I have seen enough to know,
Where I tread, Your goodness follows.
My soul is well, my soul is well.

2574. The rocks are going to cry out

(The glory of our King)

Ps 19:1; Song 1:4; Mt 1:23; Lk 19:40; Jn 20:21; 1 Pet 2:9

Jonas Myrin, Jess Cates & Matt Redman

With energy

Bm
G
a ge - ne - ra - tion worship - ping un - a - shamed;
we be-lieve You are all that You say You are.
D
1.
Asus4
A
Bm
giv-ing all for the glo - ry of our King.
Giv-ing all for the
G
2.
A
i.
Bm
G
glo - ry of our King.
A
Bm
D
G
A
Bm
D.C.(v.2)
ii.,iii.
D
G
Bm
G2
2. The
The glo - ry of our King.

Last time to Coda
D
A
Bm
G2
The glo-ry of our King.
D
A
Bm
G2
Mid section
D
A
We are, we are a cho - sen peo - ple.
You are, You are the God who saves us.
Bm
G
D
We are, we are called to fol-low. We are, we are Your
You are, You are the God who sends us. You are, You are the
A
1.
Bm
G
ge - ne - ra - tion.
God who's with us.

2. The church is waking up now
To be Your hands and feet upon this earth.
Send us in Your power,
As we take heaven to a broken world.
Stand up, stand up –
The time has come.

2575. The song of all eternity
(Creation)

Ps 19:1; 69:34; Jn 1:1, 4

Ken Riley

Steady rock feel

Verse

D Em7 C G

1. The song ___ of all ___ e - ter - ni - ty re - sounds ___

D Em7 C G D Em7

___ through time ___ and ___ space. ___ Bright burn - ing stars ___ and ga -

(v.2)

C G D Em7 C G *Bridge*

- lax - ies light up ___ in glo - rious praise. ___ You are a - ma -

(v.2)

Asus4 A C2 Asus4 A C2 *Chorus*

- zing, ___ God; ___ a - ma - zing ___ God! ___ Cre -

Em7 C G D Em7 C

a - tion ___ sings of Your glo - ry; all that You fa - shioned

G D G/B C G D
shout-ing Your name! Cre - a - tor, we give You glo - ry.
1.
Em7 C G D G D
Lord God al-migh - ty, Je-sus, the life - giv - ing Word.
Em7 C G D Em7 C
D.C.(v.2)
2. Dawn breaks
3.
D.S.S. al Coda
2.,4.
G D G D
Je - sus, the Word. All cre - Je - sus, the life - giv - ing Word.
Mid section
G D Em7 C G D
It's all for You, my Lord, it's all, it's all for You.

2. Dawn breaks into her symphony,
High mountains bow in praise,
Great oceans roar in harmony.
We join the earth to sing:
You are amazing, God;
Amazing God!

The heavens declare the glory of God; the skies proclaim the work of his hands.

PSALM 19:1

2576. The Spirit came, as promised

Jn 14:17; Acts 2:1; 1 Cor 6:19; 12:12; Eph 1:13; 2:18; 4:3, 30; 5:19; 6:6, 17

ELLACOMBE

Wüttemberg Gesangbuch 1784
Arr. David Ball

Brightly

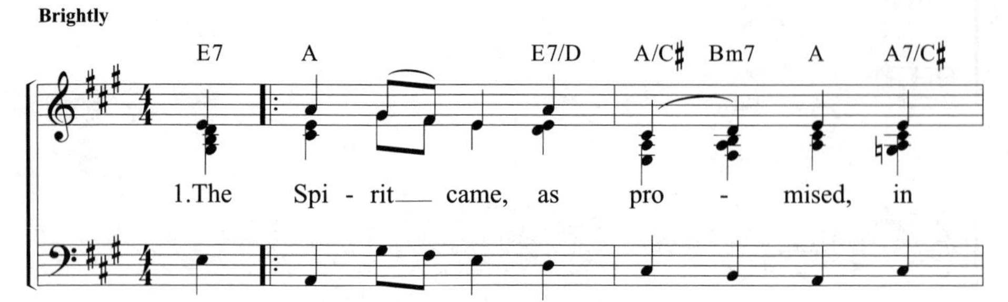

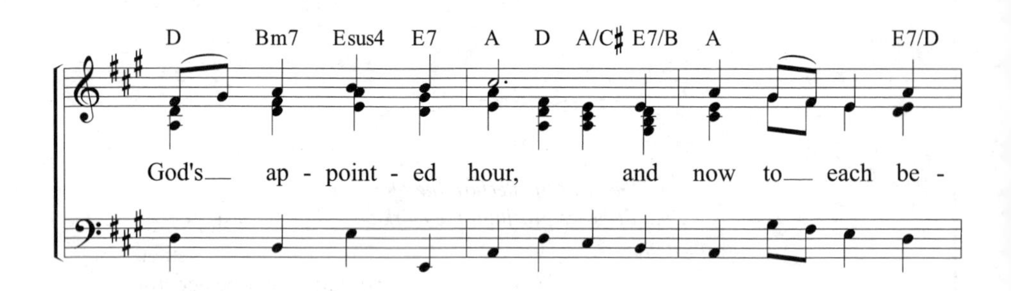

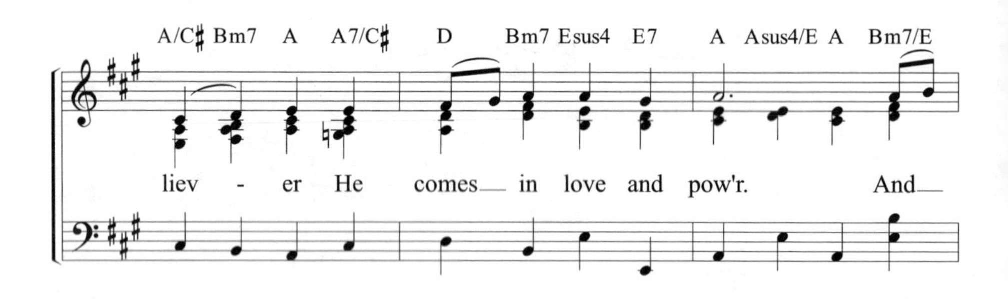

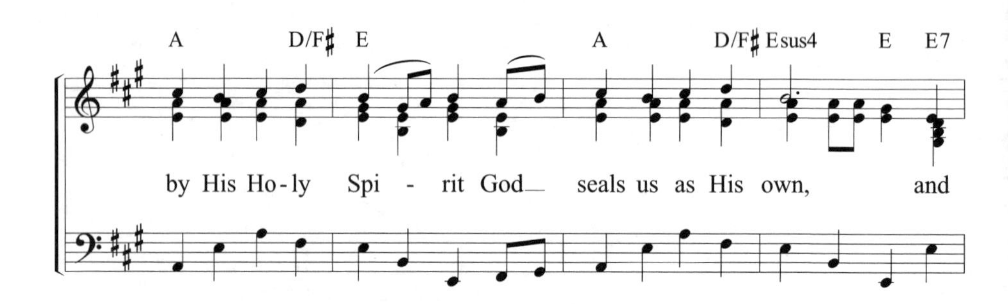

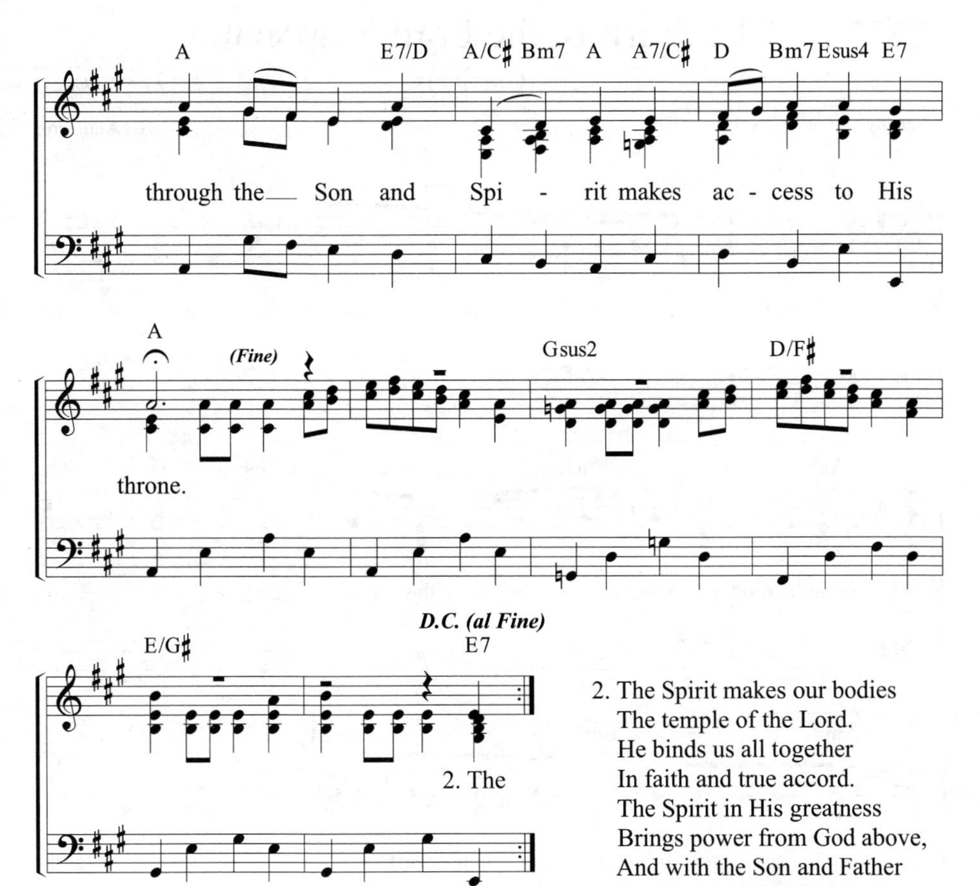

2. The Spirit makes our bodies
The temple of the Lord.
He binds us all together
In faith and true accord.
The Spirit in His greatness
Brings power from God above,
And with the Son and Father
Dwells in our hearts in love.

3. He bids us live together
In unity and peace,
Employ His gifts in blessing
And let base passions cease.
We should not grieve the Spirit
By open sin or shame,
Nor let our words and actions
Deny His holy name.

4. The word, the Spirit's weapon,
Will bring all sin to light,
And prayer, by His directing,
Will give new joy and might.
Be filled then with His Spirit,
Live out God's will and word;
Rejoice with hymns and singing,
Make music to the Lord.

J. E. Seddon (1915–83)

2577. The Spirit of the Lord is upon me

(Carrier)

Is 6:8; 9:2; 61:1, 3; 2 Cor 4:6-7; Phil 2:15

Steadily

Jared Anderson

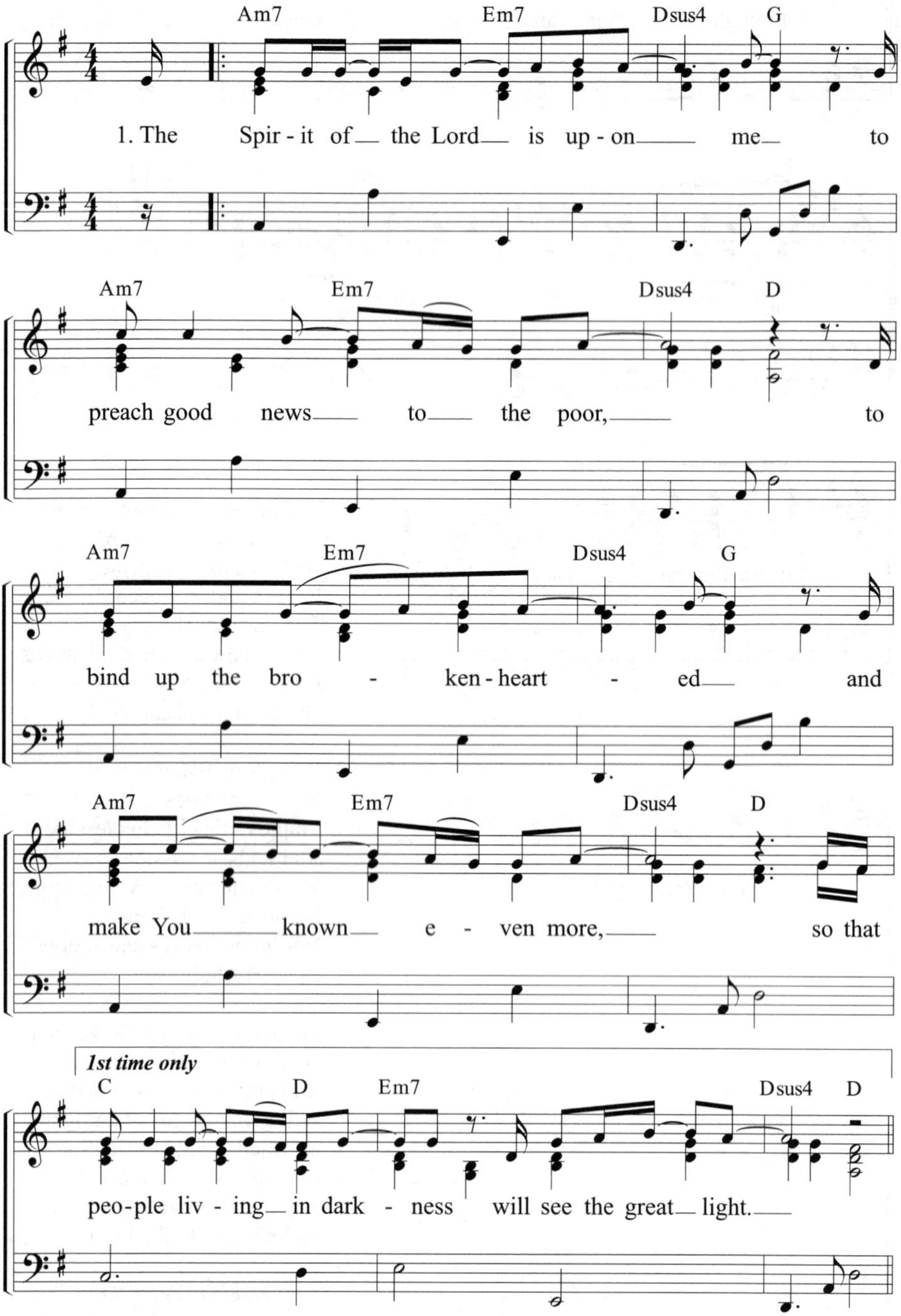

Am7 Em7 Dsus4 G
1. The Spir - it of the Lord is up - on me to
Am7 Em7 Dsus4 D
preach good news to the poor, to
Am7 Em7 Dsus4 G
bind up the bro - ken - heart - ed and
Am7 Em7 Dsus4 D
make You known e - ven more, so that
1st time only
C D Em7 Dsus4 D
peo-ple liv - ing in dark - ness will see the great light.

Chorus
G D/F♯ C/E D
I'll be the car - ri-er of love and com-pas - sion;
G D/F♯ C/E Dsus4 D
I'll be the car - ri-er of light to the world,
G D/F♯ C/E D G/B
I'll be the car - ri-er of hope and sal - va-tion; I will go,
C2 Dsus4 Em7
shine Your light to the world, I will go,
Last time to Coda
1.
C2 D Am7 Em7 Dsus4
shine Your light to the world.

D.C.(v.2)
2. Mid section
Am7 Em7 Dsus4 D Am7 Em7
2. The Here am I, send
D C Am7 Em7 D C
me, send me. Here am I; send me, send me.
Am7 Em7 D C Am7 Em7
Here am I; send me, send me. Here am I; send
D Cmaj9
D.S. al Coda
Coda
G
me, send me. And
Verse
Am7 Em7 D G Am7 Em7
2. The Spi-rit of the Lord is up-on me, free-dom and truth to pro - claim.
D Am7 Em7 Dsus4 G
Trade your ash - es for the oil of glad - ness, and your
Am7 Em7 Dsus4 D
(to Chorus)
sor-rows for gar - ments of praise.

2578. The Spirit of the sovereign Lord

(From ashes to beauty)

Is 61:1, 3; Joel 2:23; Acts 2:18

Tom Read

Chorus
G
Em7
C
G/D
D
Pour Your Spi - rit o - ver me, let Your love rain down.
Gmaj7
Em7
C2
G/D
D
Would You take these hands of mine and use me?
G
Em7
C
G/D
D
Pour Your Spi - rit o - ver me, let Your love rain down.
Gmaj7
Em7
C2
G/D
D
Would You take these feet of mine and lead me?
1.,3.
D.C.(v.2)
Last time to Coda
G
Em7
Dsus4
C2
G
Em7
Dsus4
C2
(1°)
2. The

2. The Spirit of the sovereign Lord is on me now
To go, to free, to give, to feed.
The Spirit of the sovereign Lord is on me now,
Spreading love.

2579. The wonder of the cross

Is 53:4; 1 Cor 15:55, 57; Eph 2:6, 13; Col 2:15; Heb 10:12; 1 Pet 2:9; Rev 5:12

Worshipfully

Chris & Jennie Orange

2. The triumph of the cross –
Death has lost its sting;
Swallowed up in victory
That we might live in Him.
Seated now with Christ
At the Father's side;
Out of darkness, one with Him,
Raised to glorious life.

(Chorus 2)
'Jesus, Jesus,
Jesus is the Lamb.'

2580.

This dry and desert land

(All my fountains)

Is 35:1, 6; 43:19; Hos 6:3; Joel 2:23; Jn 4:14; 7:38

Chris Tomlin, Daniel Carson
& Nathan & Christy Nockels

F
C
Am7
All my foun - tains.
F
C
D.C.(v.2)
2.
F
let it flow.
Chorus
C
O - pen the hea - vens. Come, li - ving wa - ter, all my
F
C
foun - tains are in You. You're
strong like a ri - ver, Your love is

F
run - ning through. All my foun - tains are in You.
Last time to Coda
Am7
F
C
C
Am7
F
C
Mid section
Come on and
Am7
F
C
Csus4
rain down on us, rain down on us, Lord.
C
Sing 3 times
Am7
Come on and rain down on us, rain

F
C
D.S. al Coda
Coda
down on us, Lord.
All my
F
Am7
foun - tains are in You.
F
C
All my foun - tains are in You.
Verse
Am7
F
C
2. A flood for my soul, a well that ne-ver will run dry.
Am7
F
I've ram-bled on my own, ne-ver be-liev-ing I would find
C
Am7
F
an e-ver-last-ing stream. Your ri-ver car-ries me home.
C/E
F
Let it flow, let it flow.

2581. This is a realm of Your glory

(In the presence of angels)

Rev 4:8; 19:6

Roy Fields

Steadily

G D D.C.(v.2) 2. G Dsus4 D
da, la da da. 2. In the hear the an - gels sing:
Chorus Am Em G D Am Em 1. G D
'Ho - ly, ho - ly, ho - ly, ho - ly.'
2. G Dsus4 D Verse Am Em
(v.4)
ho - ly.' 3. In the pre - sence of an - gels with God's
(v.4)
G D Am Em
glo - ry on their wings, like the voice of ma - ny wa - ters I can
1. G D 2 G Dsus4 D
hear the an - gels sing. 4. This is a see Your face.

2. In the presence of angels
   With God's glory on their wings,
   Like the voice of many waters
   I can hear the angels sing.

4. This is a realm of Your glory,
   This is a realm of Your grace.
   All my heart's desire
   Is to see Your face.

'Holy, holy, holy is the Lord God Almighty, who was, and is, and is to come.'

REVELATION 4:8

2582. This is how I know what love is

Jn 3:17; 1 Jn 3:16

(Because of Your love)

Al Gordon
& Hanif Williams

F♯m
E
D
-cing in my heart. Be-cause of Your grace
A
B
B/F♯
D
I am free. Be-cause of Your faith-ful-ness
A
F♯m
E
there's a song that must be sung, and I will
2nd time to Coda 1
3rd time to Coda 2
D
A
E
sing, I will sing be-cause of You.
A
Verse
2. This is why there's

joy with - in me, this is why my spi - rit sings:
F♯m
D
A
Je - sus, You're my great ad - ven - ture; You're my ev - 'ry - thing.
D.S. al Coda 1
Coda 1
E
Be - cause of Your
You
D
E
F♯m
came to save the world, to save
A
D
A
E
the world, to save the world.

D E F♯m
Your love can change the world, can
A D A
change the world, can change the world.
D.S. al Coda 2
Coda 2
E
Be-cause of Your
E
I will dance,
D A E
I will dance be-cause of You.
D A E
I will dance be-cause of You.

2583. This is how we know

Jn 3:16; 1 Jn 3:16; 4:19

Matt & Beth Redman

Dsus2
Bm
gave Your on - ly Son. Love a - ma-zing, so di-vine, we will
Dsus2
Esus4
E
A
love You in re - turn. For this life that You give, for this
Dsus2
Bm
Last time to Coda
(Last time)
death that You have died, love a - ma-zing, so di-vine – we will
1.
Dsus2
A
D2
love You in re-ply, Lord.
D.C.
2.
D.S.
A
D2
Dsus2
E
love You in re - ply. For You

3.
Dsus2
E
A
Mid section
love You in re-ply, Lord.
And our love will be
D
A/C♯
loud, our love will be strong; our love should be
Bm
A
E
A
hands and feet that serve You in this world.
So let it stay
D
A/C♯
true and let it en - dure,
that You will be
Bm7
D.S. al Coda
Esus4
E
glo-ri-fied and wor-shipped and a-dored.
For You

Coda
Dsus2
Esus4
E
A
love You in re - ply, Lord.
D2
A
Sa - viour of the world.
D2
Tag
A
King Je-sus, we love You, for we have been loved.
D2
A
King Je-sus, we love You, for we have been loved.
1.
D2
2.
D2
A
King Je-sus, we love We have been loved.

2584. This is Jesus
(The Saviour's song)

Ps 40:5; Jn 1:1, 4, 14; 19:30; 1 Cor 15:54; Phil 2:8

Tim Hughes, Kees Kraayenoord & Martin Smith

Steadily

C D C G/B
Sa - viour's song. Come, wor - ship Him, come,
C D Gsus4 G D
wor - ship Him. Raise Your hands and
C D C G/B
shout His name: Christ Je - sus, Christ
3° jump to Mid section
1. D.C.(v.2)
2.
C Dsus4 D D
Je - sus. 2. It is For no -
Mid section
C Em7 G C
- thing is high - er, no - one is great - er,
(no - thing)
(Vocals tacet last time)

Em7
1.
G
B
no - thing com-pares to You.
2.,3.
G
Am7
(Fine)
Chorus 2
Gsus4
G
D
Sing a - loud the
C
D
C
G/B
Sa - viour's song. Come, wor - ship Him, come,
Am7
G/B
C
G/B
wor - ship Him. Come, wor - ship Him, ev-'ry-bo-dy
Am7
G/B
C
G/B
wor - ship Him, yeah, wor - ship Him, we will

2. It is finished:
The rugged cross stands empty,
Death has been defeated,
This world is not the same.
Songs are rising –
Awe and adoration
Fill our hearts with wonder;
Endless praise is Yours.

2585. This is my prayer in the desert

(Desert song)

Gen 22:14; Is 54:17; Mt 13:24; Rom 8:17, 37; 1 Cor 3:15; 1 Pet 1:7

Moderately

Brooke Ligertwood

Verse Bm A G D

1. This is my prayer in the de - sert, when

Bm A G D Bm A

all that's with-in me feels (vv.2&3) dry; this is my prayer in my

G D 1. Bm A G D.C.(v.2)

hun-ger and need. My God is the God who pro - vides.

2.,3. Bm D/F♯ v.2 only G G *Chorus*

re - fine me, Lord, through the flame. I will bring (stand.)

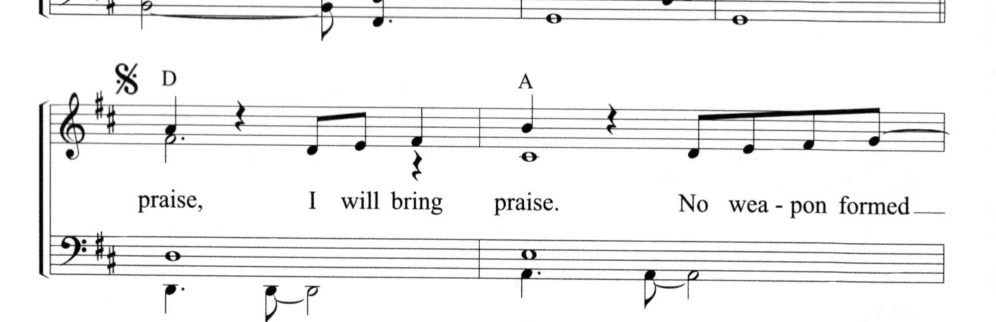

G
D
A/C♯
A
_ a-gainst me shall re - main._ I will re-joice,_ I will de-
1.,3.
Bm
G
A
Bm
A
clare: God is my vic - to-ry and He is here.
(2°)
1st time to v.3.
Last time to Coda
2.
G
D
Bm
A
G
G
A
- to-ry and He is
Bm
Mid section
D
here. All_ of my life, in_ ev-'ry sea - son, You_
Bm
A
_ are still God;_ I_ have a rea - son to sing,_ I_

2. This is my prayer in the fire,
In weakness or trial or pain.
This is a faith proved of more worth than gold.
So refine me, Lord, through the flame.

3. This is my prayer in the battle,
When triumph is still on its way.
I am a conqueror and co-heir with Christ,
So firm on His promise I'll stand.

2586.
This is our story
Mt 26:28; Eph 2:13-14; Heb 10:19-20; 1 Jn 1:7
Capo 4 (G)
Eoghan Heaslip
Rhythmic
Verse
B(G) E(C) B(G) E(C)
This is our sto-ry: Je-sus died for you, for me.
G♯m(Em) E(C) F♯sus4(D)
This is our sto - ry: the Son of God
1. E(C)
poured out for us.
2. E(C)
poured out for us.
Bridge
His
F♯/A♯(D/F♯) G♯m(Em) E(C)
love re-vealed in sa - cri-fice. His
F♯/A♯(D/F♯) G♯m(Em) E(C)
blood that frees and re - con-ciles.

B(G)
Chorus
E(C)
F♯(D)
He has made a way for us on the cross.
B(G)
E(C)
F♯(D)
He has made a way for us in all He's done.
B(G)
E(C)
F♯(D)
G♯m(Em)
Je-sus makes a way for us to come. He is
3rd time D.S.S. al Coda
1.,3.
E(C)
B(G)
our peace, He is our peace.
1st time D.C.
Last time to Coda
2.
F♯/A♯(D/F♯)
Mid section
Our sin,

G♯m(Em)
E(C)
and shame
are washed
a - way.
F♯/A♯(D/F♯)
G♯m(Em)
1.
E(C)
Our debt
is paid,
we are for-gi - ven.
2.
E(C)
- ven.
(G/B)
B/D♯
(C)
Esus2
F♯(D)
B/D♯(G/B)
Esus2(C)
F♯(D)
D.S.
He has made a way for us.
Coda
B(G)
B(no3rd)(G)

2587. This is the day that You have made

(Hosanna)

Ps 118:24-25; Lam 3:22-23; Jn 14:6; 2 Cor 4:4; Phil 2:9

Noel & Tricia Richards
& Wayne Drain

Gently rhythmic

Chorus

Gmaj7

This is the day that You have made.
New ev - 'ry morn - ing is Your love

Cmaj7 Am7 *Last time to Coda*

We will re-joice in You al-ways. Ho - san - na, ho-
fall-ing up-on us from a-bove. Ho - san - na, ho-

G D C2

san - na.
san - na.

Verse

Help us, O Lord, we pray,

Em C2

to live for You each day; keep us faith-

G C2

- ful to the end. Save us, O Lord,

(Chorus 2)
You are the way, the truth, the life.
We'll be the bearers of Your light.
Hosanna, hosanna.
You have the name above all names,
We'll be the keepers of Your flame.
Hosanna, hosanna.

2588. This is the message of the cross

Ps 85:2; Lk 22:20; Jn 19:18; Rom 8:2; 1 Cor 1:18, 20

Medium rock feel

Martin Smith

G
1.
D.C.(v.2)
2.,3.
Chorus
life. 2. This is the mes-sage of the (1.3.) You set me free
(2.) You set us free
D
G
when I came to the cross; poured out Your blood,
when we came to the cross; You poured out Your blood,
D
G
for I was bro-ken and lost. There I was healed
for we are bro-ken and lost. Here we are healed
2° D.S. al Coda
D
Em7
Csus2
and You co-vered my sin. It's there You saved me;
and You co-ver our sin. It's here You saved us;
Last time to Coda
D
G
this is the mes-sage of the cross.

2. This is the message of the cross:
That we can be free
To lay all our burdens here
At the foot of the tree.
The cross was the shame of the world
But the glory of God,
For Jesus, You conquered sin
And You gave us new life.

3. This is the message of the cross:
That we can be free
To hunger for heaven,
To hunger for Thee.
The cross is such foolishness
To the perishing,
But to us who are being saved,
It is the power of God.

2589. This joyful Eastertide

(Risen)

Ps 116:4; Lk 24:6; 1 Cor 15:14, 51-52

Moderately

Words: George R. Woodward (1848–1934)
Adpt. Graham Kendrick
Music & chorus words: Graham Kendrick

Last time to Coda
Bm D/F♯ G A Bm G A G/B A/C♯
He is ri - sen. Christ the Lord is ri -
2° D.C.(v.3)
D A/D G/D A/D D A/D G/D A/D
sen.
Verse
D(no3rd)
2. Death's flood has lost its chill since Je-sus crossed the ri-ver.
Bm7 Asus4
D.S.
Lo-ver of souls, from ill my pas-sing soul de - li - ver.
Coda
D A G A Bm G A G A
sen. He is ri - sen. Christ the Lord is ri -

3. My flesh in hope shall rest,
And for a season slumber,
Till trumpet east to west
Shall wake the dead in number.

2590. Though a thousand may fall

(Dwell)

Ps 91:1-2, 4-5, 7, 11; Is 54:17

Aaron Keyes
& Jess Cates

2. You have set me securely on high,
You've delivered me out of darkness,
And when evil surrounds my life,
You've commanded Your angels to guard me.

G
shel - ter of the most high God, I will rest in the
Gsus4 G Csus2
beau - ty of Your pre - sence. Your faith - ful - ness is a
G
shield and my great re - ward. I will not be a -
Last time to Coda
1.
D Em C2
fraid, I will trust in the Lord.
D.C.(v.2)
2.
G D/F♯ C2
2. You have set

Dsus4
Em7
Mid section
Oh, I will trust in the Lord. 'No
Csus2
D
wea - pon formed a-gainst me will pros - per, no
Em7
Bm7
wea - pon formed a-gainst me will pros - per, no
Csus2
D
wea - pon formed a-gainst me will pros - per,' says the Lord.
Em7
1.
2.
D.S. al Coda
'No

Coda
Em
C2
G
D
Em
C2
I will trust in the Lord.
G

2591.
Though I walk through waters
(Refuge)
Ps 23:4; 32:7; 91:1-2, 4, 11; Is 43:2
Capo 3 (G)
Moderately
Vicky Beeching
Verse
B♭(G)
F/A(D/F♯)
1. Though I walk through wa - ters, they won't o - ver-whelm me;
(v.2)
Cm7(Am)
Gm(Em)
F(D)
though I stand in fire, I won't be con-sumed.
Cm7(Am)
B♭/D(G/B)
Though I walk through val - leys with dark-ness all a-round me,
E♭(C)
A♭(F)
F/A(D/F♯)
Chorus
I lift my eyes to You. You are my

B♭sus4(G) B♭(G) F/A(D/F♯) Gm7(Em)
re - fuge, You are my hid - ing place, You are my
Cm(Am) E♭(C) F(D)
shel - ter where I am fin - 'lly safe. In the
Gm(Em) F/A(D/F♯) B♭(G)
sha - dow of Your migh - ty wings, for -
Cm7(Em) B♭/D(G/B) E♭(C) F(D)
ev - er I'll sing that it's true: my re - fuge is in
B♭sus4(G) B♭(G) F(D) E♭(C) B♭sus4(G) B♭(G)
You.

(Fine)
Mid section
F(D)
E♭(C)
D.C.(v.2)
E♭(C)
E - ven in the dark - ness,
Gm(Em)
F/A(D/F♯)
B♭(G)
E♭(C)
I will lift Your name up; though my heart is break - ing,
Gm(Em)
F/A(D/F♯)
B♭(G)
Cm7(Am)
still I will sing.___ (And) e - ven in the dark - ness,
Gm(Em)
F/A(D/F♯)
B♭(G)
Cm7(Am)
I will lift Your name up; though my heart is break - ing,
Gm(Em)
F/A(D/F♯)
F(D)
D.S. al fine
still I will sing.___ You are my
2. Everywhere You send me,
Angels will defend me –
Guarding me from danger
And every snare.
Though the battle's fierce,
I know that You are near;
So I put my trust in You.

Even though I walk through the valley of the shadow of death, I will fear no evil, for you are with me; your rod and your staff, they comfort me.

PSALM 23:4

2592. Through it all, You are faithful

(C♯m/G♯)
D♯m/A♯ G♯m(F♯m) E(D) B(A)
Bridge
D♯m/A♯(C♯m/G♯)
- ful-ness, have mer-cy on this world. You nev-er turn
F♯m(Em) E(D) Em7(Dm)
or change, You nev-er break the faith,
B/D♯(A/C♯) F♯m(Em) E2(D)
Chorus
yes-ter-day, to-day and al-ways. Through it all,
C♯m(Bm) G♯m(F♯m) F♯(E) C♯m(Bm) G♯m(F♯m)
You are faith - ful, through it all, You are strong.
F♯(E) C♯m(Bm) G♯m(F♯m)
As we walk through the sha -

F♯(E)
E2(D)
G♯m(F♯m)
- dows, still You shine on,
1.
D.S.(v.2)
still You shine on.
2.
D.S.S.
3.,4.
E(D)
Through it all
Still You shine on.
Mid section
B(A)
You are faith - ful, Je - sus, You are
C♯m(Bm)
1.,3.-5.
faith - ful to the end. You are
Through it all

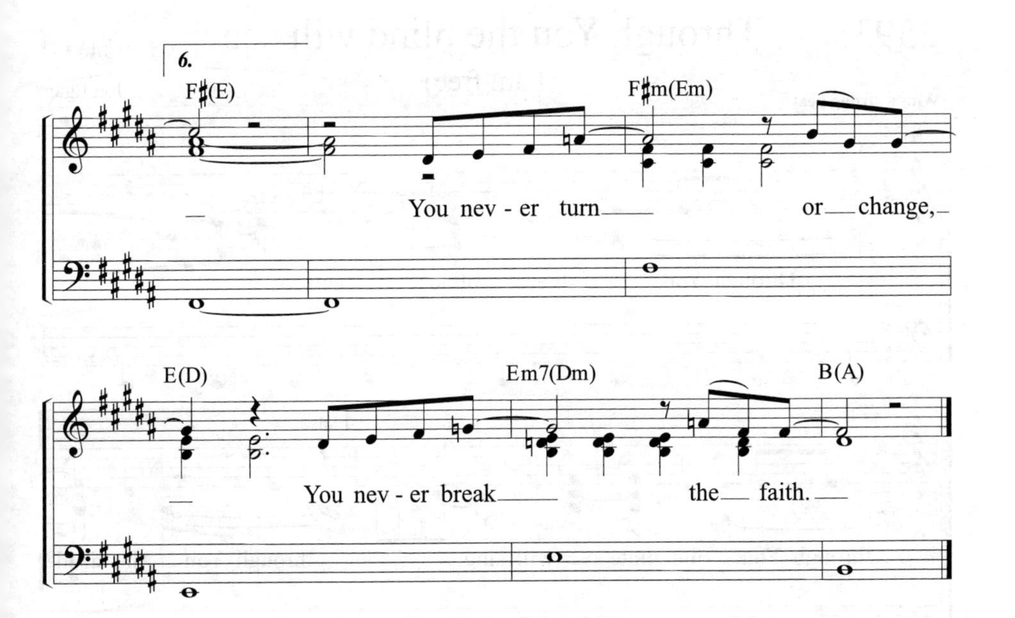

2. God of unbroken promises,
Always You keep Your word.
Glory, grace and holiness
Forever to endure.

2593. Through You the blind will see

(I am free)

Lk 4:18

Jon Egan

With a strong beat

Chorus
C
I am free to run, (I am
free to run,) I am free to dance,
F
(I am free to dance,) I am
Am7
Gsus4
free to live for You, (I am free to live for You,)
Last time to Coda
B♭sus2
I am free! (I am free!) I am free!

Dm7
(I am free!)
1.
C
F2/A
B♭sus2
C
F2/A
B♭sus2
D.C.
2.
D.S. al Coda
I am
Coda
C
(I am free!)
Csus4
I am free!
C
(I am free!)
Csus4
C

2594.
To give as You gave
(Here on the earth)
Mic 6:8; Mt 6:10; Jn 13:15; 15:12; Rom 12:1
Capo 4 (G)
Eoghan Heaslip & David Ruis
Thoughtfully
Verse
A
Bm7
To give as You gave, to love as You loved,
To walk as You walked, to serve as You served,
D
1.
A
E/G♯
we will fol - low where You lead.
2.
E/G♯
D
Bridge
lead.
We pour out our lives
E
D
F♯m
E/G♯
in wor - ship, pour out our lives for You.
Chorus
A
E/G♯
Let Your king - dom come, let Your will be done

Last time to Coda
D
E
here on the earth,
here on the earth.
A
E/G♯
Give us eyes to see,
the cou-rage to be-lieve
3rd time D.S. al Coda
D
E/G♯
here on the earth,
here on the earth.
1.
2.
D2
Asus4
A
Mid section
D
Bring-ing jus-tice,
E
F♯m
1.
C♯m
lov-ing mer-cy,
walk-ing hum-bly with our God.

2.
C♯m
D2
A
with our God.
C♯m/G♯
Dmaj7
Dsus2
D.S.
Coda
D2

2595. To God be the glory!

Ps 126:3; Lk 23:43; Jn 3:16; Heb 2:17; Rev 5:9

With strength

New music: Nathan Fellingham

2. O perfect redemption,
The purchase of blood!
To every believer
The promise of God:
The vilest offender
Who truly believes,
That moment from Jesus
A pardon receives.

3. Great things He has taught us,
Great things He has done,
And great our rejoicing
Through Jesus the Son,
But purer and higher
And greater will be
Our wonder, our worship
When Jesus we see!

Fanny J. Crosby (1820–1915)

2596. To Him who is able

Mk 13:26; Rom 8:11; 1 Cor 3:11; Eph 1:13; 1 Thess 4:17; Heb 6:19; 7:25; 10:12; Jud 24-25; Rev 5:12

With conviction

Lou & Nathan Fellingham & Gary Sadler

1.
2.,3.
A
Chorus
D/A A
home. 2. To To Him be the
D F♯m7 D
glo - ry, bless - ing and ho - nour and praise. All
D/A A D F♯m7
saints now a - dore Him, wor - ship the glo - ri - ous
D E7/G♯ A D/A A
name of Je - sus our King. To Him be the
D/F♯ A/E D D/A A
glo - ry, bless - ing and ho - nour and praise. All saints now a -

2. To Him who is able to save me completely,
Who has poured out His blood as the offering for sin,
And raised me to life by the power of the Spirit,
And sealed me for heaven to reign there with Him.

3. To Him who's returning to earth in His glory,
Clothed in His majesty, splendour and light;
And at last we'll behold Him, our glorious Saviour,
And forever and ever our worship will rise.

To him who is able to keep you from falling and to present you before his glorious presence without fault and with great joy – to the only God our Saviour be glory, majesty, power and authority, through Jesus Christ our Lord, before all ages, now and for evermore! Amen.

JUDE 24-25

2597. To see the King of heaven fall

(Gethsemane)

Mk 14:27, 35-36, 50; 15:34; Jn 8:12; 1 Cor 15:22; Heb 5:7; 1 Jn 4:10

Thoughtfully

Keith Getty
& Stuart Townend

2. To know each friend will fall away,
And heaven's voice be still,
For hell to have its vengeful day
Upon Golgotha's hill.
No words describe the Saviour's plight –
To be by God forsaken
Till wrath and love are satisfied,
And every sin is paid;
And every sin is paid.

3. What took Him to this wretched place;
What kept Him on this road?
His love for Adam's cursèd race,
For every broken soul.
No sin too slight to overlook,
No crime too great to carry,
All mingled in this poisoned cup –
And yet He drank it all.
The Saviour drank it all;
The Saviour drank it all.

2598. To You, O Lord, our hearts we raise

Mt 6:11; Jn 6:41; Heb 13:15; Rev 5:13; 22:1

GOLDEN SHEAVES

Capo 3 (D)

Music: A. Sullivan (1842–1900)
Arr. Paul Hughes

Unhurried

F(D) C/F(A/D) B♭/F(G/D) F(D) Gm/B♭(Em/G) Gm(Em)

1. To You, O Lord, our hearts we raise in hymns of a - do -

C(A) F(D) C/F(A/D) B♭/F(G/D) F(D) Gsus4(E) G(E)

ra - tion: ac - cept our sa - cri - fice of praise, our shouts of ex - ul -

Csus4(A) C(A) Am(F♯m) D(B) D/F♯(B/D♯)

ta - tion; for by Your hand our souls are fed – what

Gm(Em) F/A(D/F♯) B♭(G) Em7(♭5)(C♯m) Am7(F♯m) Dm7(Bm)

joys Your love has_ gi - ven! You_ give to us our

Gm7(Em) C7/E(A/C♯) F(D) Gm/B♭(Em/G) Gm(Em) C(A) F(D)

dai - ly bread, so give us bread from hea - ven!

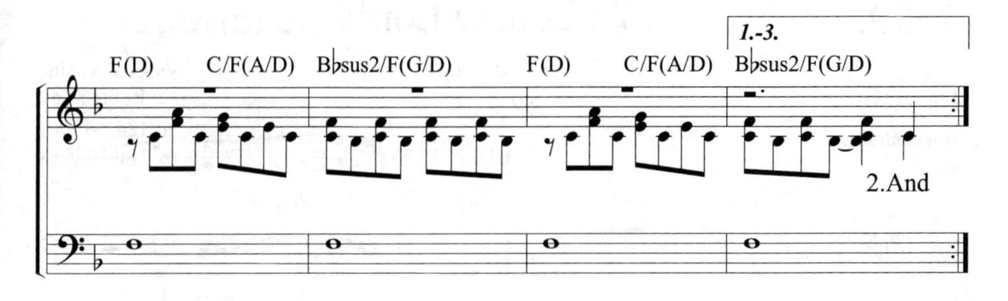

2. And now on this our festal day,
   Your love to us expressing,
   Our gifts before You, Lord, we lay,
   The firstfruits of Your blessing.
   Bright robes of gold the fields adorn,
   The hills with joy are ringing;
   The valleys stand so thick with corn
   That even they are singing.

3. Yet in Your presence we confess,
   O Lord of earth and heaven,
   Our pride, our greed and selfishness –
   We ask to be forgiven.
   And where the hungry suffer still
   Because of our ambition,
   There let our riches serve Your will,
   Your love be our commission.

4. There is a country bright as day
   Beyond the crystal river,
   Where hunger will be done away
   And thirst be gone forever;
   Where praises ring out loud and strong
   That now with ours are blending;
   Where we shall sing the harvest song
   That never has an ending.

After W. C. Dix (1837–98)

2599.
To You, O Lord
(One day)
Phil 2:10-11; Rev 4:8-11; 11:15, 17
Vicky Beeching
& Robin Mark
Capo 1 (G)
Rhythmically
(v.2)
Verse
D♭(C)
E♭(D)
1. To You, O Lord, will all the earth give glo -
Fm(Em)
A♭(G)
D♭(C)
E♭(D)
- ry. And no o-ther name will share the glo - ry too.
Fm(Em)
A♭(G)
D♭(C)
E♭(D)
Though king-doms rise, and na - tions mock Your mer -
Fm(Em)
A♭(G)
D♭(C)
E♭(D)
- cy, one day they'll stand and wor - ship on - ly You.

A♭(G)
Chorus
E♭/G(D/F♯)
Fm(Em)
Ev - 'ry knee will bow down, ev - 'ry tongue
D♭(C)
A♭(G)
E♭(D)
Fm(Em)
say out loud: 'You are the Lord of earth and hea - ven.'
D♭(C)
E♭/G(D/F♯)
Fm(Em)
Ev 'ry hand will be raised in the thun -
D♭(C)
A♭(G)
E♭(D)
Fm(Em)
- der of praise. 'You are the King of all cre-a - tion,' they'll say
D♭(C)
Last time to Coda
A♭(G)
Fm(Em)
A♭/C(G/B)
D♭(C)
one day.

2. Today we join with angels and archangels,
Who never cease, by day or night, to sing.
Yet we await the moment earth joins heaven
Around Your throne to raise an offering.

God exalted him to the highest place and gave him the name that is above every name, that at the name of Jesus every knee should bow, in heaven and on earth and under the earth, and every tongue confess that Jesus Christ is Lord, to the glory of God the Father.

PHILIPPIANS 2:9-11

2600. To You we bring our hymn of praise

(Glory be to God)

Gen 1:3; 1 Cor 15:55; Rev 4:8; 5:9, 13

Steadily

Stuart Townend, Matt Maher & Kelly Minter

3. You purchased captives for Your saints;
Glory be to God.
And opened wide the kingdom gates;
Glory be to God.

4. You overcame the sting of death;
Glory be to God.
And clothed us in Christ's righteousness;
Glory be to God.

5. Father, Spirit, risen Son;
Glory be to God.
Who was and is and is to come;
Glory be to God.

2601. Undivided love

Ps 86:11; Jn 10:3; Phil 2:6-7; Col 3:17, 23

Ben Cantelon
& Martyn Layzell

C Em7 D
I give You my life. Lord, You take con - trol;
C Em7 D
You have my heart, my soul, oh.
Am7/D
Chorus
C G
'Cause it's all for You:
D Am7 G/B C
all that I am I sur-ren - der, Je - sus, all for You.
G D Am7 G/B
Sa-viour, to You I sur - ren - der

C
Am7
G/B
C
Last time to Coda
now. I sur - ren - der now.
G
D/E
Em7
Cmaj7
1.
D
2.
D
Mid section
G
And all that I have e - ver done, and all
D/E
Em7
that I have now be - come, it's all
C
D
for You, it's all for You, God. With ev -

2. Undivided love – You gave it all,
Laying down Your majesty.
Mercy made a way, called me by name,
Welcomed me with open arms.

2602. Veiled in humanness

(The cross speaks)

Is 53:5; Mk 15:33-34; Rom 5:9; 1 Cor 15:53, 55; Col 2:15; Heb 1:3; 10:20

Building in strength

Suzanne Hanna

(v.2)
D
A/C♯
Esus4
E/G♯
Son of God bore wrath for me. In the
Bm7
A/C♯
Esus4
E
dark-ness of that awe-some day, Je-sus'
Bm7
A/C♯
Esus4
E
Chorus
A
blood would make a way. In hope-less - ness, the
D
Esus4
E
E/G♯
A
D
cross speaks hope; in fear and doubt, the cross speaks
Bm7
C♯
F♯m
C♯m
D
peace. In place of pain, the cross sup - plies our ev-'ry

2. Victor of the grave, disarming death You stand;
In radiance You reign, with power in Your hand!
Death, where is thy sting, the soul will never die;
Eternity is our reward.
And in the darkness of these final days,
Jesus' blood still makes a way!

When the perishable has been clothed with the imperishable, and the mortal with immortality, then the saying that is written will come true: Death has been swallowed up in victory.

1 CORINTHIANS 15:54

2603. Wake up, my soul

(Lift Him up)

Ps 57:8-9; 86:13; 96:2-3; Is 47:4; 63:1; Acts 4:12; 1 Cor 15:54; Jas 4:8; Rev 7:9; 14:6

With a driving rhythm

Kate Simmonds

B2
C♯m7
B2
con - quered the grave,
He is migh - ty to save.
C♯m7
B/D♯
E
F♯m7
A
Hal - le - lu - jah!
Chorus
E
A
Lift Him up, lift high the prai - ses of
F♯m7
our God and Sa - viour, our Re -
A
E
deem - er! On - ly one name saves us,

A
F♯m7
Him who died to raise us, Je - sus,
A
Last time to Coda
E
C♯m
Je - sus!
1.
D.C.(v.2)
2.
Mid section
A
A
C♯m7
And as we draw near, He will
B
A2
draw near to us. And as we draw near,
C♯m7
B
1.
A2
He will draw near to us.

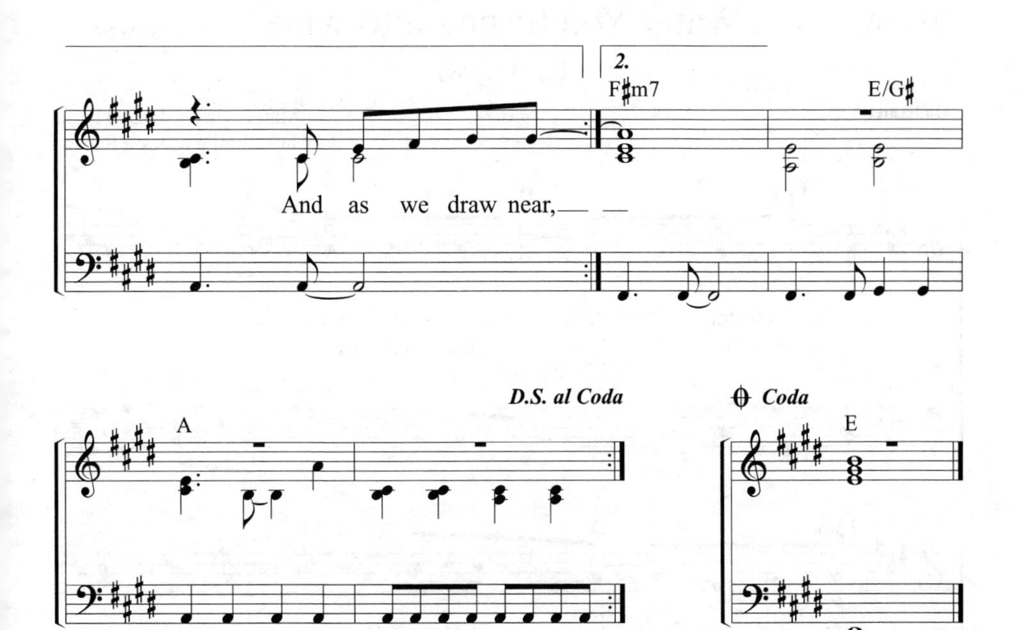

2. Who can be silent? Grace has been found;
With grateful hearts we come.
Let our love be a shout, let our praises be loud,
As we tell of all He's done.
From the ends of the earth
There's a song to be heard: our God saves!
Every tribe, every tongue,
Sing of unfailing love. Hallelujah!

2604. Water You turned into wine

(Our God)

Ps 86:8; Jn 2:9; 9:7; Rom 8:31; 2 Cor 4:6

Moderately

Matt Redman, Jonas Myrin, Chris Tomlin & Jesse Reeves

A
E/G♯
God, You are high - er than a - ny o - ther.
F♯m
D
3
Our God is heal - er, awe-some in pow - er, our God,
2° & 4° D.S. (al fine)
(Fine)
1.
A
3
Esus4
F♯m
D
our God.
D.C. (v.2)
2.
A
Esus4
F♯m
D
Mid section
A
Esus4
F♯m
(—) And if our God is for us,

D
A
then who could ev - er stop us;
and if our God is with us,
Esus4
F♯m
D
then what could stand a-gainst?
A/C♯
Esus4
F♯m
What could stand a-gainst?
D
A/C♯
Esus4
D.S.

2605. We are thirsty for You to flood our lives

(Let the rain come)

2 Chron 7:13-14; Ps 42:2; Hos 6:3; Mt 5:6; 6:9-10; Jn 17:21

Capo 3 (G)

Expectantly

Simon Brading, Kate Simmonds & Ben Hall

F/A(D/F♯)
Cm7(Am)
E♭(C)
in heaven, send the rain, fall again on us.
B♭(G)
F/A(D/F♯)
Cm7(Am)
For Your kingdom, Your glory, send the rain,
Last time to Coda
1.
E♭(C)
B♭(G)
F(D)
let the rain come, let the rain come on us.
D.C.
2.
Cm7(Am)
E♭(C)
Gm(Em)
F/A(D/F♯)
2. Holy
B♭(G)
Cm7(Am)
Mid section
Gm(Em)
Let the rain come, let the rain come,

2. Holy Spirit, the more we see of Christ,
We'll have passion to make Him known.
Then the whole world might know that You are God:
Lord, send Your revival rain.

2606. We believe You're a God who can mend

(Breathe)

Ex 15:26; Is 61:1, 3; Jer 31:13; Jn 20:22; Acts 2:21, 24

Moderately

Lou & Nathan Fellingham & busbee

G
F
C
pour out Your love from hea - ven. Come
G
F
C
breathe on us now, let this be the hour;
Last chorus D.S. al Coda
Last time to Coda
(D.S.)
come, Lord, and change us. Come
1.
D.C.
Am
G
F
C(no3rd)
Fsus2
come, Lord, and change us for-e - ver.
2.
Mid section
C(no3rd)
G
Am
F
C
ver.
Life giv - ing Spi - rit,
Bless - ing from hea - ven,
1.
2.
D.S.
G
Am
F2
F
C
Fsus2
come in this mo - ment.
show us Your
pow'r.
So

2. We believe You're a God
Who can free the captive,
Change darkness to light.
We believe You're a God
Who can rescue the sinner,
Turn death into life.
Bringing peace to the restless soul,
Giving purpose and making whole.

2607. We bow before the holy One

(Let Your rain fall down)

1 Kings 8:35-36; 18:1; 2 Chron 7:1, 13-14; Ps 46:10; Joel 2:23

Capo 3 (G)

Kate Simmonds

With awe and expectancy

B♭2/D(G/B)
E♭maj7(C)
B♭/F(G/D)
rain fall down, let Your rain fall
Last time to Coda
E♭/G(C/E)
B♭(G)
1.,3.,5.
D.S.
2.
D.C.
E♭maj7(C)
E♭maj7(C)
down on us. Let Your 2. I
4. (Optional extended tag)
E♭maj7(C)
B♭/D(G/B)
God of E - li - jah, send the rain;
E♭(C)
B♭/F(G/D)
come and fill this land a-gain with Your jus-tice and com-pas - sion,
E♭/G(C/E)
B♭/D(G/B)
with Your hope and re - sto-ra - tion. With Your gos-pel of sal-va - tion,

2. I hear the sound of heavy rain;
Let Your glory fill this place.
Oh, power of heaven, fall again;
Let Your glory fill this place.
This dry and weary land
Cries out for Your revival, mighty God.

2608. We bow our hearts

(Adoration)

Ps 95:6; 123:2; Phil 3:13-14; Rev 5:6, 11; 22:3

Brenton Brown

Chorus
G
D
Re-ceive our a-do - ra - tion, Je - sus, Lamb
Em
Em7
C
G
of God. Re-ceive our a-do - ra - tion;
1.,4.
D.C.(v.2)
D
Em
Em7
C
(Fine)
how won-der-ful You are. 2. We
3.
D.S. al fine
2.
Mid section
C
C
D
Dsus4
Re-ceive our a-do -
Ev-'ry soul You've saved sings
an - gels'
D
C
out, ev - 'ry - thing You've made re -
song, we're ga - thered to Your an - cient

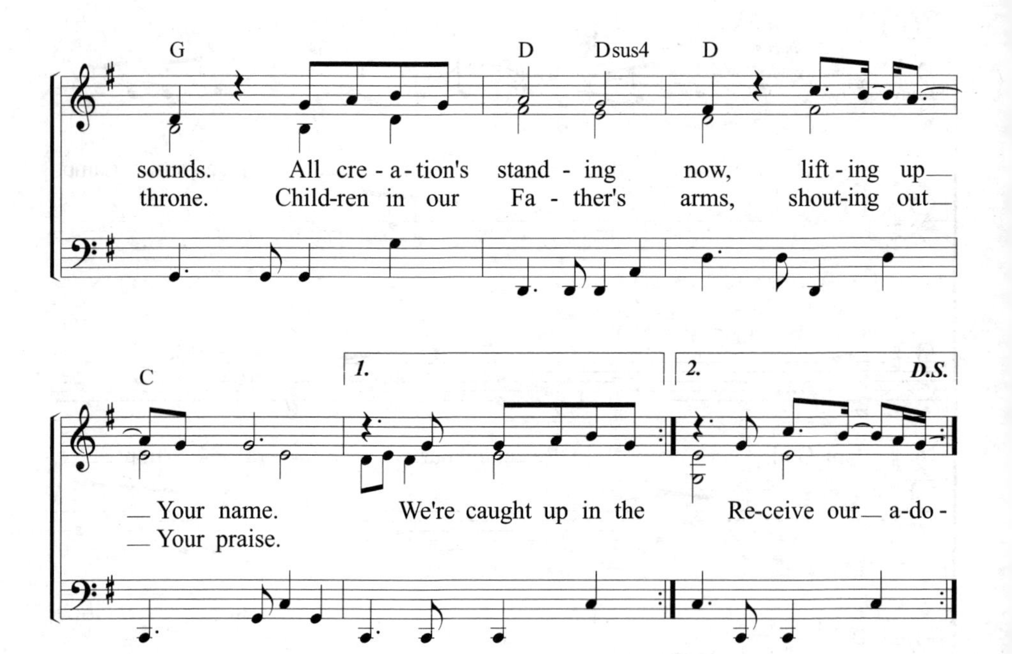
G
D
Dsus4
D
sounds. All cre - a - tion's stand - ing now, lift - ing up
throne. Child-ren in our Fa - ther's arms, shout-ing out
C
1.
2.
D.S.
Your name. We're caught up in the Re-ceive our a-do -
Your praise.

2609. We can hear it growing louder

(Amazing God)

Is 61:1, 3; Mt 11:29; Jn 12:46; 2 Cor 4:6; 1 Jn 1:7; Rev 7:9, 11

Em
Dsus2
C2
You can bear the weight of ev - 'ry hea - vy heart.
You can turn our tears in - to songs of praise.
G
1.
You can heal the
You're a - ma - zing, God.
D.C.(v.2)
2.,3.
C
Em
D
C
Mid section
G
Songs of praise sur - round us,
C
Em
songs of praise sur - round us. Hear it grow - ing loud - er.

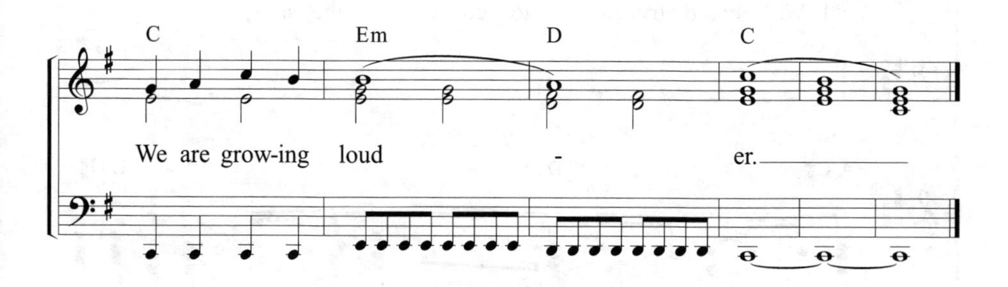

2. Beauty rises from the ashes,
Sorrow turns to gladness
When our God is near.
You speak light into our darkness,
You heal the broken-hearted,
You wipe away our tears.

2610.

We could try
(King of wonders)

2 Sam 7:22; Ps 19:1; 96:9; 147:4; Rom 1:20

Paul Baloche, Steven Curtis-Chapman, Stuart Garrard, Israel Houghton, Tim Hughes, Graham Kendrick, Andy Park, Matt Redman, Martin Smith, Michael W. Smith, Chris Tomlin, Darlene Zschech

Moderately

A/C♯
D
Bridge
Bm
Your glo-ry shines
be-fore our eyes;
A
D
the more we see,
the more we love
F♯m
E
Chorus
A
You.
King of won-ders,
we stand a-mazed;
D
there's no oth-er,
oth-er than You.
F♯m
King of won-ders,
You know the way
to our hearts,

2. You reveal and we respond –
You have shown there's no one like You, God;
Your love and mercy welcome us
Into the beauty of this holiness.

2611. # We fix our eyes on You
(We will worship You)

2 Kings 19:19; Ps 63:5; 86:10; Lam 3:22, 24; Mk 8:36; Heb 12:2

Prayerfully

Carlos Whittaker & Jason Ingram

Verse

A E
1. We fix our eyes on You, You are God a-lone.

A E
We fix our eyes on You, You're our on - ly hope,

A E Bsus4
for all we have to lose is our ve - ry souls.

B **1° D.C.(v.1)** 𝄋

Chorus

C♯m7 A E B
Save us from these com - forts,

C♯m7 A E Bsus4 B
break us of our need for the fa-mil - iar.

C♯m7 A E Bsus4 B
Spare us a-ny joy that's not of You, and we
Last time to Coda
C♯m7 A Bsus4 C♯m7 A
will wor - ship You, yeah, we will wor - ship
Bsus4 D.C.(v.2)
Mid section
G♯m7 C♯m7
1.-3.
A B
You. Hal - le - lu - jah.
4.
A B
D.S. al Coda
Coda
Bsus4
lu - jah.
You, yeah, we
C♯m7 A Bsus4 A2 E A2 E
will wor - ship You.

Verse
A
E
A
2. Sa - tis - fy us, Lord, in Your un - fail - ing love. Sa - tis - fy us, Lord,
E
A
that You would be e - nough. We have no - thing here;
E
Bsus4
B
let Your king - dom come.

2612. We have a strong and certain hope

(I know He lives)

Ps 8:1; 123:1; Acts 7:55; Col 1:15; 1 Thess 4:17; Heb 4:14, 16; 6:19-20; 10:19-20; 1 Jn 3:2; Rev 21:1

Capo 4 (C)

Graham Kendrick

1.
D.C.(v.2)
2.,3.
Chorus
B(G)
E2(C)
2. We have an
I know He lives.
B/D♯(G/B)
A/C♯(F/A)
E/B(C/G)
Je - sus is a - live and He
C♯m(Am)
A(F)
E/G♯(C/G)
Bsus4(G)
reigns in glo - ry now.
B(G)
E2(C)
B/D♯(G/B)
I know He lives,
A/C♯(F/A)
A(F)
F♯m7(Dm)
and with Him we'll rise: hal-le - lu - jah,

(D.S. last chorus repeat)
Last time to Coda
1.
B7sus4(G)
Eno3rd(C)
I know He lives.
D.C.(v.3)
2.
G6(E)
Mid section
3. We have a
lives.
We
C♯m(Am)
F♯/A♯(D/F♯)
see Him now in ma - je-sty, en - throned a-bove the
D(B♭)
ga - lax-ies, un - til His glo - ry bursts the skies and
B(G)
D.S. al Coda
all cre-a - tion joins the cry.
I know He

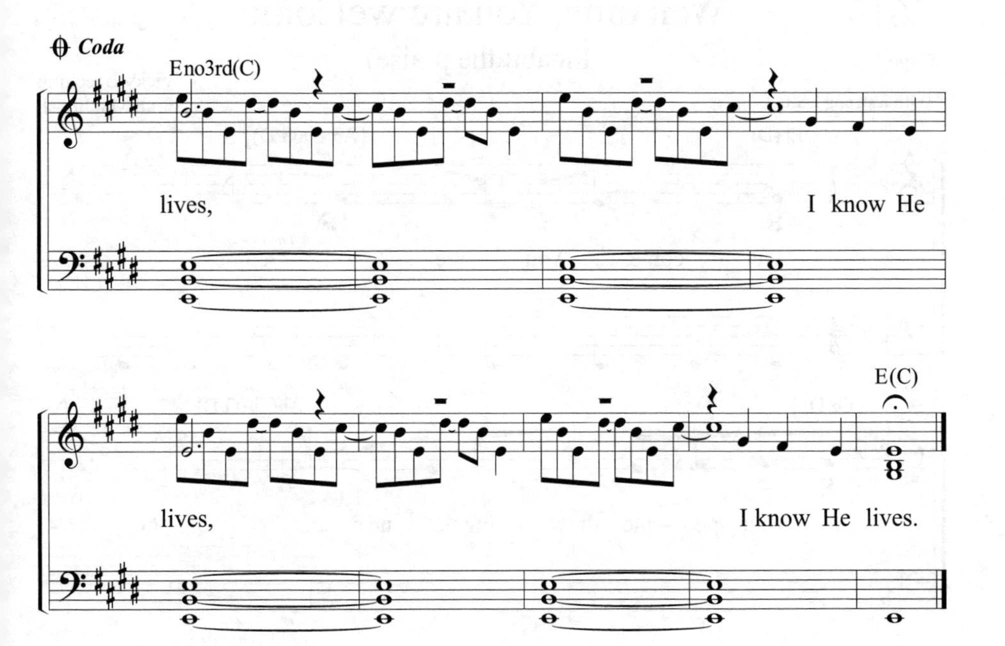

2. We have an anchor for the soul,
Since Jesus' blood has made a way
Into the deepest heart of God,
Before the Father's throne of grace.

3. We have a King high over all,
The new creation's firstborn Son.
New heaven and earth await His call;
We shall be like Him when He comes.

2613.
Welcome, You are welcome
Ps 22:3; 27:8; 63:1-2, 4
Capo 1 (D)
(Inhabit the praise)
Vicky Beeching
& Sarah MacIntosh
With a strong beat
Verse
E♭(D)
[A♭/E♭(G/D)]
(Chord v.2 only)
(Small notes v.2)
1. Wel - come, You are wel - come; see
[E♭(D)]
A♭/E♭(G/D)
Your peo - ple draw - ing near. O - ver -
E♭(D)
A♭/E♭(G/D)
whelm us with Your pre - sence; Lord,
E♭(D)
A♭(G)
Fm7(Em)
(v.2)
re - veal Your glo - ry here. We are sing - ing and bring - ing in
E♭/G(D/F♯)
A♭(G)
love songs with our hands held high.

Chorus
B♭(A) Cm(Bm) A♭(G) E♭/G(D/F♯) B♭(A) Cm(Bm)
Oh, in - ha - bit the praise of Your peo - ple, in-
A♭(G) E♭/G(D/F♯) B♭(A) Cm(Bm)
ha - bit this place as we seek You;
A♭(G) E♭/G(D/F♯) B♭(A)
vi - sit us, Lord. You're the One we're long - ing for,
Last time to Coda
A♭(G) B♭(A) A♭(G)
Je - sus, You're the One we're long - ing for.
1. D.C.(v.2)
B♭(A) Cm(Bm) A♭(G) E♭/G(D/F♯) B♭(A) Cm(Bm) A♭(G) E♭/G(D/F♯)

2.
Mid section
A♭(G) E♭/G(D/F♯) E♭(D)
Let His praises rise, let His praises rise,
E♭sus4(D) E♭(D) B♭/D(A/C♯) Cm7(Bm)
let His praises rise, let His praises rise,
1.-3. 4.
A♭(G) A♭(G) B♭(A) Cm(Bm)
let His Oh, in -
D.S. al Coda
A♭(G) E♭/G(D/F♯) B♭(A) Cm(Bm) A♭(G) E♭/G(D/F♯)
habit the praise of Your people,
Coda
B♭(A) A♭(G)
the One we're longing for.

2. Gazing at Your beauty,
   Lord, Your face will make us new.
   Thirsty for Your whispers,
   Chasing after more of You.
   We are singing and bringing in love songs
   With our hands held high.

2614. # We lift up our hearts

(Answers for this world)

Ps 8:1; 27:1; 63:4; 1 Cor 3:11; Phil 2:11

Eoghan Heaslip
& Ben Cantelon

With praise

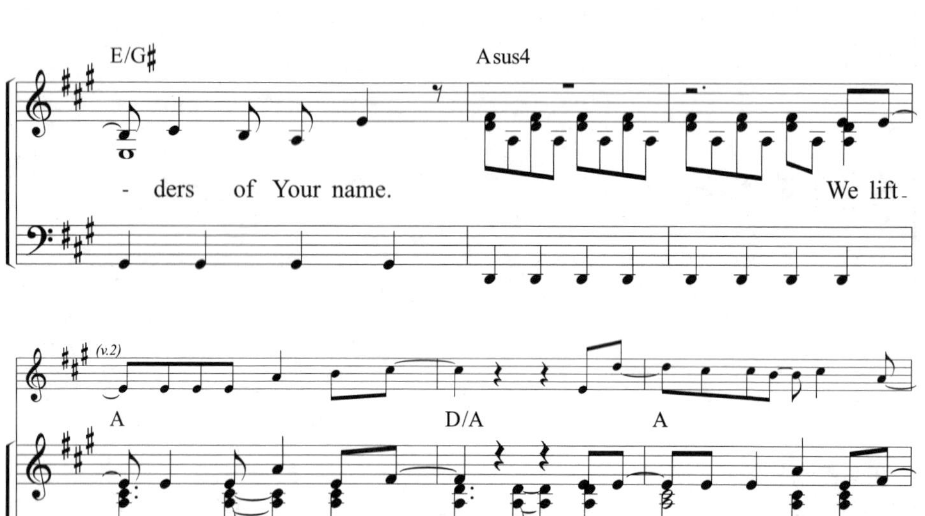

D/A
F♯m7
E/G♯
- tion, as we see the won - ders of Your name.
D2
1st time only
D
E
D
And for - e - ver we re -
E
D
D
Chorus
mem - ber:
You
A
E/G♯
are our light, joy and sal - va - tion; You sa - tis - fy, Je-
are our hope, strong, firm foun - da - tion; in ev - 'ry way, Je-
D2
E
- sus, You are the an - swer, the an - swer for
- sus, You are the an - swer, the an - swer for

Last time to Coda
1.,3.,5.
2.
D2/F♯
E/G♯
E/G♯
this world.
You
this world.
A
Asus4
A
Asus4
D.C.(v.2)
2. Let wor -
4.
E/G♯
Mid section
E
D
And for - e - ver we re -
1.
2.
E
D
E
A
mem - ber. And for mem - ber.
E/G♯
D2

2. Let worship and praise ring out,
The heavens and earth resound
To tell the world of the wonders of Your name.
Let every heart and mouth confess
The glory of Your majesty;
Jesus, the wonders of Your name.

2615. Well, the joy of the Lord

(The joy of the Lord)

Neh 8:10; Ps 27:5; 84:11; Is 52:9-10; Jn 6:68

Capo 2 (D)

Paul Simpson-Parry

Gently building

Verse

E(D)

Well, the joy of the Lord, it is my strength,
Lord, He is a sun and shield

C♯m(Bm)

and the song of the Lord, it is my hope;
who shel - ters all who run to Him,

A(G)

the pow'r of the Lord, it is His arm
and in His hands the suf - fer - ing

B(A)

laid bare.
find peace.

1.

Well, my

2.
Bridge
A/C♯(G/B)
(A/C♯)
B/D♯ E(D)
And in my heart, I know
A/C♯(G/B)
(A/C♯)
B/D♯ E(D)
A/C♯(G/B)
with-out You I'd be lost. In You there's ev -
(A/C♯)
B/D♯ E(D)
A(G)
E(D)
Chorus
- 'ry - thing.
I need You,
B(A)
C♯m(Bm)
A(G)
Re - dee - mer;
my Sav - iour;
You have the words of e - ter - nal life
Last time to Coda
E(D)
B(A)
F♯m(Em)
and I will fol - low You.

E(D)
C♯m(Bm)
After rpt, D.C.
(Well, the)

Coda
F♯m(Em)

2616.
We're not ashamed
(Not ashamed)
Lk 9:62; 19:40; Jn 14:6;
Rom 1:16; 2 Tim 1:12
Ben Cantelon
& Nick Herbert
Moderately
Verse
G
Bm
1. We're not a-shamed of the One
A
D/F♯
(v.2)
we love; there's a King of love who takes
G
a-way our shame. The cross
Bm
A
of Christ is our vic - to-ry;
D/F♯
the Sa-viour set us free, the Sa - viour, He's a-live.

G
A
G
Chorus
Oh no, we
A
Bm
G
A
Bm
won't stay si - lent, we'll shout it out from the roof-tops, sing - ing:
G
A
Bm
we're not a-shamed, we're not a - shamed of
D
A
2° D.S. (chorus 2)
G
You, Je - sus. Whoa,
A
Bm
(3 times)
1.
D
A
D.C.
whoah.
2. No turn -

2. No turning back, now to live for You,
   And tell the world it's true – You're the one and only way.
   No backing down, let the streets resound:
   Sing it louder now for all the earth to hear.

   (Chorus 2)
   The time is now or never
   To tell the world You're the only Saviour.
   We're not ashamed, not ashamed of You, Jesus.

2617. We're the forgiven

(We are the free)

Jer 20:9; Eph 2:6; Rev 14:3

Jonas Myrin
& Matt Redman

Chorus
Am
G
D
— We are the free, the free - dom ge-ne-ra-tion,
Em
C
G
sing - ing of mer - cy. You are the One who set
D
Em
C
us all in mo-tion; Yours is the glo - ry. There's a fire
G
Bm7
in our hearts and it burns for You; it's
Em
C
G
ne-ver going to fade a-way. We are the free, and

1.
G
Bm
Em
Yours is the glory!
D.C.(v.2)
2.,3.
C
Em
C
G
Yours is the glo - ry!
Last time to Coda
Bm
Em
C
Mid section
C
Up from the grave You rose again. Up from the grave You rose, and we will
- to the world that You so love, in - to the world we go, and we will
G
1.
rise up, rise up. In -
rise up, rise up,

2. We are the risen,
Living alive in You,
And our passion will not die,
No, our passion will not die.
Nothing can stop us;
We'll be running through the night,
And our passion will not die,
No, our passion will not die.

2618. We sing the song of saving grace

(Saving grace)

Ps 22:3; 86:13; 134:2; Rom 8:38-39; Eph 2:8; Col 1:14, 27

Neil Bennetts & Eoghan Heaslip

Joyfully

Chorus
A
Praise, praise, praise, lift your hands
Praise, praise, praise to our God
E/G♯
D
to hea - ven, for His love has res - cued us
for e - ver, for the glo - ry of His name,
1.
A/C♯
F♯m
E
from the sha-dow of the grave.
Last time to Coda
2.
A/C♯
D
E/G♯
we sing the song of sav - ing
1.
A
E/G♯
A
grace.

D.C.(v.2)
2.
E/G♯
D
Mid section
grace. A love stron - ger than death
A/C♯
F♯m
has lift - ed our heads; and
E
we find peace in the pre - sence of God.
D
A/C♯
Love high - er than moun - tains
D
still is the rea - son we sing, the rea -

2. Your hope in us, it shines the way;
You bring us freedom.
For all our sin and all our shame
You have forgiven.

2619. We thank You, God

Is 58:3; Mic 6:8; Mt 6:11; Phil 4:19

Noel & Tricia Richards & Tom Lane

Reflectively

3. Open our eyes: we need to care.
Move in our hearts, teach us to share
Your riches everywhere:
Love beyond compare.

2620.
We've got nothing to lose
(No reason to hide)
Ps 40:5; Jn 6:68; Rom 8:18, 39; Phil 2:10
Matt Crocker
& Joel Houston
Capo 3 (D)
Quite quickly
Verse
F(D)
1. We've got no - thing to lose,
B♭(G)
(v.2,2)
we've got no rea - son to hide,
we'll see Your name lif - ted high;
Dm(Bm)
we've got the an - swer in - side of us;
'cause there is no - bo - dy else for us,
1.
B♭(G)
(v.2)
it's time we took the dis - gui - ses off.
We'll see Your glo - ry re-vealed,
2.
Je - sus, You are the on -

B♭(G)
Chorus
F(D)
- ly One. Whoa, You're a - live
(chor 2) Your love has spo -
B♭(G)
Dm(Bm)
and we are free,
- ken and we be - lieve,
You are ev - 'ry - thing, ev -
1.
F(D)
B♭(G)
F(D)
- 'ry - thing we need, yeah!
D.C.(v.2)
2. There's not a mi - nute to waste,
2.,4.
D.S. (Chorus 2)
3.,5.
B♭(G)
B♭(G)
yeah! Whoa,

F(D)
E♭maj7(C)
Whoa,
whoa,
Gm(Em)
B♭(G)
Last time to Coda
whoa.
F(D)
Mid section
E♭(C)
No - thing com - pares to You,
no - thing could
Gm7(Em)
e - ver se - pa-rate us now,
Your love
(3.) this love.
1.,2.
B♭(G)
is ours.
3.
B♭(G)
D.S.
Whoa,

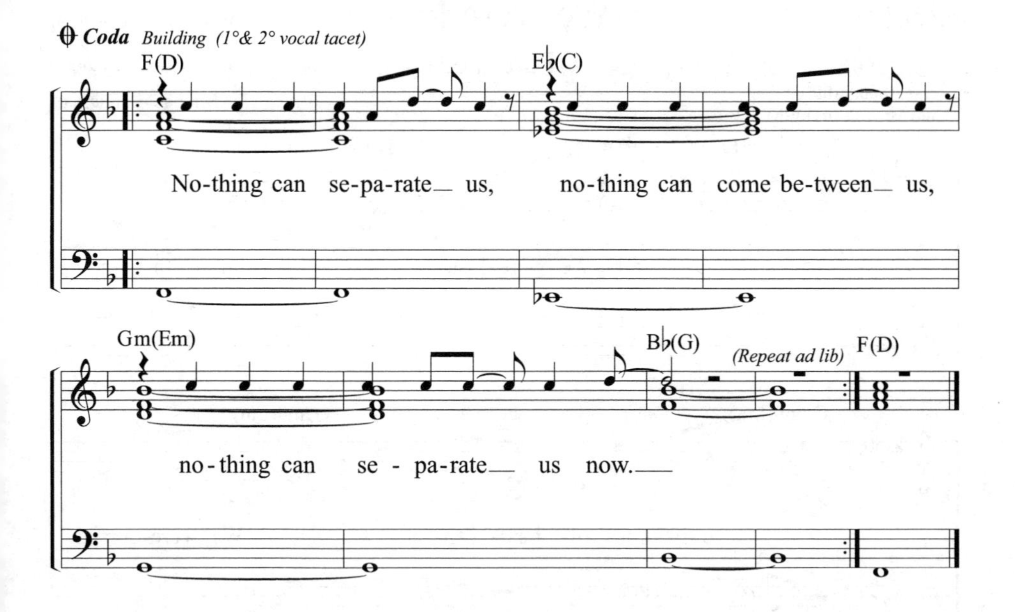

2. There's not a minute to waste,
Not a second to lose,
'Cause there's a city that waits for us;
It's time we took all the lamp shades off.
We'll see Your glory revealed,
And see Your name lifted higher;
'Cause there is nobody else for us,
Jesus, You are the only One.

2621.

We were lost
(Pardoned)

Mk 14:24, 36; Rom 6:14; 1 Cor 7:23; 2 Cor 5:21; Eph 2:6, 12, 14; 3:3; 1 Jn 1:7

Capo 4 (G)
Verse: thoughtfully
Chorus: with strength

Michael Sandeman

Chorus
B(G)
C♯m/B(Am/G)
F♯/B(D/G)
B(G)
Par - doned and se - cure in the Fa - ther's love,
C♯m/B(Am/G)
F♯sus4(D)
F♯(D)
seat - ed in the heav'n - ly realms.
B(G)
C♯m/B(Am/G)
F♯/B(D/G)
G♯m(Em)
Re - con - ciled to God, we're for - gi - ven,
Last time to Coda 2° & 4° D.S. (chor 2)
B(G)
C♯m/B(Am/G)
F♯sus4(D)
F♯(D)
B/D♯(G/B)
E(C)
ne - ver bound by sin a - gain. Praise the King who
B/F♯(G/D)
F♯(D)
B/D♯(G/B)
E(C)
saved us through His suff - 'ring, for His life was

2. Dividing walls now destroyed,
And wrath that stood against us.
Christ the man drank that cup,
As through the cross . . .

(Chorus 2)
See the glory,
Sense the majesty,
Know the mystery of God.
Revelation of His wisdom,
Shown to us in Jesus Christ.

2622. We will dance, we will dance

(For Your glory)

2 Sam 6:14; Ps 24:7; Acts 4:12; Rom 12:1

Ben Cantelon
& Matt Redman

Moderately paced

Verse

A

1. We will dance, we will dance for Your glo - ry, we will dance, we will dance for Your glo - ry,
up a shout to a - dore You, ev - 'ry sound that we make, it is for You,

G D/F♯

we will dance for Your glo - ry, Lord.

5th time jump to 𝄋𝄋

A

1.,4.

2. We will lift

2.,3.

Bridge

For sal - va -

G

- tion's in this place, You're the name

D/F♯
A
by which we're saved: Je - sus, Je-sus.
G
Let Your name be lift - ed high,
D/F♯
as our thank - ful hearts now cry: Je - sus,
F♯m
G
Chorus
Je - sus. Lift
A
F♯m7
up your heads, you an - cient gates. Be lift-ed up, you
up a shout to shake the skies. Lift up a cry: 'Be
G
an - cient doors: the King is com-ing in, the
glo - ri - fied!' The King is com-ing in, the

D
1.,3.,5.
2.,6.
D.C.
King is com-ing in. We lift
1. We will dance
King is com-ing in.
4.
A
Mid section
We're the
A
peo - ple of God with a song to sing, and we're
cross is the hope that we hold up high, as we
bring - ing our lives as an of - fer - ing; we will
tell the whole world of Your love and life; we will
G
D
4th time to Coda
A
dance for Your glo - ry, Lord.
1.,3.
2.
D.S.
Coda
And Your
Lift
A

2623. We will fill up this place with Your praise

(There is none like You)

2 Sam 7:22; Is 63:1; Lk 15:4; Jn 15:15; 2 Cor 3:18; Rev 21:5

Country rock feel

Robin Mark & Johnny Parks

F G
bro - ken, still You love it so.
E Am F
Though our hearts are prone to wan - der, still You
seek us and You find us, call - ing us back
1° D.C. (chor 2 & v.2)
2° D.C. (chor 1) al Mid section
Mid section
G
home. You're the God
Gsus4 G
You, my
C Am Fmaj7
friend. There is no one like You, there is

(Chorus 2)
You're the God who is mighty to save;
There is none like You,
There is none like You, my friend.
You're the One who has conquered the grave;
There is none like You,
There is none like You, my friend.

2. All the wonders of creation,
   Formed and found in You.
   Work in us this transformation,
   Changed from glory
   Into glory,
   Making all things new.

2624. We will sing, sing, sing

(Sing, sing, sing)

Ex 13:21; Ps 9:2; 43:3; 69:34; Jn 20:31

Chris Tomlin, Jesse Reeves,
Matt Gilder, Daniel Carson & Travis Nunn

D
x4
Verse
D(no3rd)
1. What's not to love about You? Heaven and earth adore You,
2. You are the love that frees us, You are the light that leads us.
Bm7
kings and king - doms bow down.
like a fi - re burn-ing,
Son of God,
Asus4
1.
You are the One, You are the One
G(no3rd)
we're liv - ing for.

2.
Asus4
G(no3rd)
You are the One
we're liv - ing for.
D
D.S.
Mid section
Csus2
Gsus2
We will
D
D.S.
Coda
D

2625. We worship a wonderful Saviour

2. We worship a wonderful Saviour;
In the form of this child is the fullness of God.
His infinity hides in His weakness,
His divinity beats in His human heart.

3. We worship a wonderful Saviour;
He was born as a man, yet was fully divine.
He is God, come to dwell with His people,
He's the Word become flesh, He is Jesus Christ.

2626. We, Your children pray
(King of the broken)

2 Chron 7:14; Lk 11:2; Jn 20:22; Rev 21:4; 22:2

Capo 1 (G)

Paul Baloche, Steven Curtis-Chapman, Stuart Garrard, Israel Houghton, Tim Hughes, Graham Kendrick, Andy Park, Matt Redman, Martin Smith, Michael W. Smith, Chris Tomlin, Darlene Zschech

Steadily, building

(C/E) (D/F♯) Chorus
Fm7(Em) D♭(C) E♭(D) D♭/F E♭/G A♭sus4(G) A♭(G)
Fill us, breathe up-on us. Je - sus,
Last time to Coda
(Last chorus)
E♭/G(D) Fm7(Em) D♭(C)
Je - sus, heal-er of na-tions, hope of sal - va - tion.
(Last chorus) hope of the world.
A♭sus4(G) A♭(G) Cm7(Bm) Fm7(Em)
Je - sus, Je - sus, King of our hearts,
(Last chorus)
Last time D.S. al Coda
1.
D♭(C) A♭(G)
King of the bro - ken
(Last chorus) hope of the world.
A♭sus4(G) A♭(G) A♭sus4(G) A♭(G) D.C.(v.3)

2. Healing King of nations,
   Let Your kingdom come.
   Purify Your church, Lord,
   Your glory over us.

3. Lover of the wounded,
   Defender of the weak,
   Friend of the forgotten;
   You wipe away our tears.

2627.

Whatever comes

Job 13:15; Ps 2:1; Rom 8:19, 22; Eph 6:13; Phil 3:14; 1 Tim 1:17

G2
D.C.(v.2)
4.,6.
2. What - e - ver comes, what - e - ver comes,
D
Chorus
D
D/F♯
Al - migh - ty, im -
G
D/F♯
mor - tal, al - ways on Your throne, the
G
Asus4
A
D
sov - 'reign in con - trol. Un - chang - ing,
D/F♯
G
D/F♯
pre - vail - ing, though the na - tions rage, You're

2. Whatever comes,
Cultures will rise as nations fall,
Troubles will challenge and assault,
Your word will stand above them all.
Whatever comes,
All that we cannot comprehend –
Disasters will break the pride of men –
You will be faithful till the end,
Whatever comes.

3. Whatever comes,
Nothing on earth escapes Your gaze,
All of creation groans and waits
For the revealing of Your name.
Whatever comes,
Our enemies will intimidate,
This is the testing of our faith,
Still we will stand our ground and wait,
Whatever comes.

2628. What grace is mine

Is 40:31; Lk 9:23-24; Eph 2:8, 13; Heb 7:25; 1 Pet 2:24

Capo 3 (G)

LONDONDERRY AIR

Words: Kristyn Getty
Music: Irish traditional melody

Refrain
E♭6(9)/B♭(C/G)
(D) (C/E) (D/F♯)
F E♭/G F/A B♭sus2(G) B♭(G) E♭(C)
known? So I will go wher-ev - er He is
Dm7(Bm) Gm(Em) E♭(C) Gm7(Em) E♭(C) B♭2/D(G/B)
call - ing me. I lose my life to find my life in
(C/E) (D/F♯) (G/B) (C♯m)
E♭/G(C/E) F(D) E♭/G F/A B♭(G) B♭7/D E♭(C) Em7♭5
Him. I give my all to gain the hope that
(Em) (C) (Em)
B♭/F(G/D) Gm7 E♭ E♭m(Cm) B♭/F(G/D) Gm7add4 Cm(Am) F(D)
ne-ver dies. I bow my heart, take up my cross and fol-low

2. What grace is mine to know His breath alive in me?
Beneath His wings, my wakened soul may soar.
All fear can flee, for death's dark night is overcome:
My Saviour lives and reigns forever more.

It is by grace you have been saved, through faith – and this not from yourselves, it is the gift of God – not by works, so that no-one can boast.

EPHESIANS 2:8-9

2629. What heart could hold?

(Holy)

Capo 3 (G)

Ex 3:14; 15:11; 1 Cor 2:9; 13:12; Eph 3:18-19; Phil 2:9; 1 Pet 4:5; Rev 1:7, 16; 4:8

Jonas Myrin, Matt Redman & Jason Ingram

Building in intensity

E♭(C)
B♭(G)
2.
Chorus
(small notes chor 3°, 5° & 6°)
F(D)
Gm7(Em)
E♭(C)
You are ho - ly, ho - ly,
E♭(C)
B♭(G)
Fsus4(D)
F(D)
Gm7(Em)
E♭(C)
ho - ly, God most high and God most
E♭(C)
B♭(G)
Fsus4(D)
F(D)
Gm7(Em)
E♭(C)
wor - thy. You are ho - ly, ho - ly,
Fsus4(D)
F(D)
Gm(Em)
E♭(C)
ho - ly, Je - sus, You are, Je - sus, You are.

1.
D.C.(v.2)
2.,4.
D.S.
Fsus4(D) F(D)
2. Your name a
Fsus4(D) F(D) Fsus4(D) F(D)
You are
5.,6.
(small notes opt. last time)
Fsus4(D) Gm(Em) E♭(C)
Je - sus, You are Je - sus, You are.
(Fine)
D.C.(v.3) al fine
3.
F(D)
3. And You will
Fsus4(D)
Je - sus, You are
Gm(Em) E♭(C) Fsus4(D) F(D) Fsus4(D) F(D)
Je - sus, You are.
Mid section
E♭(C) B♭(G) F(D) Gm(Em)
Who shall we say You are? You're the liv - ing God.

2. Your name alone has power to raise us.
Your light will shine when all else fades.
Our eyes will look on Your glorious face,
Shining like the sun.
Who is like You God?

3. And You will come again in glory
To judge the living and the dead.
All eyes will look on Your glorious face,
Shining like the sun.
Who is like You God?

2630. What hope we hold
(Emmanuel/Hallowed manger ground)

Mt 1:17, 23; 2:2, 6; 27:29, 54; Lk 1:35; 2:7; Jn 1:14; Col 1:19-20; 1 Jn 1:1

Reverently

Ed Cash
& Chris Tomlin

Chorus
A
E
A2/C♯
D Dsus2
A/C♯
D
A/E
ma - nu - el, Em - ma - nu - el, God in - car-nate, here to
E
A
E
A2/C♯
Dsus2
A/C♯
dwell. Em- ma - nu - el, Em - ma - nu - el, praise His
Last time to Coda
D
A/E
A
D2/F♯
A/E
D2/F♯
Verse
name – Em - ma-nu - el. 3. The
A
D2/F♯
E
Son of God here, born to bleed; a crown of thorns would
D/F♯
A
A/C♯
D
Dsus2
pierce His brow. And we be-held this of-fer-ing, ex -

2. What fear we felt in the silent age –
Four hundred years – can He be found?
But broken by a baby's cry;
Rejoice in the hallowed manger ground.

The virgin will be with child and will give birth to a son, and they will call him Immanuel – which means, God with us.

MATTHEW 1:23

2631. What if I held in my hands?

(Glorify)

Mt 13:44; Col 1:27; Heb 6:19

Capo 2 (D)

Adam Carmichael
& Ken Riley

B(A) C♯m7(Bm7) A(G) E(D)
all I am to call Your own; let my life bring glo - ry to You.
Bsus4(A) B(A) A(G) E(D)
No - thing, Lord, can take Your place,
B(A) C♯m7(Bm7) A(G) E(D)
You de - serve the high - est praise; let my life bring glo - ry to You.
1.
D.C.(v.2)
2.,3.
Mid section
Bsus4(A) B(A) Bsus4(A) B(A)
3. When my heart
Glo - ri - fy,
A(G) E(D) B(A) C♯m7(Bm7) A(G) E(D)
glo - ri - fy You, God, glo - ri - fy You with my life.

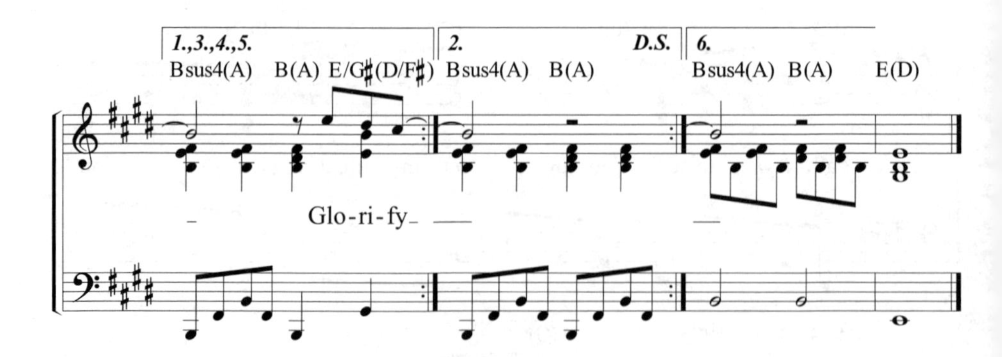

2. If my world's shattered in pain
   And if hope's fading away,
   The strength I have burning inside:
   Christ in me, Christ in me.

3. When my heart centres on You,
   And Your word anchors my soul,
   Then everything, all that I am,
   Worships You, worships You.

The kingdom of heaven is like treasure hidden in a field. When a man found it, he hid it again, and then in his joy went and sold all he had and bought that field.

MATTHEW 13:44

2632. What kind of throne?

Ps 22:3; Mt 2:11; Lk 2:7; Jn 8:12

2. What kind of Saviour makes weakness His strength,
   In frailty depending on those He would save,
   And veiling the power that always belonged to His name?
   What kind of child causes heaven to sing,
   With angels proclaiming the hope that He brings?
   This is the glory of God; this is Jesus, the King.

2633. What love is this?

(Everlasting love)

Ps 103:17; Jer 31:3; Rom 5:5; Phil 3:9-10, 14; Col 2:14; Heb 12:6; 1 Jn 4:18

Stuart Townend
& busbee

2. What love is this that purges fear
And cancels every sin,
Yet loves enough to lead me through
The fires of discipline?
The suffering that works in me
The jewel of humility:
Everlasting love,
Everlasting love,
Everlasting love,
Be my comfort and guide.

3. What love is this, what priceless gift,
So freely poured on me?
If all the wealth of earth was mine,
No richer would I be.
The greatest prize, to know the King,
And know that I am loved by Him:
With everlasting love,
Everlasting love,
Everlasting love,
Be my hope and my light.

2634. When everything's breaking

(We shall not be shaken)

Ex 3:14; Deut 32:4; Ps 62:2; Mal 3:6

Matt Redman
& Jonas Myrin

Chorus
Asus4
D2
F♯m7
G
D
Our God, You are all that You say You are;
are faithful in all Your ways;
Last time to Coda
Bm7
F♯m
You ne - ver change, You ne - ver fail, You ne - ver
for - ev - er You stand, for - ev - er You reign, fo - ev - er re -
1.,3.
2.
G
fade. Our God, You main. And we shall not be sha - ken.
Bm
A(no3rd)
We shall not be sha-ken.
D.C.
When ev-'ry-thing's

4.
G
Mid section
D/F♯
main. And we shall not be sha - ken.
(small notes 3°&4°)
(1.,3.) We shall, we
(2.,4.) You are, You
G2
shall not be sha - ken. We shall, we
are ne - ver chan - ging. You are, You
D
A/C♯
shall not be sha - ken when all a - round is sink-ing sand.
are ne-ver chan - ging. You will stand, the great I Am.
1.-3.
4.
D.S. al Coda
G
(1.,3.) For
(2.) No,
The great I Am. Our God, You
Coda
G
main. And we shall not be sha - ken, we shall not be sha - ken.

He is the Rock, his works are perfect, and all his ways are just. A faithful God who does no wrong, upright and just is he.

DEUTERONOMY 32:4

2635.
When I am lost
(The Father's name)
Ps 23:1; Mt 28:19; Lk 15:4; 24:2; Jn 14:27
Capo 3 (G)
Mark Niedzwiedz
Worshipfully
Verse
Chorus
(v.2)
B♭2(G) B♭(G) E♭6/B♭(C/G) E♭2/B♭(C/G)
1. When I am lost, the Lamb of God
shep-herds me back home.
(C/G) (C/G) E♭6/B♭ E♭/B♭
When I'm un-done,
E♭6(C) E♭2(C) B♭2(C)
Je-sus, You come and roll a-way my stone.
F(D) E♭6(C) B♭sus2(G) B♭(G)
You're the One who car-ries me o-ver moun-tains,
E♭6(C) B♭sus2(G) B♭(G) E♭maj7(C)
ri-vers deep. You're the joy my heart pro-claims

1.
F(D)
Bbsus2(G)
(G) Bb(no3rd)
(C) Eb6(9)
D.C.(v.2)
in the Fa - ther's name.
2.
F(D)
Bbsus2(G) Bb(G)
Eb6(C)
Bbsus2(G)
in the Fa-ther's name. You're the One who res-cues me,
Bb(G)
Eb6(C)
Bbsus2(G) Bb(G)
fills my life with in - ner peace. You're the Christ my
Eb2(C)
F(D)
Bb(G)
heart pro-claims in the Fa - ther's name,
Eb2(C)
rit.
F7sus4(D)
Bb(G)
in the Fa - ther's name.
2. When I have less,
Lord, I am blessed
With more than I know.
When on my knees,
Then I am freed;
Chains – they have no hold.

2636. When I am lost

(I have been redeemed)

Is 53:5; Eph 1:7; 1 Jn 1:7

Wendy O'Connell

Chorus
G A Asus4 A D A
so I can know: Now I am for - gi -
G A D A
- ven, I have been set free; through the blood of Je -
G A Bm A
- sus I have been made clean. Now I know of His mer -
G A Last time to Coda
- cy be-cause He died for me; I have been re-deemed.
1. D.C.
D A/C♯ D A/E D G A D

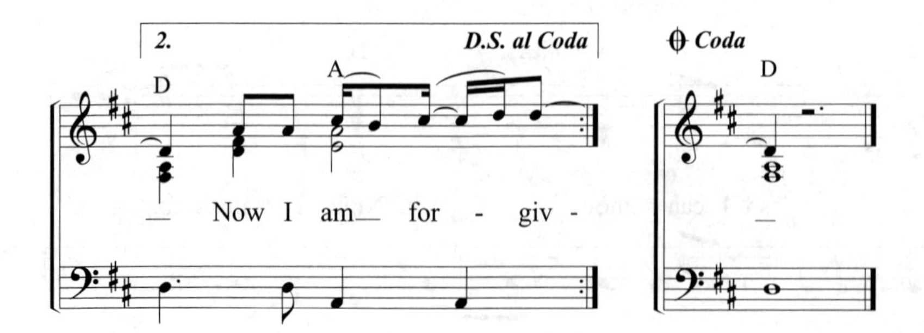
2.
D.S. al Coda
Coda
D
A
D
Now I am for - giv -

2637. When I draw near You

(Mercies)

Ps 113:3; Lam 3:22-23; Jas 4:8

 SoF 5

1.
A
- cies are new ev - 'ry morn - ing, Your love
B7
ne - ver end - ing. Your mer -
2.
A
D
- cies are new ev - 'ry morn - ing, Your love is ne-ver
1.,3.
Last time to Coda
D.C.
E
A
D2/A
A
D2/A
end - ing. Yeah. When
2.
Mid section
E
D
end - ing. From the ri - sing of the sun to its

F♯m
1.
E
go - ing down a - gain, the Lord's name is to be
praised. From the
2.
E
name is to be praised.
A
D2/A
A
D2/A
A
D2/A
E
D.S. al Coda (inc. rpt)
Your mer -
Coda
A
D2/A
A
D2/A
A
D2/A
A

2638. When I feel I'm not enough

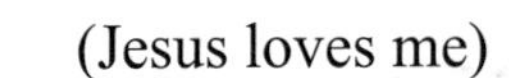

(Jesus loves me)

Deut 32:10; Lk 15:17; Rom 8:38-39; Heb 1:3

Aaron Keyes
& Ben Smith

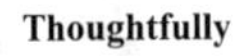

Thoughtfully

F
Verse 1 only
Am
Dm9
all out for-sa - ken You, oh,
I re-mem-ber:
(After mid section)
Verse 2 only
G
Chorus
Fmaj9
Je - sus loves me,
Last time to Coda
C
Dm7
Je - sus loves me, Je - sus
1.
G
C
D.C.(v.2)
loves me so.
2. When I

2.
G
C
D.S.
4.
Dm/G
loves me so.
loves me
C
Csus4
C
D.S. al Coda
3.
G
C
so.
O
loves me, this I know.
Mid section
Dm7
C/E
Nei-ther death nor life, not an-gels or de-mons, not
F
Gsus4 G Gsus2 G
Dm7
a-ny-thing that is to come; nei-ther depth nor height, nor
C/E
F
1.
G
all of cre-a-tion, can se-pa-rate me from Your love. Nei-ther

2. When I think about the way
You spoke the word, and worlds were made,
Yet You call me child,
The apple of Your eye;
When I lie down to sleep,
My heart skips a beat
At the thought so sweet.

2639. When I fix my eyes on You

(From the inside out)

Rom 12:1; 2 Cor 4:16; Heb 9:14; 12:2

G D A
is Yours a-lone. Ho-ly Spi - rit, re-store me. Lord, I bow
G D Em7 3 A
be-fore Your throne. Ev-'ry breath, ev-'ry thought: Lord, take
D A/C♯ Bm G
them and make them pure. Please cap - ti-vate, please cap-
A D
- ti-vate me from the in - side out.
1. D.C. 2. Mid section
Bm G D Dsus4 D
When I I'm

Bm
F♯m7
thir-sty, Lord, for more of You. Please
G
A
1.
Bm
take me and mould me, make me new. I'm
2.
Bm
D
new. From the in - side out, from the in -
Bm
G
A
- side out, You change me, Lord, from the in - side out.
D
Dsus4
D

2640. When I'm dry and thirsty, Lord

(Your love is everything)

Ps 42:2; 77:2, 11; 103:2-4; Jer 31:34; Lk 1:37; Phil 4:19

G/B
Em
Your love fills my ev - 'ry need, Your love is ev - 'ry thing to me,
D
C
Your love is ev - 'ry-thing. Your love heals ev' - ry di-sease,
G/B
Em
Your love fills my ev - 'ry need, Your love is ev - 'ry-thing to me,
1.
D
C
Em
G/B
C2
Your love is ev - 'ry-thing.
Em
G/B
C
D.C.
2.,3.
D/F♯
Mid section
I will not forget,

C
(1.,2.,5.,6.) I won't for - get Your pro -
(3.,4.) that no - thing is im - pos -
D
Em
- mi-ses.
- si - ble.
I will not for-get,
I won't for-get Your love.
1.-3.,5.
4.
D.S.
Last time
D/F♯
D(no3rd)
I will not for-get
Optional verse (Chris McClarney/Mark Woodward/Anthony Skinner)
Em
G2/B
G
2. I was all messed up in - side, full of pain, I bought the lie,
Cmaj7
C6
but some-one said that You loved me. And then You snuck
in like a thief, stole the lie that I be-lieved; now
I know I can trust in Your love.

2641. When I'm filled with doubt and fear

(Hallelujah)

Ex 3:14; Jn 1:29; 8:58; 19:30, 34; Acts 2:23-24; Rom 1:16; 12:1; Eph 1:7, 10; 1 Pet 2:24

With a celtic feel

Derri Daugherty, Katie Gustafson & John Hartley

Verse

D

1. When I'm filled with doubt and fear, con-dem -

G/D D (v.3) Bm G

na - tion e-ver near, I will praise You through my tears: hal-le-

Asus4 D G

lu - jah! Hope that fills me with Your peace, grace that

D/F# (v.4) Bm G

sets my heart at ease; in Your pre-sence there's re - lease: hal-le-

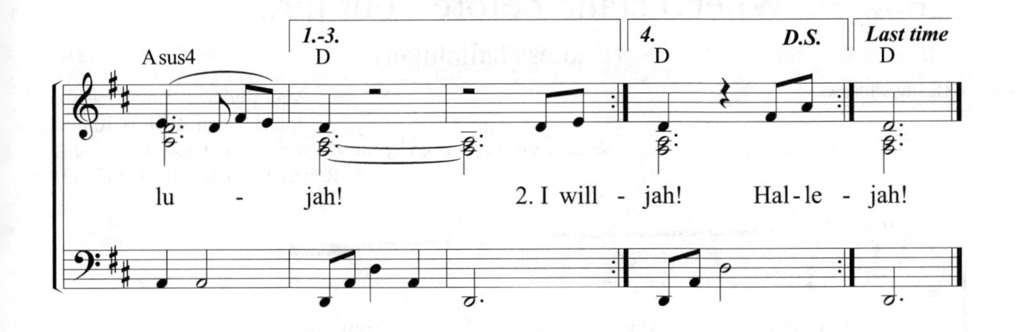

2. I will never be ashamed,
For Your mercies I'll proclaim;
There is power in Jesus' name:
Hallelujah!
On the cross He bore my sin,
When He died and rose again,
And ascended into heaven:
Hallelujah!

3. Let creation see the One
Who with breath gave earth a Son,
Redeeming all, the battle won:
Hallelujah!
'It is finished!' was His cry
As the blood flowed from His side;
Lamb of God, be glorified:
Hallelujah!

4. All our days on earth will be
Sacrificed to God our King,
For Your blood has set us free:
Hallelujah!
For we see salvation's plan,
Shown to us through Christ the man;
Eternal One, the great I Am:
Hallelujah!

Hallelujah, hallelujah,
Hallelujah, hallelujah.

2642. When I stand before Your throne

(Endless hallelujah)

1 Cor 13:12; Rev 7:9; 19:6, 8; 21:4

Gently, with awe

Matt Redman, Tim Wanstall, Jonas Myrin & Chris Tomlin
Verse words adpt. from hymn *'When this passing world is done'*, Robert M. McCheyne (1813–43)

C2
Dsus4
D
Chorus
ev - 'ry-thing as it was meant to be. And we will
C
D
Em7
G/B
wor - ship, wor - ship. For -
C
D
G
D/F♯
e - ver in Your pre - sence we will sing. We will
C
D
G/B
Em7
wor - ship, wor - ship You; an
3rd time to Instrumental section
Last time to Coda
1.
Am7
D
G
end - less hal - le - lu - jah to the King.

D.C.(v.2)
2.
Em7
C
Dsus4
D
Gsus4
G
Mid section
Em7
Bm7
No more tears, no more shame, no more
C
D
G
sin and sor - row e - ver known a - gain. No more
Em7
Bm7
C
fears, no more pain, we will see You face to face,
D
G
Em7
see You face to face.

D.S. al Instrumental section
Instrumental section
C
Gsus4(G)
And we will
G
Em7
C
Csus2
Gsus4
G
G/D
D
Am7
C2
Am7
C2
G
D.S. al Coda
And we will
Coda
G
Verse
G
Em7
2. I will see You as You are, love You with un - sin - ning heart, and
C2
Dsus4
D
see how much You paid to bring me home.
G
Em7
Not till then, Lord, shall I know, not till then, how much I owe;
C2
Dsus4
ev - 'ry - thing I am be - fore Your throne.

2643.
When my soul is weak
(My praise overflows)
1 Cor 9:24; 2 Cor 12:10; Rev 21:4
Capo 4 (G)
Jamie Rodwell
& Tom Field
Gently, building
Verse
B(G)
G♯m(Em)
1. When my soul is weak, You bring strength for me.
E(C)
B(G)
When the dark - ness clouds, You're the light I see.
F♯(D)
B(G)
(v.2)
When all hope seems lost, I re -
G♯m(Em)
E(C)
(v.3)
mem - ber Your cross, when I'm strug - gling and bound,
(v.3)
B(G)
F♯(D)
Chorus
You break the walls that sur - round. My

B(G)
F♯(D)
G♯m(Em)
praise o - ver - flows from my heart, from the
E(C)
B(G)
F♯(D)
depths of my soul. My praise o - ver - flows from my
Last time to Coda
G♯m(Em)
E(C)
B(G)
heart, from the depths of my soul.
1.,3.
1° D.S.(v.2)
2° D.C.(v.3)
2.
Mid section
F♯(D)
G♯m(Em)
E(C)
E(C)
2. When I'm
To my
E(C)
F♯(D)
God who reigns, the on - ly One who's

G♯m(Em)
F♯(D)
wor - thy of praise, who con - quered death and
E(C)
F♯(D)
rose from the grave, oh, how I love
B(G)
1.
F♯(D)
You. Je - sus, I love You. To my
2.
F♯(D)
E(C)
You. Oh, how I love You. Je - sus, I love
F♯(D)
G♯m(Em)
You. Oh, how I love You. Je - sus, I love

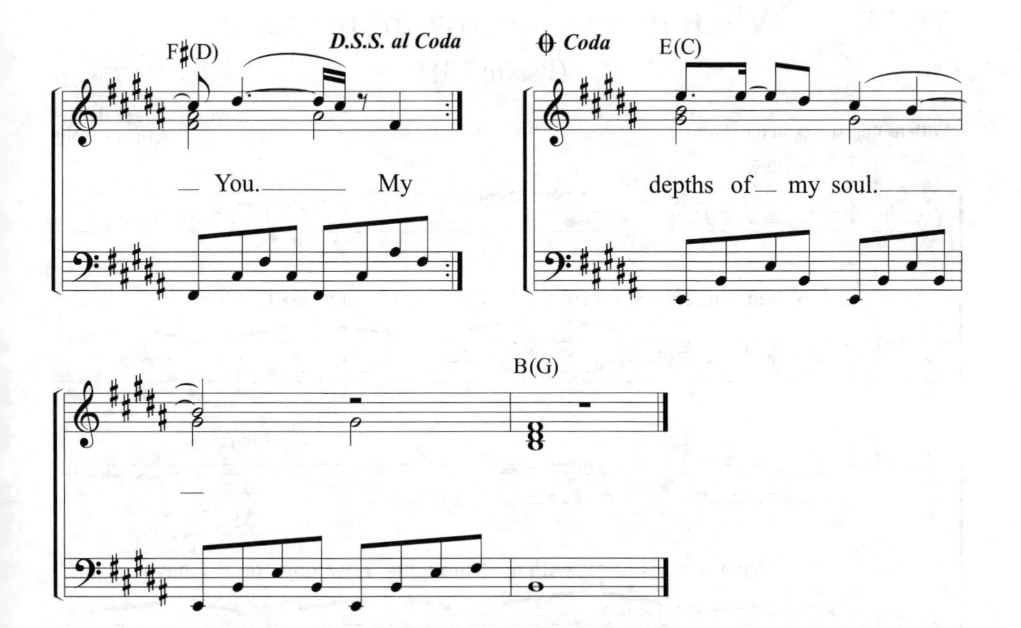

2. When I'm empty and dry,
   Hurting and broken inside,
   I can call on Your name:
   Jesus Christ, You sustain.

3. When I've run this race,
   Only by Your grace,
   You will lead me home
   To where I belong.
   My hope – secure in Your name;
   No more hurt, no more pain.
   I am forever Yours,
   You are forever mine.

2644. When there's sorrow in my heart

(Psalm 13)

A
E
long, how long for Your
F♯m7
E
D
mer - cy and Your king-dom to come? How
A
E
1.
long, how long to
D
D.C.(v.1)
wait? 1. When there's
2.,3.
E
Dmaj7
E
F♯m
E/G♯
to wait?

2. When the laughter and the joy is stripped away,
And the silence in my heart is like a heavy weight;
When I'm running through the darkness
And my eyes can't see Your light:
Hear my cry, hear my cry.

Though the fig-tree does not bud and there are no grapes on the vines, though the olive crop fails and the fields produce no food, though there are no sheep in the pen and no cattle in the stalls, yet I will rejoice in the LORD, I will be joyful in God my Saviour.

HABAKKUK 3:17-18

2645. When the sun no longer shines

(God will send His angels)

1 Thess 4:16-17; Heb 4:12; 2 Pet 3:12; Rev 1:7; 21:4

Kees Kraayenoord, Paul Field & Henk Pool

Steadily

Verse

C
1. When the sun no longer shines and the stars begin

Am7 F2
to fall, heaven will tremble

G C
for the Lord of all.
When He's sweeping through

Am7
the clouds, then we all will see His face;

F2 G C
the Messiah is coming to take His place.

Chorus
C
G/B
And God will send His an - gels wher - e - ver love is
Am
F
C/E
Dm7
found; they will lead us home to ho - ly ground.
G
C
G/D
(2°)
G/B
And God will send His an - gels wher - e - ver love is
Am
F
C/E
G
found; they will lead us home to ho - ly
Last time to Coda
C
1.
D.C.(v.2)
2.
Mid section
ground. 2. Face the fu - ture filled with They will

F C/E F C/E F
(2°,4°)
lead us home, they will lead us home, they will lead us
1.,3.
C/E Gsus4 G
home to ho-ly ground. They will
2.
Gsus4 G C
home to ho - ly ground.
4.
Gsus4 G C
D.S. al Coda
They will home to ho - ly ground. And God will send His
Coda
F C/E G C
They will lead us home to ho - ly ground.
F Dm7 Gsus4 G C
They will lead us home to ho - ly ground.

Verse
C
Am7
2. Face the fu - ture filled with hope, and be-lieve the Word that lives:
F2
G
C
a cru - ci - fied Sa-viour and a Fa-ther who for - gives.
Seek His Spi-rit day by day while your life and breath
Am7
F2
re-main; your tears will be wiped a - way
G
C
when Je-sus comes to reign.

2646. When we were in the darkest night

(God of our yesterdays)

Ps 30:5; 88:12-13; 139:5-6, 12; Mt 6:34; Mk 4:37-38; 1 Cor 10:13; Heb 12:2; 13:8; Rev 4:8

Moderately

Matt Redman

Em7
yes - ter - days. We praise You, the God who is
A/C♯
Am7 G/B
here to - day. We praise You, our God, as to - mor - row
1.
2.3.
Csus2
Csus2
comes. 2. So, what - ev - er lies comes. We thank
G
You for grace in our yes - ter - days. We thank
Bm/F♯
You for peace in our hearts to - day. We thank

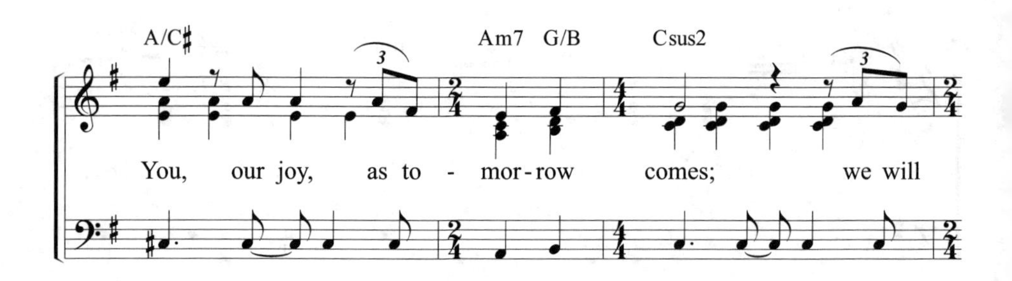
A/C#
Am7 G/B
Csus2
You, our joy, as to - mor-row comes; we will

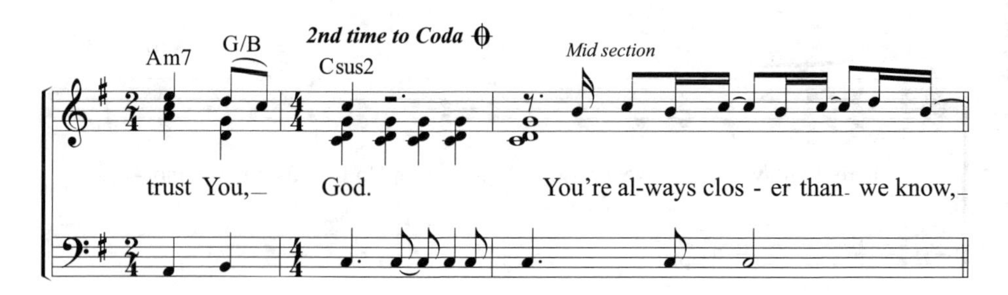
2nd time to Coda
Mid section
Am7
G/B
Csus2
trust You, God. You're al-ways clos - er than we know,

G/B
Csus2
G/B
al-ways more in-volved and in con - trol.

Csus2
G/B
We will trust our lives to You, the One

F
D/F#
D
D.S. al Coda
who was and is and is to come. We praise

2. So, whatever lies ahead,
   Whatever roads our grateful hearts will come to tread,
   You'll be there, Lord.
   And we will fix our eyes on You,
   And know that there is grace enough to see us through;
   You'll be there, Lord.
   You'll be there in the struggle,
   You'll be there in the fight,
   You'll be there all the time.

2647.
Where can we go?
(Cling to the cross)
Jn 10:10; 19:30; Acts 5:31; Rom 10:9; Heb 9:12
Capo 2 (G)
Thoughtfully, building
Cathy Burton
F♯m(Em) Verse D(C)
1. Where can we go to find for-give - ness?
(v.2)
F♯m(Em) E(D) D(C)
Where can we go with the bur-dens of life? We
(v.2)
(v.3)
Bm(Am) E(D)
look to the cross, where our Sa-viour longs to meet us; He
1.
Bm(Am) F♯m(Em) E(D) D.C.(v.2)
of - fers His love and sa-cri-fice.
2.,3.
Bm(Am) F♯m(Em) E(D) Chorus
we can have life for-e - ver more. Let us fall

A(G)
E(D)
F♯m(Em)
to our knees,
let us cling
to the cross,
D(C)
Bm(Am)
E(D)
and a-ban
-
don our-selves
to
Je -
Dmaj7(C)
1.
D.C.(v.3)
2.
Mid section
- sus.
I will fall
Bm(Am)
F♯m(Em)
A(G)
to my knees
at the foot
of the
cross,
E(D)
Bm(Am)
F♯m(Em)
I will fall
at the feet
of Je-

2. There on the cross He died to save us,
There on the cross He did it all;
He rose from the dead so that we can know forgiveness,
That we can have life forever more.

3. Where can we go to find the answers?
Where can we go with a questioning heart?
Who can we trust, when there's no one to listen?
Who knows and loves us as we are?

2648. Where there's no song for the silent

(King of compassion)

Ps 68:5; Is 55:7; 58:6; 61:1; Jn 20:23

Peter Semple

Steadily

Verse

G D

1. Where there's no song for the si - lent and no
Your strength to the weak and Your

C D Dsus2 D

har - vest for the hun - gry, where Your
free - dom for the pris - 'ner, to bring

G D

jus - tice is de - nied, there You have called
Your peace to the fear - ful; there You have called

C | 1. D Dsus2 D | 2. D

us, there You have called us. To bring us.
us, there You have called

Bridge
Em
B
C
Je - sus, make Your glo - ry known.
D
Chorus
G
D
King of com-pas - sion, Lo-ver of mer - cy, Fa-ther of jus-
C
D
- tice, ho - ly and pure. Friend to the friend -
G
D
- less, light in the dark - ness, strength to the weak -
C
1.,3.
D
Dsus4
D
- est, stead-fast and sure. King of com-pas -

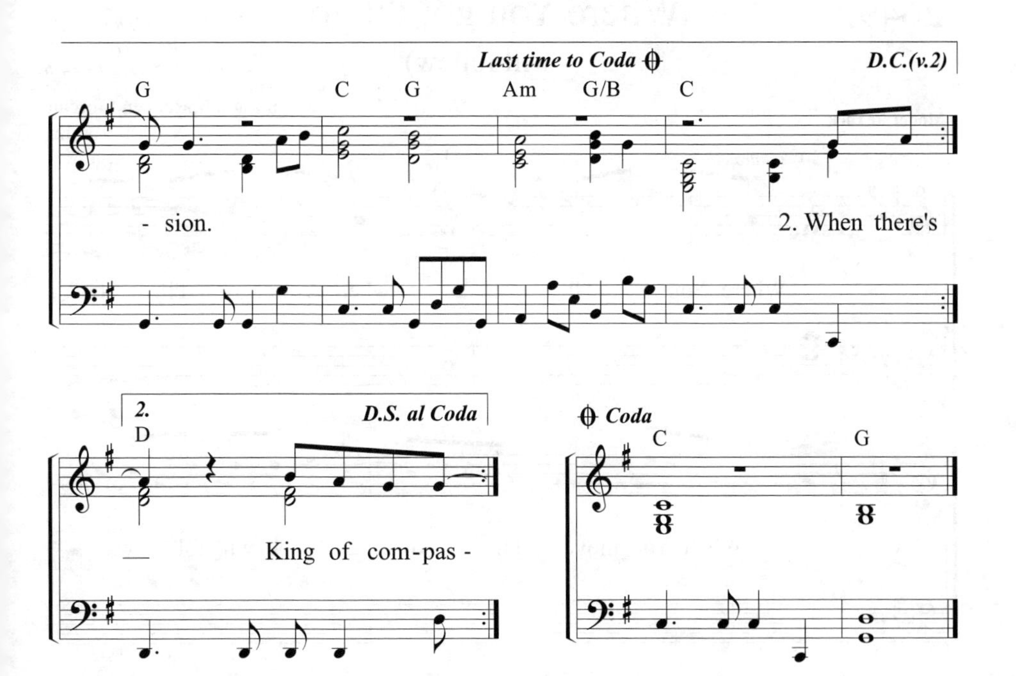

2. When there’s no tears left to cry
And no family for the orphan,
No companion for the lonely,
There You have called us,
There You have called us.
To bring Your love to the lost,
Your forgiveness for the sinner,
To bring healing to the broken;
There You have called us,
There You have called us.

2649. Where You go, I'll go

(I will follow)

Num 9:17; Ruth 1:16; Ps 16:11; Is 55:9; Lk 9:24; Jn 8:12; 2 Cor 4:6

D
F♯m
E
Higher than my sight, high above my life; I will
(v.2)
A
E/G♯
D
E
trust in You alone.
F♯m
Chorus
D
Where You go, I'll go; where You stay, I'll stay.
A
E
When You move, I'll move; I will fol - low You.
F♯m
D
Who You love, I'll love; how You serve, I'll serve.

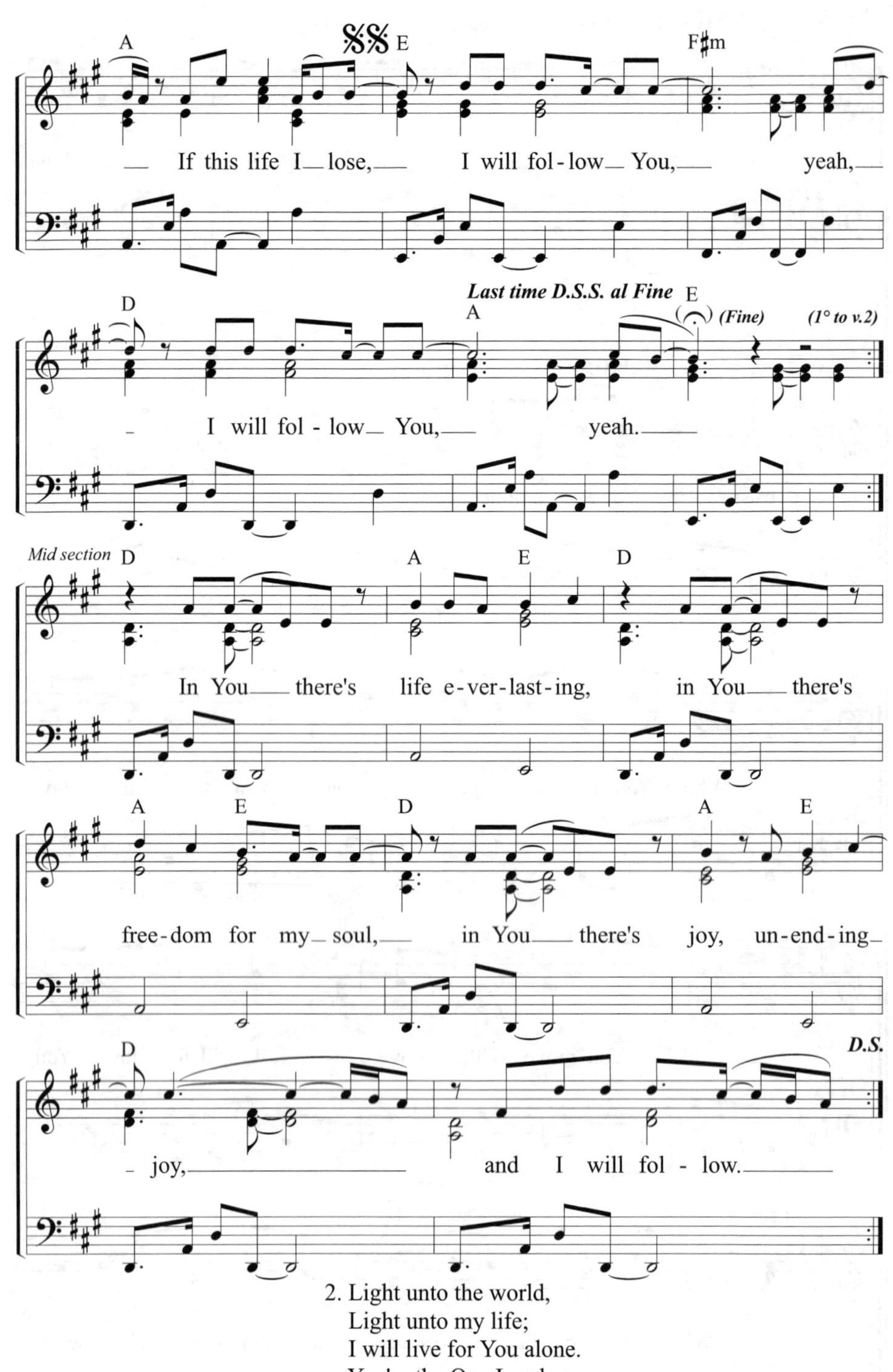

2. Light unto the world,
Light unto my life;
I will live for You alone.
You're the One I seek,
Knowing I will find
All I need in You alone,
In You alone.

2650. Who am I that You are mindful of me

(Friend of God)

Ps 8:4; Jn 15:15; Jas 2:23

Michael Gungor
& Israel Houghton

Joyfully

- zing! It's a-ma - zing!
Chorus
D
Bm7
I am a friend of God, I am a friend of God,
Em7(add4)
I am a friend of God: He calls me friend.
D
I am a friend of God,
Bm7
Em7(add4)
I am a friend of God, I am a friend of God:

D
(Fine)
D.C.
He calls me friend.
Mid section
G2
D2/F♯
God Al - migh - ty, Lord of glo - ry,
Em7
1.-3.
G2
You have called me friend.
4.
Asus4
D.S. al fine

2651. Who am I that You would know me?

(You have saved us)

Ps 8:4; Jer 32:40; Eph 1:5; 2:4-5, 6, 8, 19

With energy

Paul Baloche
& Ben Gowell

A
Esus4
Chorus
D
A
cause of what You've done.
You have saved us,
E
F♯m7
D
A
E
You have raised us up with You.
You have saved
D
A
E
F♯m7
D
A
us,
called us out and made us new,
Last time to Coda
Esus4
D
A
1.
E
F♯m7
D
A
yeah.
D.C.(v.2)
E
F♯m7
2.
E
F♯m7
D
A
You have saved us, yeah.

2. Turn our hearts from earthly idols,
Turn our eyes to You, Lord.
Only You can heal what's broken,
Only You can restore.
We are daughters, we are sons,
All because of what You've done.

Because of his great love for us, God, who is rich in mercy, made us alive with Christ even when we were dead in transgressions – it is by grace you have been saved.

EPHESIANS 2:4-5

2652. Who can ever tell?

(He is faithful)

Deut 29:29; Ps 19:1; 30:5; 148:3; Lam 3:22-23

Moderately

Neil Bennetts

G
Asus4
A
D
Chorus
en-dures for-e - ver.
1. O praise Him,
2. O praise Him,
Last time to Coda
1.
A
Bm
G
all God's peo-ple wor-ship;
He is
e - ver - last-ing in love;
Bm
A
D
faith-ful.
D.C.(v.2)
2.,4.
G
G
And is
D.S. (ch.2) (al Coda)
3.
Bm
A
Em7
faith-ful.
He is

D/F♯
A
Asus4
A
faith - ful.
Bm
A
Mid section
G
Bm
A
And His pro - mise ne - ver fails,
G
Bm
A
G
and His fa - vour lasts a life - time,
Bm
A
G
Bm
A
and His arms are strong to save,
G
Bm
A
Em7
and His gaze is al - ways on us.

2. Who could ever know all the Father knows?
The secrets of this world are in His hands.
He desires our good, He is glorious,
And His love endures forever.

2653.
Who could understand?
(Christ crucified)
Acts 1:11; Rom 8:34;
1 Cor 1:18; 23; 2:16; 1 Jn 1:7
Capo 3 (D)
Lou & Nathan Fellingham
Slow, gradually building
Verse
Dm(Bm) C/E(A/C♯) F(D) Gm(Em)
1. Who could un - der - stand the depth of Your plan,
Dm(Bm) C(A) B♭2(G) Dm(Bm) C/E(A/C♯)
to bring sin - ners home? Will we e - ver know
F(D) Gm(Em) Dm(Bm) C(A) B♭2(G)
the size of the cost, the shame of the cross?
Bridge
Gm7(Em) F(D) E♭2(C) B♭2(G)
So fool - ish to hu - man wis - dom,
Gm7(Em) F(D) C/E(A/C♯) B♭/D(G/B) C(A) B♭/D(G/B)
Chorus
but to Your chil - dren it's life and pow - er. We preach

F(D)
C/F(A/D)
Bb/F(G/D)
Dm(Bm)
Christ cru - ci-fied; it's the on - ly way for
Last time to Coda
Bb(G)
F/A(D/F#)
Csus4/F(A/D)
souls to be saved who have gone a - stray. We preach
Christ raised to life, and now He reigns in - ter -
C(A)
1.
Bb2(G)
ced-ing for us till He comes a - gain.
D.C.(v.2)
2.
Mid section
Gm/D(Em)
It has the pow'r to break in
One day He will come a - gain,

2. Self-sufficient ways run through our veins,
Fighting Your grace.
But Your grace invades, stronger than flesh,
Demanding a change.

The message of the cross is foolishness to those who are perishing, but to us who are being saved it is the power of God.

1 CORINTHIANS 1:18

2654. Whoever dwells in the secret place
(His love upon me)
Capo 3 (G)
Deut 7:7; Ps 91:1, 4-6, 9-11, 14
Mark Niedzwiedz
Prayerfully
F(D) Bb(G)
1. Who-ev - er dwells in the se - cret place of the Most High,
F(D) Bb(G)
(v.2)
under the wing of Al - migh-ty God they shall a-bide.
Eb(C) Cm7(Am)
(v.3)
Co-vered in fea-thers, re-fuge I take;
Bb(G) Dm(Bm) Eb(C)
(vv.2&3)
safe in His sha-dow. Each day I wake be - cause the Lord has
F(D) Bb(G) F/A(D/F♯) Eb(G) Bb(G) F/A(D/F♯)
set His love up-on me, His love up-on

2. Whoever dwells in the house of God
   Nothing shall fear.
   His truth, a shield from the hunter's bow,
   No arrow can pierce.
   Days filled with darkness shall not befall,
   God will deliver, answer my call,
   Because the Lord has set
   His love upon me,
   His love upon me,
   His love upon me.

3. Whoever dwells in the peace of God
   Will be at rest.
   The charge of angels, who keep a watch,
   Makes us so blessed.
   In times of trouble, salvation own.
   To God the Father my name is known,
   Because the Lord has set
   His love upon me,
   His love upon me,
   His love upon me.

4. Whoever dwells in the secret place
   Of the Most High,
   Under the wing of Almighty God
   They shall abide.
   Covered in feathers, refuge I take;
   Safe in His shadow.
   Each day I wake
   Because the Lord has set
   His love upon me,
   His love upon me,
   His love upon me.

2655. # Who I have become in You

(Highly favoured)

Rom 8:11, 15

2. Who I have become in You
Is grace beyond all measure;
Raised to life and crowned with love:
Jesus, Yours forever.

3. A child of grace I have become,
Adopted into favour.
Now I sing Your Spirit's song,
Crying, 'Abba Father.'

2656. Who is this King of glory?

(His name is wonderful)

Capo 2 (G)

Gen 1:27; Ps 24:10; Is 9:6; Mk 10:45; Lk 1:34; Jn 1:1, 3; Acts 2:23-24; 3:15; 10:38

Brenton Brown

Driving

E(D) *Verse* D2(C)

1. Who is this King of glo - ry, ma - ker of

A(G) E(D) D2(C)

all the hea-vens, au-thor of all cre-a - tion? What is His

A(G) E(D)

name? Who is the One who formed us,

D2(C) A(G) E(D)

made us in - to His i-mage? At whose voice will

D2(C) A(G) *Chorus*

all of hea - ven one day bow in praise? His name is

E(D)
A(G)
Won-der-ful, His name is Coun-sel-lor, His name is
E(D)
A(G)
Prince of Peace, the li-ving Word. His name is
E(D)
A(G)
migh-ty God, e-ter-nal Fa-ther. His name is
Last time to Coda
1.
E(D)
D2(C)
A(G)
Je-sus, His name is Lord.
D.C.(v.2)
E(D)
D2(C)
A(G)

2.
A(G)
Mid section
E(D)
A(G)
Ran-somed for my re - lease, He came to set me free.
E(D)
D(C)
Oh, how a - ma-zing is my Sa-viour's love for me.
A(G)
Chorus
D.S. al Coda
Coda
E(D)
His name is
His name is Je - sus,
D2(C)
1.
A(G)
2.
A(G)
His name is Lord.
Lord.

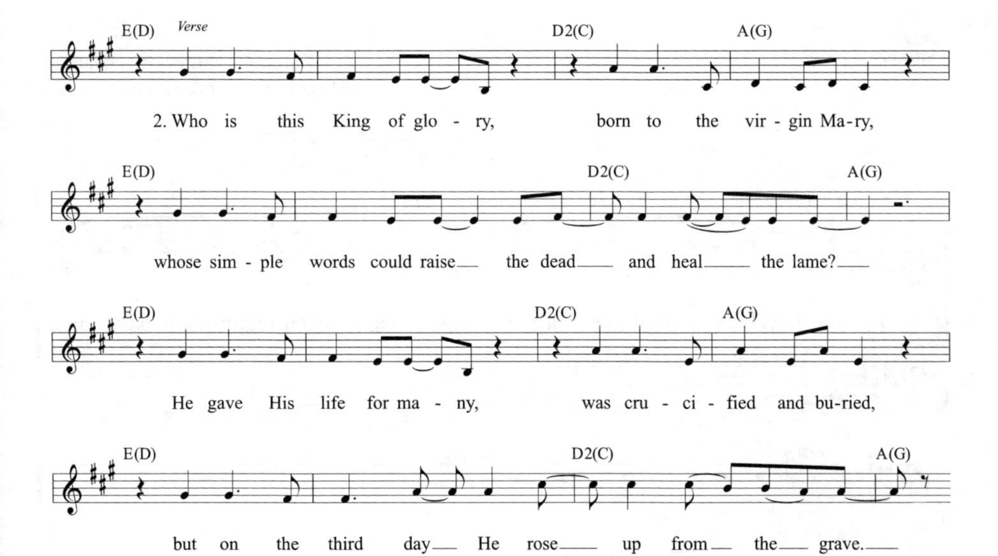
E(D)
Verse
D2(C)
A(G)
2. Who is this King of glo - ry, born to the vir - gin Ma-ry,
E(D)
D2(C)
A(G)
whose sim - ple words could raise the dead and heal the lame?
E(D)
D2(C)
A(G)
He gave His life for ma - ny, was cru - ci - fied and bu-ried,
E(D)
D2(C)
A(G)
but on the third day He rose up from the grave.

2657. Who is this Love amazing?

Ps 24:8-10; 32:10;
Lam 3:22-23;
1 Jn 1:9; Rev 4:11; 5:12

Steadily

Chris McClarney, John Hartley,
Miriam Webster & Katie Gustafson

F♯m7
Bridge
D
'Cause You are wor - thy, King of glo -
A
Esus4
F♯m7
- ry, King of glo - ry; You're for - e - ver wor -
2° D.S.
Last time to Coda
D
A
Esus4
- thy, King of glo - ry, King of glo - ry.
A
Chorus
Esus4
O - pen up, o - pen up, you an - cient gates;
(After v.2 D.S. al Coda)
F♯m7
D
o - pen up, o - pen up for the King is com - ing.

2. Who is this King of glory?
The Lord so strong and mighty.
He's always faithful to forgive.
His favour goes before me,
His perfect love surrounds me;
Now I can't help but sing, oh.

2658. Who, O Lord, could save themselves?

Capo 4 (G)

(You alone can rescue)

Ps 86:8, 13; 89:48; 123:1; Lk 15:20; Rom 5:8; Heb 10:20

Steadily

Matt Redman & Jonas Myrin

G♯m(Em) E(C) F♯(D)
save. You a - lone can lift us from the grave.
G♯m(Em) E(C) F♯(D)
You came down to find us, led us out of
G♯m(Em) E(C) F♯(D)
death. To You a - lone be - longs the high - est praise.
1. D.C.(v.2) 2.,3.
Bsus4(G) B(G) Bsus4(G) B(G) G♯m(Em)
To You a - lone be -
E(C) F♯(D) G♯m(Em)
longs the high - est praise. To You a - lone be -

2. You, O Lord, have made a way,
The great divide You healed;
For when our hearts were far away,
Your love went further still.
Yes, Your love goes further still!

2659. Why do You stand?

(Carry me)

Ps 13:1-2, 4-5

Godfrey Birtill

(Fine)
F(D) Csus4(A) C(A) Chorus F(D) F/A(D/F♯)
Car-ry me o'er the moun-
B♭(G) F/A(D/F♯) Gm(Em) Csus4(A) C(A) F(D) Csus4(A) C(A)
- tains, car - ry me a-way. Car-ry me
F(D) F/A(D/F♯) B♭(G) F/A(D/F♯) Gm(Em) Csus4(A) C7(A)
o'er the moun - tains, car - ry me a-way.
1. D.C.(v.2)
F(D) B♭(G)
2. D.S.
F(D) C(A)
Car-ry me
3. D.S.S. al Fine
B♭(G)
2. How long, O Lord,
2. How long, O Lord,
Must I fight, fight with my thoughts?
How long to stand in this mud?
My enemy taunts me,
And my foes rejoice when I fall.
Still I will trust in Your love.

2660. Will You hide me in Your shelter?

(Healing streams)

Gen 31:40; Ps 23:4; 30:5; 91:1, 4; Is 55:1; Mt 11:28; Jn 14:16; 20:27; Rom 2:4

John Hartley, Stuart Townend & Kelly Minter

Gently

Verse

C F/C C F
1. Will You hide me in Your shel-ter? Will You shade me with Your

C G/B Am7
wings; when the heat of day con-sumes me, let me

G F G
drink from heal-ing streams, drink from heal-ing

1. D.C. (v.2) | 2.-4. (Fine)

C
streams? 2. Will You

Chorus

F
And when the joy of morn-ing

C F Am
tar-ries, when the waves of dark-ness roll, will You

2. Will You lift my heavy burdens?
Will You pave my path with peace;
When the road is steep and stony,
Let me bathe in healing streams,
Bathe in healing streams?

3. Will You lead me to repentance?
Will you make temptations flee?
When I'm filled with condemnation,
Will You show Your scars to me,
Show Your scars to me?

2661. Wonder of a newborn Son

(Angels sing their song tonight)

Is 7:14; 9:6; Mt 1:21, 23; 2:9, 11; Lk 1:33; 2:7, 14, 20; Jn 1:14

Noel & Tricia Richards

C2
Dsus4
D
G
God has come with us to dwell.
Chorus
D/F♯
C2/E
D
An - gels sing: 'Glo - ry
C2
G
be to God.'
D/F♯
C2/E
D
Christ has come: hope for
Last time to Coda
C2
A/C♯
all is birthed when hea-ven kis - ses earth;

1.,2.
C
Dsus4
D
an - gels sing their song to-night.
D.S. (v3.,4.)
3.
D.S.S. al Coda
G
Dsus4
D
song.
Coda
C
Dsus4
D
C2/E
an-gels sing their song, an - gels sing
D/F♯
C2/E
Dsus4
D
their song, an-gels sing their song to-night.
G
3. Seek the star that burns so bright,
Let it be your guiding light
To a stable cold and bare –
You will find the Saviour there.
4. Wise men, lay your treasure down,
Worship on this holy ground;
Bow before the Prince of Peace,
For His kingdom will not cease.

Glory to God in the highest, and on earth peace to men on whom his favour rests.

LUKE 2:14

2662. Worthy is the Lamb

(Revelation song)

Rom 16:27; Rev 4:3, 5, 8; 5:9, 12; 17:14

Jennie Lee Riddle

Quite slow, celtic feel

D *Verse* Am2

1. Wor - thy is the__ Lamb who was slain;__

Cmaj7 G D

ho - ly, ho - ly is__ He.__ Sing a new song,__

Am2 Cmaj7 G *(1° rpt v.1)*

to Him who sits on__ hea - ven's mer - cy__ seat.__

D
Am7
With all cre - a - tion I sing praise to the King of kings;
C
G
You are my ev - 'ry - thing and I will a - dore You.
D.C.(v.2.,3.)
D
Am7
C
G (Fine)
D
Am2
Cmaj7
2. Clothed in rain - bows of liv - ing co - lour, flash - es of light - ning, rolls
G
D
Am2
of thun - der. Bles - sing and ho - nour, strength and glo - ry and po - wer be
Cmaj7
G
to You, the on - ly wise King.
D
Am2
Cmaj7
3. Filled with won - der, awe - struck won - der, at the men - tion of Your name.
G
D
Am2
Je - sus, Your name is po - wer, breath, and liv - ing wa - ter;
Cmaj7
G
such a marv'l - lous my - ste - ry.

2663. You alone are worthy

(We bow down)

Capo 2 (C)

Ps 48:1; Lk 2:14; Eph 2:4-5

Al Gordon, Luke Hellebronth & Hanif Williams

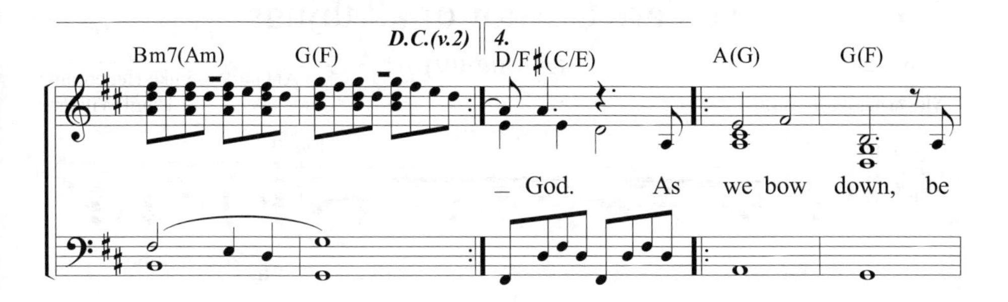

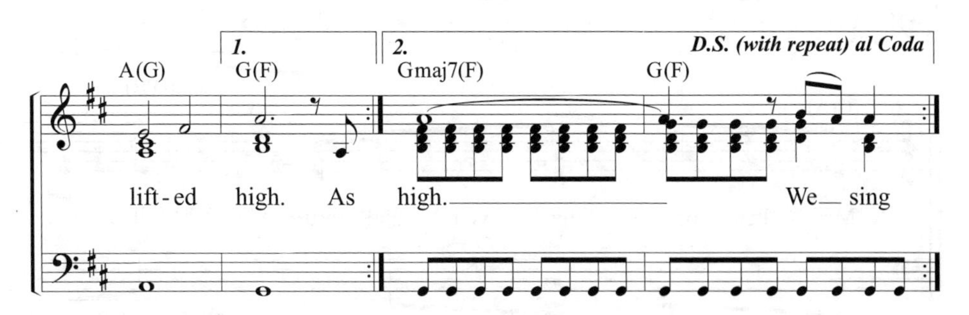

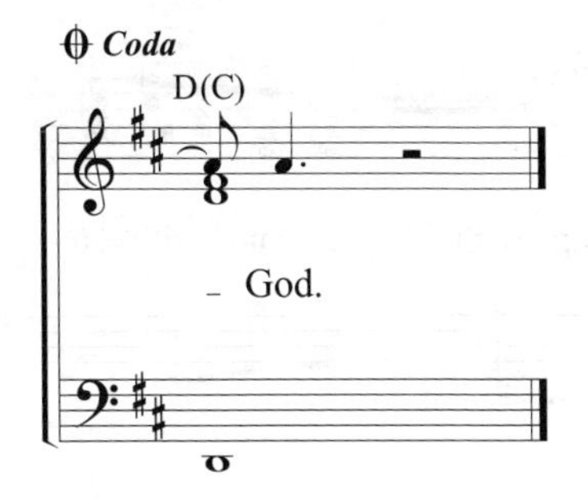

2. For Your love and mercy,
For the beauty of Your saving grace,
We have come to thank You.
We have come to worship You today.

2664. You are Creator of all things

(Almighty)

Capo 3 (D)

Ps 78:4; Is 47:4; Jn 1:3; Rev 4:11; 7:9-12

With increasing intensity

David Lyon

Verse F(D) B♭(G)

1. You are Cre - a - tor of all ___ things,

C(A) B♭(G)

Ma - ker of hea - ven and earth. ___

F(D) B♭(G)

Now, as we wor - ship, we're join - ing with kings ___ and with an -

Csus4(A) F/A(D/F♯) B♭(G) 𝄋 *Verse* F(D)

- gels. 2. You are our hope ___ and Re-deem -

(v.3)

B♭(G) C(A) B♭(G)

- er, Sa - viour to all ___ who would come.

F(D)
B♭(G)
C(A) F/A(D/F♯)
You are the love that is reach - ing to saints and to re-bels.
B♭(G)
Bridge
C(A)
Gm7(Em)
F/A(D/F♯)
B♭(G) C(A)
Glo-ry and ho-nour and pow-er are Yours for - ev-er.
B♭/D(G/B) C/E(A/C♯)
Chorus
F(D)
Al - migh - ty, we are
F/A(D/F♯)
B♭(G)
F(D)
stand-ing in awe of Your great-ness. Al - migh - ty,
Last time to Coda
1. D.S.(v.3)
2.,4. D.S.S.
F/A(D/F♯)
B♭(G)
B♭(G) (al Coda)
we are hum-bled and we are a-mazed. Al -

3. Each generation will praise You,
Grateful for all You have done.
Each generation
Will tell of Your fame and Your wonder.

Our Redeemer – the LORD Almighty is his name – is the Holy One of Israel.

ISAIAH 47:4

2665.
You are good
(We see love)
2 Sam 7:22; Ps 100:5; Is 30:18; Jn 14:9, 26; 16:14
Capo 1 (D)
Worshipfully
Gareth Robinson
Verse
E♭(D)
You are good and Your love en - dures for - ev - er.
A♭(G)
Fm(Em)
Ne-ver chan - ging, al-ways faith-ful You are.
B♭(A)
B♭7(A)
E♭(D)
E♭/D♭(D/C)
Ho - ly God, there is no one else a-bove You.
A♭(G)
Fm(Em)
B♭(A)
Just and gra - cious, full of mer - cy You are.
E♭(D)
Chorus
B♭6/D(A/C♯)
A♭maj7(G)
Spi - rit, show us Je - sus.

E♭(D)
B♭6/D(A/C♯)
A♭maj7(G)
Je - sus, You show us the Fa - ther.
Fm7(Em)
B♭(A)
E♭(D)
When we see You, we see love. When we see
A♭6(G)
B♭(A)
E♭(D)
1.
2.
You, we see love.
You are

2666. You are good
(Forever reign)

Ps 85:2; 100:5; Jn 8:12; 1 Cor 15:55; Phil 2:11

Reuben Morgan & Jason Ingram

Gradually building

2.,3.
Csus4 C Csus4 C
Chorus
C
Oh, I'm run-ning to Your
(—)
G/C
arms, I'm run-ning to Your
Am
arms. The ri-ches of Your
G
love will al-ways be e - nough.
F
No-thing com-pares
Am G F
— to Your — em-brace. — Light of the world, —
3° D.S. al fine
Am G
for-ev - er reign.
(Fine)
F
1. D.C.(v.3)
3. You are
2.
Mid section
Am
My heart will sing

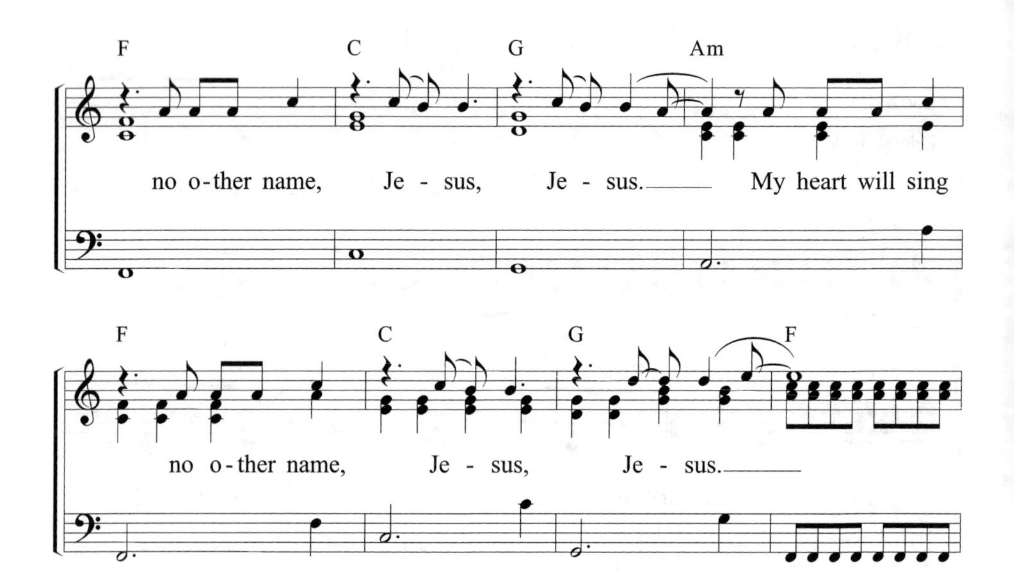

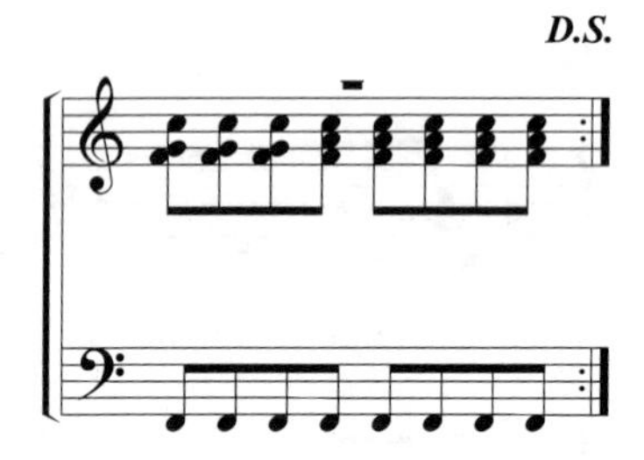

2. You are peace, You are peace,
   When my fear is crippling.
   You are true, You are true,
   Even in my wandering.
   You are joy, You are joy,
   You're the reason that I sing.
   You are life, You are life;
   In You death has lost its sting.

3. You are more, You are more
   Than my words will ever say.
   You are Lord, You are Lord,
   All creation will proclaim.
   You are here, You are here;
   In Your presence I'm made whole.
   You are God, You are God;
   Of all else I'm letting go.

2667.
You are my refuge
(Always faithful)
Ps 18:2; 46:1; Mal 3:6; Rev 11:15
Nicole Brown & Eoghan Heaslip
Capo 4 (D)
Moderate rock
(v.2, 2°)
Verse
F♯(D)
B(G)
1. You are my refuge, my shield and strength;
You are my fortress, my solid ground;
Jesus, I trust in You.
Jesus I trust in You.
Bridge
C♯(A)
D♯m(Bm)
A♯m(F♯m)
In the darkest hour, when hope seems lost, I look to You.
Chorus
For You are the rock on which I stand, the

D♯m(Bm)
rock on which I stand; You ne - ver change, fail,
B(G)
1.,4.
F♯(D)
2.,5.
F♯(D)
(Fine)
You're al-ways faith-ful. You're the
A♯m7(F♯m)
D.C.(v.2) 3.
F♯(D)
2. Each
A♯m7(F♯m)
D♯m(Bm)
B(G)
Al-ways faith-ful.
Mid section
C♯(A)
D♯m(Bm)
When the storms and tri - als of this life rage, Your love,

2. Each moment of history
Is in Your hands;
Jesus, I trust in You;
Our world is redeemed
As Your kingdom reigns;
Jesus, I trust in You.

2668.
You are my refuge
(Refuge)
Ps 18:2, 50; 46:1, 10; 62:1-2; Song 1:4; Is 55:3; Heb 7:26
Capo 3 (D)
Moderately
Cathy Burton
F(D)
Verse
(v.2-ii)
1. You are my re-fuge, You are my strength,
You see me fal-ter, You see me fall,
C(A)
You're e-ver pre-sent in ev-'ry-thing. And I will
You ne-ver leave me, I can stand tall. And I will
Gm7(Em)
1.
B♭(F)
walk with You, I will walk with You.
walk with You, I will walk
2.
B♭(F)
Bridge
C(A)
B♭/D(G/B)
C/E(A/C♯)
with You. I will be still and know that You are:
Chorus
F(D)
(1.,3.,6.) Ex-al-ted in the hea-vens, ex-al-ted on the earth;
(2.,4.,5.) Our God can-not be sha-ken, our for-tress safe and true;

Dm7(Bm)
the Lord of hosts is with us, the migh - ty rock, and I will
I pour my heart out to You, my soul finds rest, and I will
1.,3.,5.
2.,4.,6.
Gm7(Em)
C(A)
run to You, I will run to You.
run with You, I will run with You.
Gm7(Em)
run with You, I will run
run to You, I will run
Last time to Coda
1.
D.C.(v.2)
C(A)
B♭2(G)
with You.
to You.
2.
B♭2(G)
Mid section
Am(F♯m)
I will run to You when my world
B♭2(G)
F(D)
crum-bles to the sea.
When the wa-

Am(F♯m)
B♭2(G)
- ters roar, and my dreams are swal-lowed with me,
Dm7(Bm)
Gm7(Em)
I will not fear; I will be
Am7(Em)
B♭maj9(G)
still and know You are near.
F(D)
Our God can - not be sha - ken.
F(D)
D.S. (Ch 2)
Our God can - not be sha - ken.

2. Your word has spoken and I have heard;
Your love is steadfast, Your love is sure,
And I belong to You, I belong to You.
I wait in silence for You alone;
You're my salvation, You are my home
And I belong with You, I belong with You.

2669. You are the reason

(God of all)

Gen 1:1; Ps 148:2-3, 7, 9; Lk 2:13-14

Moderate rock

Ben Cantelon
& Robin Hardingham

A
G
so we join with an - gels
(v.2)
Bm
A/C♯
Chorus
Bm
(small note last time)
and pro - claim: You are God of all
G
D
A
Bm
cre-a - tion, and the stars a-bove
G
D
A
G
sing al - le - lu - ia, and to - ge - ther as
Last time to Coda
3rd time D.S. al Coda
Bm
F♯m
G
A
one voice - we de - clare: You are

1.
D.C.(v.2)
Bm
G
A/D
Bm/E
God.
2. You are for - e -
2.
(repeat 3 times)
Bm
A
G
Bm
A
G
God.
Mid section
G2
A
Glo - ry, glo - ry in the high - est.
G
A
Glo - ry, glo - ry in the high - est.
Bm
A/C♯
D.S.
Glo - ry, glo - ry in the high - est. You are

2. You are forever strong and mighty,
You are eternal King of majesty.
Even the mountains and the seas below
Cry out: 'Holy is the Lord of all.'

2670. You are the rock that I cling to

(Hallelujah to the Lord Almighty)

Capo 3 (D)

With strength

Ps 18:2; 118:14; Lk 15:24; Jn 9:25; 10:10; Acts 4:12; Rev 19:6; 22:13

Martin Cooper

B♭(G)
Csus4(A)
— and stand - ing on Your pro - mise I sing: —
Chorus
F(D)
Csus4(A)
Hal-le - lu - jah — to the Lord — Al - migh - ty, —
Gm7(Em)
B♭(G)
Csus4(A)
hal-le - lu - jah to the One — who saved my
F(D)
Csus4(A)
soul. Hal-le - lu - jah, 'cause I've — found mer - cy: —
Last time to Coda
Last chorus D.S.
Gm7(Em)
B♭(G)
Csus4(A)
liv - ing free, — I will be — walk-ing in — the full-ness of life. —

B♭(G)
Csus4(A)
F(D)
Mid section
Let an-gels a-bove,
Cadd4/E(A/C♯)
Gm7(Em)
a-mazed at such love,
sing: 'Wor-thy is the
B♭(G)
Csus4(A)
F(D)
Cadd4/E(A/C♯)
King of grace.'
Let voi-ces ring out,
let all the earth
Gm7(Em)
B♭(G)
Csus4(A)
B♭(G)
shout:
'You a-lone shall
have our praise.'
Csus4(A)
B♭/D(G)
Csus4(A)
D.S. al Coda

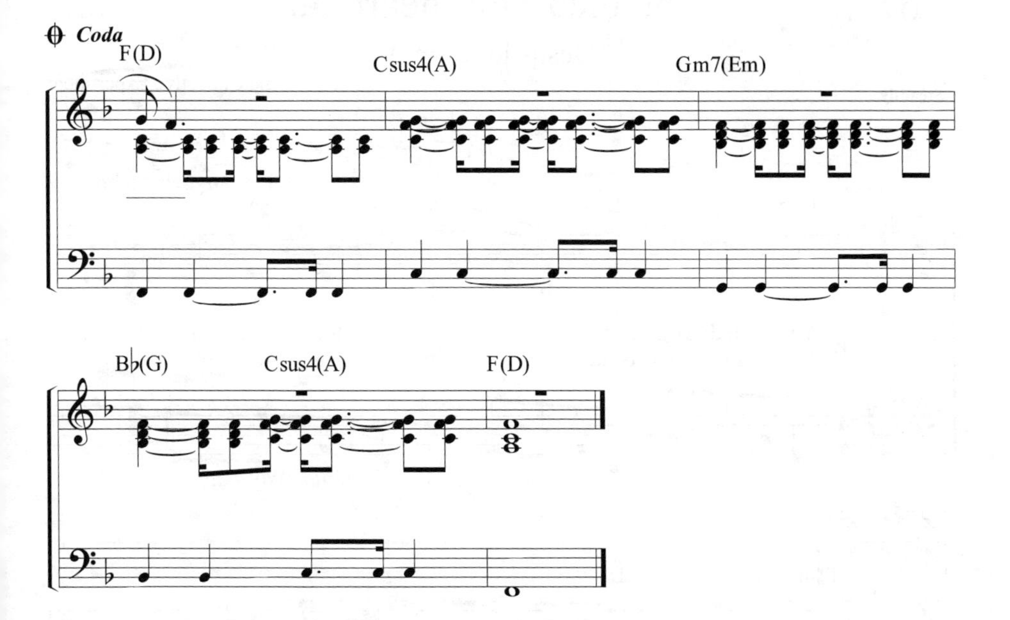

2. You are the only salvation,
You are the end and the start.
You are the God of creation,
You are the King of my heart.
Once blind, now I see,
You've set this life free,
And standing in Your goodness I sing:

2671. You bled Your heart out

(Jesus loves me)

Is 35:10; 61:3; Gal 2:20; Phil 2:6-7

Rend Collective Experiment

Steadily

D
A
E
how bound - less is Your love, is Your love.
Last time to Coda
F♯m
D
1.,3.
A
How won-der - ful, sa-cri - fi - cial, is Your love for
E
F♯m
D
A2
C♯m7
me.
F♯m
D
A
D.C.(v.2)
2.
A
is Your love for
E
Mid section
D
A
Bm7
me.
Yes, Je-sus loves me.
Yes, Je-sus

2. You put on our chains,
Sent us out through the open door;
How wonderful.
You took our sadness,
Crowned us with joy and real peace;
How wonderful.
You left Your perfection
And fought for our redemption, oh.

2672. You bring peace

Ps 23:4; Is 9:2, 6; Mt 1:23; Jn 14:27; 2 Cor 4:6

Sam Hargreaves

Calmly

Verse

Em7 Bm7 C Dsus4 D Em7 Bm7 C Dsus4 D

You bring peace, but not as the world gives;
You bring joy in the midst of our grief.
You're the light who shines in our darkness;
You bring hope when we struggle to see.

Chorus

G/B C Dsus4 D G/B C Dsus4 D Em7 C Dsus4 D Am7 G/B

Prince of Peace, everlasting Father,
mighty God, so wonderful to

Last time to Coda

1.
3.
D.S. al Coda
2.
C
D/C
C
C
me. You bring me. He's the me.
D/C
Mid section
G
D/F♯
Those walk-ing in dark-ness have seen a great light as the
F
C
G
dawn breaks, shat-ter-ing sha-dows. The val-ley of death holds no
D/F♯
F
1.
C
fear in the night, for He's with us; God is with us. Those
2.
C
D.S.
God is with us. He's the
Coda
C
me. He's so

Am G/B C Am7 G/B
won - der - ful to me. You're so won - der - ful to
C D/C C D/C
me. You bring peace, but not as the world gives,

C D/C C2
You bring peace.

2673. You came to save the world

Dm(Bm)
B♭(G)
but death was swal-lowed up in vic-to-ry.
C(A)
Chorus
F(D)
For You a-rose on the third
on the third
C(A)
Gm7(Em)
Last time to Coda
day. Hal-le-lu-jah we cry, Your
day; we are ful-ly a-live in the
1.,3.,5.,6.,7.
2.,4.
B♭(G)
B♭(G)
life is our life.
(6°) (pow'r of Your life.)
Yes, You a-rose pow'r of Your life. You're a-live.
1.
F/C(D/A)
C(A)
B♭(G)

2. Just as You arose,
Bursting out in power,
We are raised to life,
Reigning with You now and forever.
Just as You returned
To the Father's glory,
I've been made His child
Living to enjoy You forever.

The Son of Man must suffer many things and be rejected by the elders, chief priests and teachers of the law, and he must be killed and on the third day be raised to life.

LUKE 9:22

2674. You came to search and rescue

(Where would we be?)

Lk 15:20; 19:10; Jn 8:12; Rom 5:6, 8; Tit 3:5; Heb 10:20; 2 Pet 2:9

Capo 4 (G)

Steadily

Matt Redman,
Jonas Myrin & Jason Ingram

Verse

G♯m(Em) E(C) B(G) F♯(D) G♯m(Em) E(C) B(G) F♯(D) E(C) G♯m(Em) F♯(D)

1. You came to search and res - cue; in love, the Fa - ther sent You, broke through the dark - est night. You came to seek and save us, You came to li - be-rate us; Je - sus, You heard our cry, Je - sus, You heard our cry.

Chorus
B(G)
Where would we be with - out Your love? We'd
(chor 2) safe in the arms of Your em - brace,
still be lost in dark - ness.
breath - ing in Your free - dom;
G♯m(Em)
Where would we be with - out Your cross? You
lift - ing a song of high - est praise and
made a way to save us.
breath-ing out Your an - them.
C♯m(Am)
G♯m(Em)
Oh, Your love, oh, Your love.
1.
F♯sus4(D)
G♯m(Em) E(C)
B(G) F♯(D)
G♯m(Em) E(C)

D.C.(v.2)
2.,4.
D.S. (chor 2)
G♯m(Em)
F♯(D)
F♯(D)
2. You are the
We're
3.,5.
Last time to Coda
F♯(D)
C♯m(Am)
G♯m(Em)
We're sing-ing: Oh, Your love, oh, Your love.
F♯(D)
Mid section
E(C)
B(G)
We could-n't es - cape the sin and the shame that kept us bound.
F♯(D)
E(C)
B(G)
We could-n't break through, we could-n't reach You, so
G♯m(Em)
F♯(D)
D.S. al Coda (inc. rpt)
You reached down.

2. You are the hope eternal,
You are the light of this world,
Jesus, our rescuer.
We live our lives to thank You;
How could we not adore You,
Jesus, our rescuer,
Jesus, our rescuer?

2675. You came to us, the Servant King

(Great is our God)

Capo 1 (G)

With energy

Ps 24:8; 27:8; Lam 3:22; Mk 10:45; Heb 10:20

Jim Elliott
& Cathy Burton

Fm7(Em)
A♭(G)
and show the world Your pow - er and Your mer -
E♭(D)
B♭no3rd(A)
D♭(C)
Bridge
- cy.
What an awe -
E♭(D)
D♭(C)
- some God,
what a-maz - ing love,
and for-e-
E♭(D)
Chorus
- ver we will sing:
Great is our God,
Fm7(Em)
A♭(G)
E♭(D)
hal - le - lu - jah.
Great is our God,
strong and migh - ty,
King

B♭no3rd(A)
Fm7(Em)
A♭(G)
He will not fail, His love will ne - ver
for - e - ver more, He reigns for - e - ver
1.,3.,5.
E♭(D)
B♭no3rd(A)
2.
E♭(D)
fail. Great is our God, more,
B♭no3rd(A)
Fm7(Em)
A♭(G)
E♭(D)
yeah.
B♭no3rd(A)
D.C.
4.
E♭(D)
B♭no3rd(A)
D.S.
more,
6.
E♭(D)
B♭no3rd(A)
Fm7(Em)
more, Great is our God,

E♭(D)
B♭sus2/D(A/C♯)
1.
D♭6(C)
Great is our God.

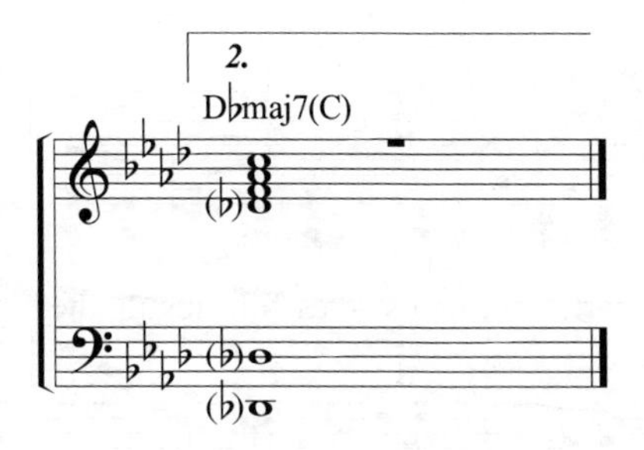
2.
D♭maj7(C)

2676. You dwell in the songs

(Restless)

1 Sam 3:10; 1 Kings 19:12; Ps 22:2-3; Mt 11:28; Jn 15:5

Chorus
D
Em7+4
D/F♯
G
rest - less, I'm rest - less till I rest in You, till I
Bm
Asus4
D
Em7+4
rest in You. I am rest - less, I'm rest - less till I
Last time to Coda
1.
D/F♯
G
Bm
Asus4
D
rest in You, till I rest in You, O God.
D.C.(v.2)
F♯m7/C♯
Bm
F♯m
A
I want to rest in You. 2. Oh
2.
Bm
Asus4
Gmaj7
D2/F♯
rest in You. I wan-na

Mid section
Gmaj9
Bm
A/C♯
Gmaj7
rest in You.
Still my heart,
(2°)
D2/F♯
Gmaj7
Bm
A
Gmaj7
hold me close, let me hear a still, small voice. Let it grow,
1.
D2/F♯
Gmaj7
Bm
A/C♯
let it rise into a shout, into a cry. Oh,
2.
D.S. al Coda
Bm7+4
A/C♯
G2
to a cry. Oh,
And I am

Coda
Bm Asus4 D A/C♯
rest in You, O God. Let me rest in
Bm F♯m A D
You.
Verse
D A/C♯
2. Oh, speak now, for my soul is list - 'ning. Say that You have
Bm F♯m A D
saved me; whis-per in the dark, the dark, 'cause I know You're more than my sal -
A/C♯ Bm F♯m A
va-tion: with-out You I am hope-less. Tell me who You are. You are the keep -
Em7 Bm Asus4 A Em7 Bm Asus4 A
- er of my heart. You are the keep - er of my heart.

2677. # You forgive, then forget
(No condemnation)

Ps 103:12; Is 43:25; Jer 31:34; Jn 8:7, 9, 11; Rom 6:14; 8:1-2; Jas 2:13

Brian Doerksen & Philip Janz

Capo 3 (D)

Rock feel

C(A)
Chorus
C(A)
F(D)
Now there's no con-dem-na - tion,
C(A)
B♭(G)
no con-dem-na - tion for all of us,
Gm7(Em)
F(D)
C(A)
all who be-long in Je - sus. Now there's
F(D)
C(A)
no con-dem-na - tion, no con-dem-na - ion; there's
Last time to Coda
1.
D.C.(v.2)
B♭(G)
Gm7(Em)
F(D)
free-dom found on-ly in Je - sus. 2. Ac-cu-sers leave

2. Accusers leave stones of hate,
As mercy triumphs over judgement
For that woman who remained.
As love reclaims, then restores,
You mend our broken hearts
And make our lives stronger than before.

Therefore, there is now no condemnation for those who are in Christ Jesus, because through Christ Jesus the law of the Spirit of life set me free from the law of sin and death.

ROMANS 8:1-2

2678.

You give me strength

(Catch me)

Ps 40:2; 91:1; Mt 28:20; 1 Cor 10:13

Paul Baloche, Steven Curtis-Chapman, Stuart Garrard, Israel Houghton, Tim Hughes, Graham Kendrick, Andy Park, Matt Redman, Martin Smith, Michael W. Smith, Chris Tomlin & Darlene Zschech

A
E
e-ver I fall I know You'll catch me,
when-
Bm7
Dmaj7
E
e-ver I'm down You're there to lift me,
where-
A
C♯m7
e-ver I go I know You're with me;
You are
Bm7
Last time to Coda
1. Dmaj7
D.C.(v.2)
with me, al - ways You are with me
3. Dmaj7
E
D.S. al Coda
2. Dmaj7
with me. When- with me

Mid section
E
Oh, You're my shel - ter, You're my home,
Dmaj7
You're my peace - when I'm a - lone,
A
E
my peace when I'm a - lone.
Oh, You're my great - est dream come true,
Dmaj7
F♯m7
and I'm so in love with You,
I'm so in love with You,

2. You give the joy that keeps me strong,
You're the reason to go on;
All I need is found in You.
Hope surrounds me every day,
You're never far away.
All I need is found in You,
Whatever life brings.

2679. You have shown us

Is 58:6; Amos 5:23-24; Mic 6:8; Jas 1:27

Paul Baloche, Steven Curtis-Chapman, Stuart Garrard, Israel Houghton, Tim Hughes, Graham Kendrick, Andy Park, Matt Redman, Martin Smith, Michael W. Smith, Chris Tomlin & Darlene Zschech

Chorus
D C D Em7 Bm7
To do just - ly and to love mer - cy, and to -
C D Em7
walk humb - ly with You, God. You said to
C D Em7 Bm7
do just - ly and to love mer - cy, and to
Last time to Coda
1.
C D G
walk hum - bly with You, God.
D.C.(v.2)
3. D.S.S. al Coda
Em7 G
2. You have shown To

2. You have shown us the riches of Your love,
You have shown us Your heart for those in need.
Lord, You're opening our ears to the cries of the poor;
You have called us to be Your hands and feet.

Away with the noise of your songs! I will not listen to the music of your harps. But let justice roll on like a river, righteousness like a never-failing stream!

AMOS 5:23-24

2680.
You hold the broken-hearted
(God of hope)
Lk 4:18; Jn 11:39; 20:1; Acts 26:17-18
James Gregory & Guy Bastable
Warmly
Verse
1. You hold the bro - ken - heart - ed,
2. Your heart is for the out - cast,
You stand be-side the weak.
for those we call the least.
You go to those in dark - ness
You lift the bro - ken spi - rit
and so must we.
and so must we.
1.
2.,3.
Chorus
God of hope,
God of fu - tures, You can take a bro - ken heart and make it sing.
God of life, new to - mor - rows, You can shine
2nd time to Coda
(v.2)
(v.3)

3. You go to those forgotten,
The faces we don't see.
You give Your life to save them
And so must we.

2681. You inhabit the praises of Your people

(The wonder of Your love)

Ps 22:3; Mt 3:17; Rev 4:8; 7:9, 11

Steadily

Jack Mooring, Leeland Mooring
& Marty Sampson

Verse

E/G♯ A B

1. You in - ha - bit the prai - ses of Your peo - ple, You de-

E/G♯ A B

light in the glo - ry of Your Son. In the

E/G♯ A B

love of the Fa - ther we will wor - ship, in the

E/G♯ A B

king - dom of God we find our home.

Bridge

The

E/G♯ A B C♯m

won-der of Your love will break the chains that bind us. The

E/G♯ A B
pow - er of Your touch re - leas - es us to wor - ship.
Chorus
E C♯m
Sing out to God, sing hal - le - lu - jah; with all we are we will
Last time to Coda
B
1.
A
wor - ship You. Ho - ly is Your name, ho - ly is Your name, O
D.C.(v.2)
2.,3.,5.
D.S. al Coda
E Esus4 E Esus4
A
God. And to - ho - ly is Your name.
4.
A E Esus4
ho - ly is Your name, O God.

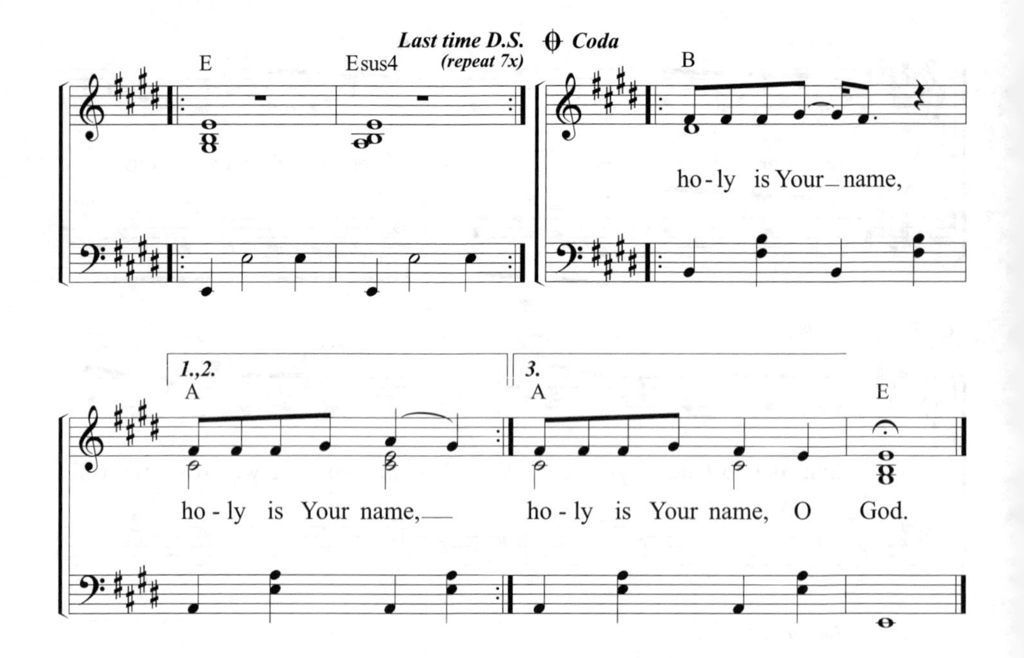

2. And together we'll lift the name of Jesus,
   And together we sing of Your great love.
   We will join with the angels to praise You;
   May our voices be pleasing to You, God.

You are enthroned as the Holy One; you are the praise of Israel.

PSALM 22:3

2682. You lead us through the wilderness

Lk 4:1-2, 4; 9:23-24; Rom 8:14, 26; 1 Cor 10:13; 2 Cor 1:4; Heb 11:9, 40

Capo 2 (D)

Flowing

Sam Hargreaves

Verse

B7sus4(A) B(A) Esus4(D) E(D) C♯m(Bm)

1. You lead us through the wil-der-ness and give us grace for

F♯m(Em) B(A) A(G) E/G♯(D/F♯) B(A) E(D)

trials__ and tests. Your Ho - ly Spi - rit shows the way, and

C♯m(Bm) F♯m(Em) B7(A) A2(G) *Chorus*

in our weak - ness teach - es us to pray. We'll

E(D) A/E(G/D) E(D) C♯m(Bm) A(G)

wor-ship in the wil - der-ness, a dry and thirs-ty land. We

2. As Jesus fasted forty days,
So help us turn from selfish ways;
To trust in You and learn to give,
For when we die to self we'll truly live.

3. You join us in our brokenness,
And comfort us in our distress,
For You're the hope of all who mourn,
You lead us to Your resurrection dawn.

(Chorus 2)
We'll worship in the wilderness,
And trust the path You've planned.
You're faithful in the wilderness,
And by Your grace we'll reach the promised land.

2683. You light up our way

(Oh, this God)

Ex 20:3; Mt 5:16; Lk 9:62; Phil 3:13; Heb 12:2

Brightly

Matt Redman & Jonas Myrin

C
G
D
we are look - ing straight a - head;
Em
C
ne - ver turn - ing back, count - ing on Your faith - ful - ness.
D
Chorus
C
Oh, this God is our God,
e - ven till the end.
G
Stand - ing strong
C
Em
o - ver us, time and time a - gain, e - ven till the end.
1.
D.C.(v.2)
2.
D.S.
3.
D
D
D
Tag
Oh, this God
Je - sus,

C
G
You will al - ways be our God, and
Em
D
we won't take our eyes off You. Je - sus,
C
G
You'll for - e - ver be the One; we'll
Em
1.
D
have no o - ther god but You. Je - sus,
2.
D
G
2. We've walked through storms
And we have walked through sorrow;
Still You won't let them
Steal away tomorrow.
We are going to shine,
Now we are going to shine for You.
We leave the old behind;
It will not define us, no.
Yesterday is gone,
Now anything is possible.

Let us fix our eyes on Jesus, the author and perfecter of our faith, who for the joy set before him endured the cross, scorning its shame, and sat down at the right hand of the throne of God.

HEBREWS 12:2

2684. Young and old

(So great)

Ps 136:1; Mt 11:28; 1 Jn 1:7, 9

Capo 3 (D)

Paul Baloche, Steven Curtis-Chapman, Stuart Garrard, Israel Houghton, Tim Hughes, Graham Kendrick, Andy Park, Matt Redman, Martin Smith, Michael W. Smith, Chris Tomlin & Darlene Zschech

Steady, building

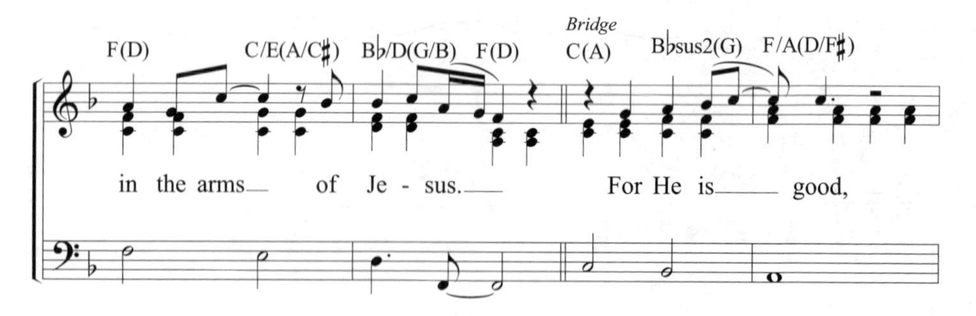

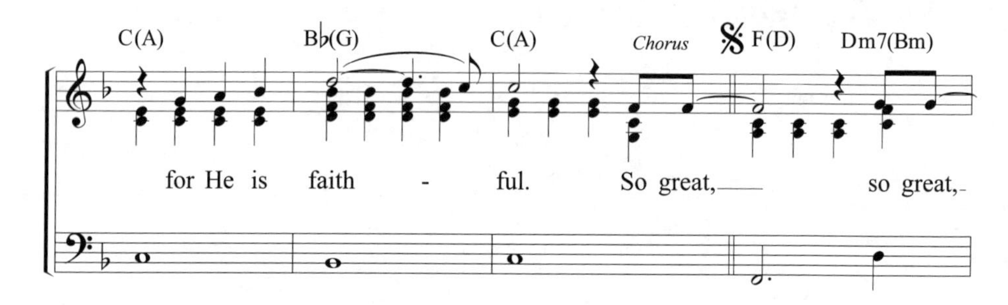

2. Beautiful, majesty,
Glorious, holy One.
Rugged cross, sovereign grace,
Oh, the blood of Jesus.

2685. You reach beyond imagination

(The way that You father me)

Ps 139:4; 145:19; 1 Cor 2:9

Eoghan Heaslip & David Gate

Moderately

A/C♯
E
F♯m7
beau-ti-ful
God of love.
You've al-ways been
D
A/C♯
E7
A
faith-ful in
the
way that You fa - ther me.
Last time to Coda
1.
D.C.
Asus4
E7
A
Asus4
E7
You reach
2.
Asus4
E7
Mid section
A
Our God is
good,
our God is
E/G♯
G2
faith - ful,
our God is
strong,
our God is

1.
D/F♯
2.
D/F♯
D.S. al Coda
a - ble. Our God is a - ble. He is

Coda
Asus4
E7
A

2686. You're calling us

(Call the seeker)

Is 56:7; Mal 3:10; Jn 20:25, 27; 1 Pet 2:5

Graham Kendrick

F♯m7
B7sus4
B7
and prai - ses rise from the off - 'ring of our lives. Let's
F♯m7
A2
Bsus4
Chorus
E
fill this house, let's fill this house. Call the seek - er,
B/D♯
C♯m7
F♯m7
Bsus4
call the stran - ger, call the chil - dren; let's hear their prai - ses.
E
B/D♯
C♯m7
Call the lone - ly, call the bro - ken; young and old will
F♯m7
Bsus4
B
F♯m7
sing ho - san - nas. Let's fill this house, let's fill

2. We're living stones,
Built together here with nail-pierced hands –
Oh, teach us holy fear.
And prayer will rise for all nations,
And open skies will pour Your glory down,
And there'll be praise, for the Lord is in this place.
Let's fill this house,
Let's fill this house.

2687. You're King, and You reign

1 Chron 29:11; Col 1:16; Rev 5:12; 11:15

Capo 3 (D)

Geraldine Latty
& Carey Luce

3 part round
16 shuffle groove

3. *(Women)*
O - ver the in - vi - si - ble, o - ver the vi - si - ble, o -

2. *(Women)*
Je - sus, the

1. *(Men)*
F(D) F/A(D/F♯)
You're King, and You reign o - ver all

- ver all po - wers and king - doms. O-ver the in-vi-si-ble, o - ver the vi - si-ble, o-

glo-ry goes to You. Je - sus, to

B♭(G) F(D) Dm(Bm)
things. You're King, and You reign o - ver all.

- ver all pow - wers and king - doms. O-ver the in-vi-si-ble, o - ver the vi - si-ble, o-

You all praise is due. Je - sus, we

Gm7(Em) B♭/C(G/A) F(D) F/A(D/F♯)
You're King, and You reign o - ver all

- ver all po - wers and king - doms. You're King and You reign o - ver all.
choose to wor - ship You. You're King, and You reign o - ver all.
B♭(G)
F/C(D/A)
B♭/C(G/A)
things. You're King, and You reign o - ver all.

To repeat
Last time
F(D)
F(D)
You're King

2688. You're mighty and strong to save

Is 63:1; Lk 19:40; Phil 2:7-8; Tit 2:14

2.
Am
G
Chorus
C
er.
Oh, what a Sa - viour! Free-dom for -
mer - cy can-not stay
Am
G
1.
- e - ver, we lift our hands with chains un -
- si - lent; we sing the song of
2.
Last time to Coda
F
done. Hearts that know sav - ing love.
C
F6/9
D.C. al Coda
You're
Coda
You're migh-ty and strong to save, You're

Am
G
migh-ty and strong to save, You're migh-ty and strong to
1.
2.
F
F
save, Res-cu - er. You're er,
C
F6/9
C
F6/9
C
Res-cu - er.

2689.
You're my solid ground
(Fix my eyes)
Capo 1 (G)
Ps 8:1; 18:2; 46:3; 123:2; Heb 12:2
David André Østby
Moderately
A♭(G)
Verse
1. You're my so - lid ground
when the waves come crash - ing down,
When I'm far from home,
You are hope be - yond my own,
Fm7(Em)
E♭(D)
D♭maj7(C)
1.
come down.
2.
my own.
Bridge
B♭m(Am)
You are God a-bove my
A♭/C(G/B)
hopes and fears,
D♭(C)
You are God a-bove the

G♭(F)
D♭/F(C/E)
E♭(D)
A♭/C(G/B)
Chorus
air I breathe.
So I'll
D♭maj7(C)
E♭(D)
B♭m7(Am)
fix my eyes on You; no - thing in this world
Fm(Em)
E♭(D)
D♭maj7(C)
E♭(D)
will do. So I'll fix my eyes on You, the
Last time to Coda
1.
B♭m7(Am)
Fm7(Em)
E♭(D)
D♭maj7(C)
One that I can hold on to.
D.C.(v.2)
3.
D.S. al Coda
2.
Fm(Em)
E♭(D)
Fm7(Em)
E♭(D)
Fm7(Em)
E♭(D)
on to. So I'll
on

2. You are in control,
Always there to break my fall, my fall.
There's no need to crawl
On these hands and knees no more, no more.

2690. You restore the wasted years

(I am not the same)

Joel 2:25; Jn 19:30; Acts 2:32, 36; Rom 8:15; 2 Cor 5:17; 2 Tim 1:12; 1 Jn 4:18; Rev 11:15

Ben Smith, Pat Barrett, Matt Redman & Aaron Keyes

Capo 3 (G)

Rock

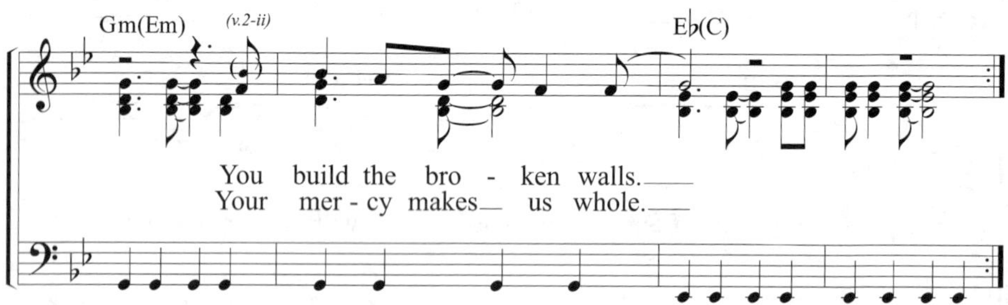

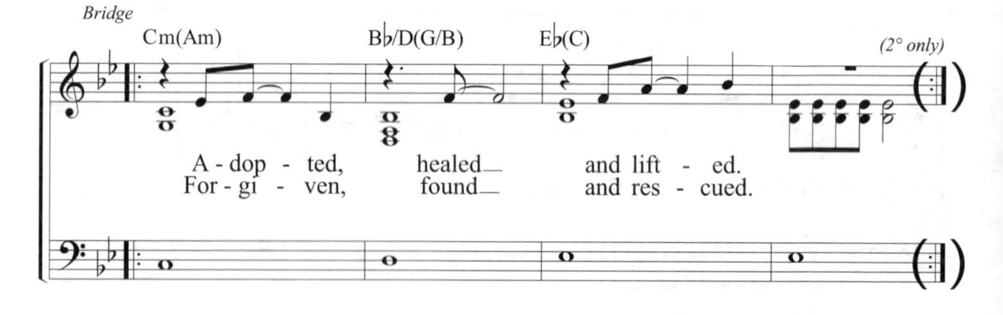

1.,4.
E♭(C)
B♭(G)
F(D)
I am not the same a - ny more.
2.,5.
B♭(G)
Dm(Bm)
A-ny more.
1° D.C.(v.2)
Last time to Coda
3.
B♭(G)
Dm(Bm)
F(D)
Mid section
You have
E♭(C)
B♭(G)
F(D)
Gm(Em)
o - ver - come, it is fin-ished, it is done. Now my
E♭(C)
B♭(G)
F(D)
E♭(C)
heart is fin - 'ly free, ev-'ry chain un -

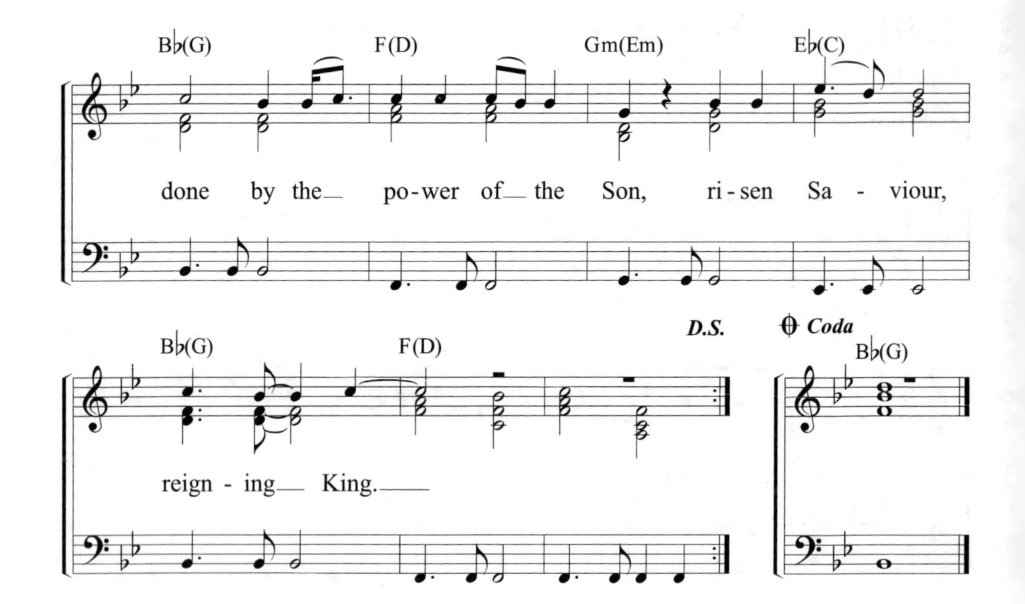

2. I bow before Your cross,
A broken life made new;
Amazed at all You are
And who I am in You.

2691. You're the air that I breathe

(Found in You)

Ps 118:14; Lk 15:24; Phil 3:9; 4:11

Capo 3 (G)

Moderately

Beth Croft & Tim Hughes

1° only
B♭(G)
F(D)
C(A)
B♭(G)
F(D)
C(A)
B♭2(G)
Verse
C(A)
1. I've searched this world for some-thing that en-
B♭2(G)
C(A)
B♭2(G)
dures be-yond this life;
but on-ly You,
(v.2)
C(A)
B♭2(G)
whose days will ne-ver cease, can sa-tis-fy.
1.
C(A)
B♭(G)
Dm(Bm)
I'm found in You,

D.C.
2.
D.C.
F(D)
Gm(Em)
C(A)
on - ly in You. You're the You. You're the
Coda 1
B♭(G)
Dm(Bm)
F(D)
My soul sings, 'Hal-le-lu - jah, Sa - viour King.'
C(A)
B♭(G)
Dm(Bm)
For I was lost and now I'm found in You,
1.
2.
D.C.
F(D)
Csus4(A) C(A)
Gm(Em)
I am found in You. You're the
Coda 2
C(A)
B♭(G)
F(D)
C(A)
Je-sus, You are all that I need. Je-sus, You are
B♭(G)
F(D)
C(A)
all that I need.
2. Now to live a simple life of praise,
In every way.
I'm letting go of treasures on the earth,
I'm holding on to You.

2692. You're the God of this city

(God of this city)

Ps 18:28, 31; Jn 14:12

Passionately

Aaron Boyd, Richard Bleakley, Peter Comfort, Peter Kernaghan, Andrew McCann & Ian Jordan

Am7
G/B
F2
(v.2) 8va
There is no one like our God.
Gsus4
Chorus
F2
For great - er things have yet to come, and
G
C
G/B
F2
great-er things are still to be done in this ci-ty.
F2
3rd & 5th time to Coda
G
Great-er things have yet to come, and great-er things are still to be done in this
C
G/B
F2
1.
ci-ty.
You're the God of this

2.,3. D.S. al Coda
F2
Coda
G
C
great-er things are still to be done here.
F2
C
F
Am7
F2
C2
F2
1.
Am7
G/B
F2
D.S.S.
2.
C
There is no one like our God.

2693. You're the greatest sign and wonder

(Great and glorious)

Gen 1:1; 1 Chron 29:11; 2 Chron 7:1; Is 60:19; Hos 6:3; Lk 11:2; Acts 3:15; 2 Pet 1:19

Rock feel

Ken Riley

Verse C(no3rd)

1. You're the great - est sign and won - der, You're the bright - est

Am7

shin - ing star; Ma - ker of the earth and hea - vens,

(v.3)

G **1.**

shine Your light, Your ma - jes - ty and pow'r. My

B♭sus2 C **D.C.(v.2)**

God, let it shine!

(v.3)
2.,3.
B♭sus2
C(no3rd)
Rain down, send Your fire! Yeah.
Chorus
C
Great and glo - ri - ous, God al - migh - ty,
Am7
Lord of hea - ven, Lord of ev - er - last - ing
3rd time D.S. al Coda
Last time to Coda
F2
Dm7
C
Csus4
light, You are great.
1st time D.C.(v.3)
Mid section
C
Csus4
Dm
Am
Breathe in me, Lord, a

2. You're the greatest of adventures,
You're the hope that burns inside;
Author of the life eternal,
Send Your passion, glory and Your fire.
Rain down, send Your fire!

3. You're the One of new beginnings,
Writer of redemption's song,
Healer of the lost and broken,
Yours the kingdom, glory and the power.
My God, Your kingdom come!

2694. Your grace is enough

(This is our God)

Mt 8:8; 20:28; Acts 2:23-24; Rom 8:2; 2 Cor 12:9; Heb 9:14

Reuben Morgan

3. Jump to 𝄋𝄋 al fine
1.,2.
(1st time to v.2)
A(F)
E(C)
Free-ly You gave
B(G)
F♯m(Dm)
C♯m(Am)
A(F)
E(C)
𝄋𝄋
Mid section
E(C)
Free - ly You gave it all for us,
from death to life,
B(G)
sur - ren - dered Your life u - pon that cross.
for - ev - er our God is glo - ri - fied.
1.
F♯m(Dm)
Great is the love poured out for all.
Ser - vant and King

2. Your presence in me,
Jesus, light the way
By the power of Your word.
I am restored,
I am redeemed.
By Your Spirit I am free.

2695. Your innocence forsaken

(Your name high)

Capo 3 (D)

Ps 27:8; 123:1; Mk 15:34; Lk 11:2

With energy

Joel Houston

Verse

Dm(Bm) F/C(D/A) Dm(Bm)

1. Your in - no - cence for - sa - ken, up - on that cross
   Our bro - ken past re - placed in a se - cond chance;

F/C(D/A) B♭(G) **1.** Dm(Bm) C(A)

You gave Your - self for us; car - ried in - to Your free - dom. (v.2)
the chains have come un - done. Death de -

2. Dm(Bm) C(A) B♭(G)

fied in the Fa - ther's love. We are

Chorus

F(D) C(A)

li - ving to make Your name high, Je - sus;

Dm(Bm) C(A) B♭(G)

li - ving to make Your name high, Je - sus. You gave what the

Dm(Bm)
F(D)
B♭(G)
world could-n't of - fer us. Say what they want, say
3rd time D.S. al Coda
Dm(Bm)
F(D)
B♭(G)
what they want, we are free! Woah-oah - oah.
Rpt 1st time only (to v.2)
Last time to Coda
F(D)
C/E(A/C♯)
Dm(Bm)
F(D)
B♭(G)
(Woah-oah) oah. Woah-oah - oah.
Mid section
B♭(G)
C(A)
With eyes on high we praise You,
Dm(Bm)
C(A)
B♭(G)
and with one voice we come to-ge-ther. Our one de - sire:

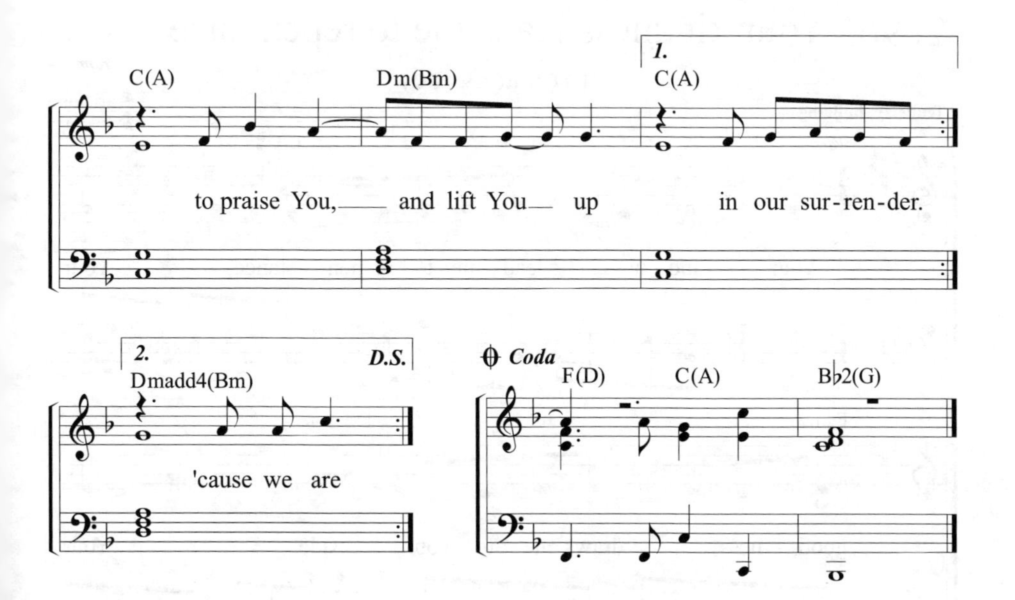

2. The atmosphere is changing.
Oh, can You hear the people rising up
In the hope of Your freedom?
Our former ways are breaking;
We seek Your face.
God, let Your kingdom come;
In our praises be lifted up.

2696. Your kindness leads me to repentance

(You are good)

Ps 100:5; Rom 2:4

Kari Jobe

Chorus
G Esus4 E A
You are good, You are good,
E/G♯ F♯m7
You are good and Your mer - cy is for-
Dmaj7 Esus4 E A
e - ver. You are good, You are good,
E/G♯ F♯m7
You are good, and Your mer - cy is
Dmaj7 A A/G♯ F♯m7
for-e - ver.

1.
D.C.
2.
Tag
Dmaj9
D2
A
Your kind -
Your
kind-ness is for-e - ver,
Your
E/G♯
F♯m7
good-ness is for-e - ver,
Your
mer-cy is for-e - ver,
for-
1.-3.
4.
D2
D2
e - ver.
Your
e - ver.

Enter his gates with thanksgiving and his courts with praise; give thanks to him and praise his name. For the LORD is good and his love endures for ever; his faithfulness continues through all generations.

PSALM 100:4-5

2697. Your love has opened my eyes

Ps 40:2-3; Mt 5:16

Am
— it's a new — life, — it's a new —
Em
C
— start — for ev - 'ry heart — that's found — You; Je -
G
- sus, we've found You. New hope, — full of Your —
Am
Em
— joy; — it's a new — start — for ev -
C
1.,3.
- 'ry heart — that's found — You; Je - sus, we've found You.

G
Am
Woah,
woah,
Em
C
(Fine)
woah.
Em
Verse
C
G
2. We have been healed and re - stored, ev - 'ry -
D
Em
C
G
thing we have is Yours; we'll shine for You.
D.S.
2.
D/F♯
G
- sus, we've found You,

we've found You.
Mid section
C
G
D
Light the way. You lead me in Your
Light the way. With You it is a
Em
C
G
per - fect ways; I'm not a - fraid: You're with
bright - er day; I'm not a - fraid: You're with
D
1.
2.
G
me.
me.
D.S.S. al fine
It's a new

2698. Your ways are always greater

(Never let me go)

Ps 36:7; 118:14; 119:11; 1 Pet 1:25

Ben Cantelon
& Tim Hughes

D
E/G♯
A
D
-ness is sur-round-ing, still You love me so, yes, You
E/G♯
A
1.,3. D.C.(v.3)
D
(Fine)
2.
D
Mid section
Bm
A
love me so. You are strength for to-day
F♯m
A
E
and bright hope for to-mor - row. You are strength
Bm
A
F♯m
A
for to-day and bright hope for to-mor-
E
Bm
A
F♯m
- row. You are strength for to-day and bright hope

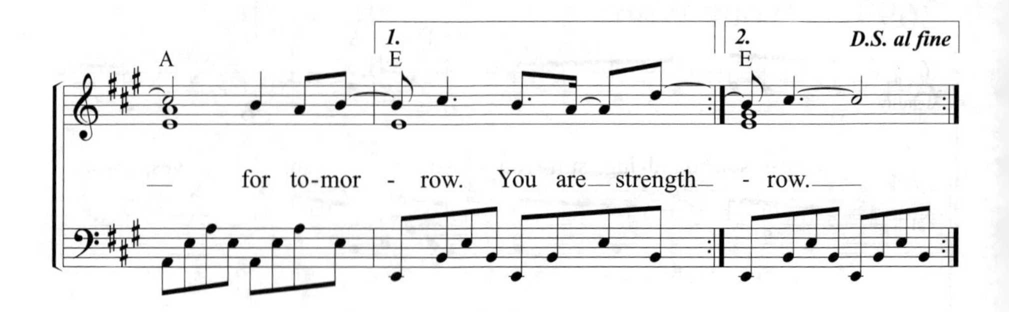

2. I look to You, my Saviour,
When I am weak.
I find rest in the shadow of Your wing.

3. Your word is never-failing,
Strength for today.
I have hidden Your word in my heart.

2699. Your Word is a lamp unto our feet

(When God speaks)

Ps 119:105; Mt 11:5; Jn 6:63; 17:17

Steadily

Allan McKinlay

Em D C D G Dsus4
people are healed, hearts are set free, oh. When God
G D/F♯ Em D
speaks, deaf ears can hear, blind eyes can see,
C D G D 1. G D/F♯ Em Dsus4
the dead are raised to life.
C Dsus4 G D D.C. 2.,3. Mid section G D/F♯
So speak Your words of life,
Last time to Coda
Em D C D G D
speak Your words of life o - ver us.

G D/F♯ Em D C D
Speak Your words of life, speak Your words of life o -
G D Am9 G/B C2 D
- ver us. Joy, life, re - sto - ra - tion, sal - va - tion.
Am9 G/B C2 D Am9 G/B
Joy, life, re - sto - ra - tion, sal - va - tion. Joy, life,
C2 D Am9 G/B C2
re - sto - ra - tion, sal - va - tion. Joy, life, re - sto - ra - tion.
D.S. al Coda
D
When God
Coda
G
- ver us.

2700. You saved my life from death

(God be praised!)

Is 55:12; Acts 2:24; Rev 5:9; 12:11

David & Alena Moore

Capo 2 (G)

With intensity

Verse

D2(C) F♯m(Em) E(D) A/C♯(G/B)

1. You saved my life from death when I was all but de -

Dsus2+4 (C) D(C) D2(C) F♯m(Em) E(D) A/C♯(G/B)

feat - ed. You spoke Your pro-mis - es and brought life to my

Dsus2+4 (C) D(C) D2(C) F♯m(Em) E(D) A/C♯(G/B)

weak-ness. Came as a con-qu'ring King and You warred for my

Dsus2+4 (C) D(C) D2(C) F♯m(Em) E(D)

free - dom. My soul can't help but sing hal-le -

A(G) E/G♯ (D/F♯) | **1.,2.** F♯m(Em) E(D) D(C) E(D) A(G) ***D.C.(v.2,3.)*** | **3.** F♯m(Em) E(D)

lu - jah. jah, hal - le -

2. You opened up my eyes;
For the first time I saw You.
Your love, commanding life
And deserving devotion.
You told me who I am,
Now in faith I believe it.
My soul can't help but sing hallelujah.

3. You've made a place for me,
Silenced all my accusers.
Leading me forth with peace,
Filled with joy I will follow.
Your cross demands my life,
Now Your grace is my anthem.
My soul can't help but sing, 'hallelujah.'

2701. You sent Your Son

(Light the sky)

Neh 9:12; Mal 3:2; Jn 8:32; Heb 10:20

Moderately

Jamie Rodwell, Sam Parker & Tom Field

D E/D D E/D D E/D D E/D
let Your light shine, burn - ing bright - er.
Chorus
A Bm7
So light the sky, I want to see Your fire
F♯m Dmaj7
burn-ing bright - er still, burn-ing bright - er still.
A Bm7
Shine like the stars, and lead me home to You,
F♯m D
I'll fol - low Your fire, I'll fol - low Your

Last time to Coda
1.
A
Bm
D
fire, yeah.
D.C.(v.2)
2.
Bm
D
Mid section
yeah. I will fol - low
F♯m7
A
(v.2)
You, I will fol - low You to the ends of the earth,
1.,3.
E
Dmaj7
ne - ver turn - ing back. I will fol - low
2.
E/G♯
D
I will fol - low
4.
D.S. al Coda
E/G♯
So

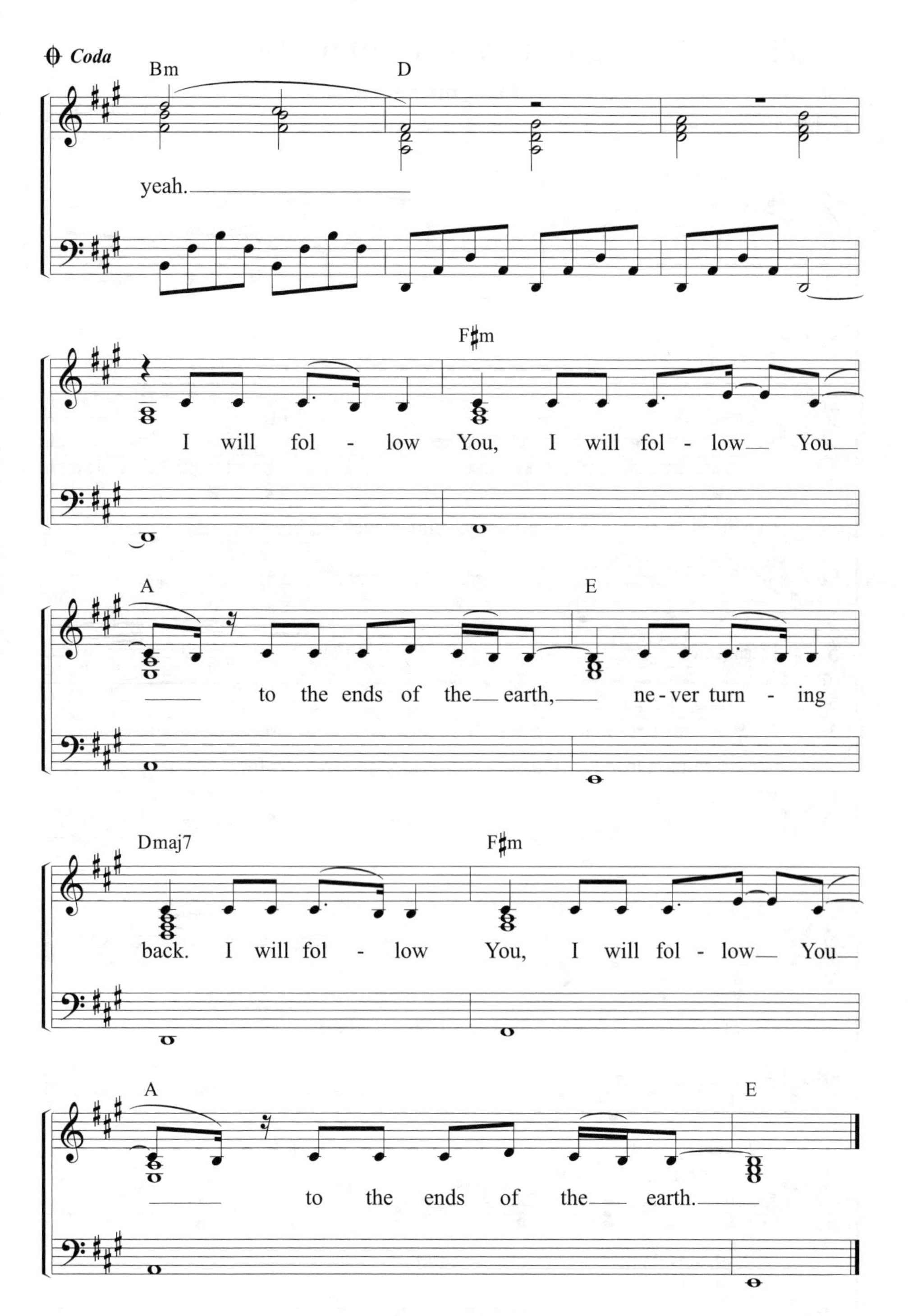

2. Open my eyes that I may see
The wonder of Your majesty.
And now I walk, knowing the truth:
It set me free, it set me free.

2702. You show Your majesty
(Magnificent)

Ps 86:8; Rom 1:20; 2 Cor 4:6

Capo 2 (D)

Moderately

Matt Redman & Jonas Myrin

E/G♯(D/F♯)
A(G)
clo - ser than our eyes could e - ver see. You
Chorus
C♯m(Bm) A(G) E(D) B(A)
are mag-ni-fi - cent, You a-lone are ho - ly;
C♯m(Bm) A(G) Bsus4(A) B(A)
no one else as glo - ri-ous as You. Mag-ni-fi -
C♯m(Bm) A(G) E(D) B(A)
cent, Je - sus, You are wor - thy;
C♯m(Bm) A(G) B(A)
who can shine as bright - ly as You do? Mag-ni-fi -

C♯m(Bm) A(G) E/G♯(D/F♯) B(A) C♯m(Bm) A(G)
cent, You're so mag - ni - fi - cent.
1. D.S.(v.2) 2.,3.
Bsus4(A) B(A) Bsus4(A) B(A) C♯m(Bm) A(G)
Mag - ni - fi - cent,
Last time to Coda
E/G♯(D/F♯) B(A) C♯m(Bm) A(G) B(A)
Bridge 2
You're so mag - ni - fi - cent. You are
F♯m(Em) B(A)
high - er than we e - ver could i - ma - gine, and
E/G♯(D/F♯) A(G) E/G♯(D/F♯)
clo - ser than our eyes could e - ver see. We are

F♯m7(Em)
B(A)
C♯m(Bm) A(G)
pour-ing out our hearts here in Your pre - sence.
D.S.S. al Coda
E(D) B(A) C♯m(Bm) A(G) Bsus4(A) B(A)
Mag-ni - fi -
Coda
Bsus4(A) B(A) A2(G)
2. You're lighting up our lives;
Illuminate our hearts
With everything You are.

2703. You spoke, and, behold, the dawn of time

Capo 2 (G)

Gen 1:3; Is 60:1-2; Mt 2:2; Jn 8:12; 2 Cor 4:6; 1 Jn 2:8; Rev 22:5

Moderately

Ken Riley & Matt Redman

Chorus
A(G)
E/G♯(D/F♯)
F♯m7(Em)
Je - sus, Je - sus, You light up the world, You
D(C)
A(G)
E/G♯(D/F♯)
light up our lives! Lord Je - sus, Je - sus, Your
F♯m7(Em)
1.,3.,4.
D(C)
2nd time
D.S. al Coda
1st time D.C.(v.3)
Last time to Coda
light is a-live in me.
2.
D(C)
E(D)
Mid section
Lord.
No hint of dark -
F♯m7(Em)
D(C)
- ness can stand in Your light, can stand in Your light,

2. They followed the star, Your guiding light,
That led them to You, led them to life.
God of this world, in mystery,
We see You shine,
We see You shining.

3. Your word has foretold the end of time,
The glory of You, our only light.
Saviour and King, eternally,
We'll see You shine,
We'll see You shining.

2704. You turned my way

(You lifted me out)

Ps 30:2-5, 11; Is 60:1; 63:1; Jn 3:19

Chris Tomlin, Matt Redman, Louie Giglio, Jesse Reeves & Matt Gilder

D2
but with the light I am see - ing,
E
Chorus
A
I am sing - ing. You lift - ed me out,
E
F♯m7
You lift - ed me out, and set me danc-
D
A
- ing, danc - ing. Free, now I am free!
E
F♯m7
Your love res - cued me; now it's the an-
1st time D.C.(v.2)
3rd time D.C. al Coda
Mid section
D
E
- them I'm sing - ing.
(2°)

2. Many will see, many will hear,
And find You strong enough to save.
Many the wonders You have done,
Your light has come;
I am seeing,
I am singing.

2705.
You urge us, Father
(Living sacrifices)
Rom 12:1-2;
2 Cor 5:15; Rev 7:11
Quite slowly
Kees Kraayenoord
F♯m
Verse
D
You urge us, Fa-ther, in view of Your mer - cy,
A
E/G♯
F♯m
to wor-ship You a - lone. Now we ac-cept, Lord,
D
A
E/G♯
Your in-vi-ta - tion to come be-fore Your throne.
D
Bridge
A/C♯
So touch our heart, O God, re-new our mind;
Bm
F♯m
E
we hear Your voice to - day.

D
A/C♯
You laid down Your life so we might live,
Bm
A/C♯
A
E
Chorus
A
and walk up-on Your way. Here we are, as liv-ing sa-cri-
E/G♯
Bm
A/C♯
D
fi-ces, ho-ly and pleas-ing un-to You. Here we
Last time to Coda
1.
A
E/G♯
Bm
A/C♯
are, sur-ren-der-ing our lives and of-fer-ing our hopes and dreams to You.
D
E
A
Asus4
D.C.
We wor-ship You.

3.
D.S. al Coda
2.
Bm
A/C♯
D
E
hopes and dreams to You.
Here we
hopes and dreams to You.
Mid section
F♯m
We wor - ship.
We hum-bly bow at the cross.
We see Your suf - fer - ing;
for You died to give us
Esus4
D.S.
life, and that is what we bring.
Here we
Coda
A
Dmaj7
hopes and dreams to You.
We wor - ship You.

2706.
You've granted perfect merit
(Mercy from the throne)
Jn 10:28; Rom 3:23-24; Eph 1:4-5
Capo 1 (G)
Steadily
Nathan Fellingham & busbee
Verse
Fm7(Em) E♭/G(D/F♯) A♭(G)
1. You've gran - ted per - fect me - rit,
You have de - clared for - give - ness
D♭(C) A♭(G) E♭/G(D/F♯)
where there be - fore had been none.
for all the wrongs I have done.
B♭m(Am) A♭/C(G/B) Fm(Em) E♭(D)
So un - de - serv - ing of this love, Je - sus, I am
D♭(C) E♭(D) (C/E) D♭/F E♭/G(D/F♯)
Chorus
A♭(G)
Yours for - e - ver. Mer - cy from the throne
E♭sus4(D) E♭(D) B♭m(Am)
tells me I've been re - deemed, meet - ing my deep -

Fm(Em) E♭(D) A♭(G)
- est need: thank You, Lord. Grace that won't let go,
E♭sus4(D) E♭(D) B♭m(Am)
through Je - sus' sa - cri - fice, I am re - stored
Last chorus D.S. al Coda
Last time to Coda
(D.S.)
Fm(Em) E♭(D) B♭m7(Am) A♭/C(G/B)
to life: thank You, Lord, thank You, Lord.
1.
2.
Mid section
D♭sus2(C) D♭sus2(C) E♭/G(D/F♯) A♭(G) A♭/C(G/B)
No scheme or plan
D♭(C) E♭/G(D/F♯) A♭(G) A♭/C(G/B)
could e - ver stem the pow'r of Your hand.

2. You sent Your Holy Spirit,
Adopted me as Your child.
A Father like no other,
Your love not cheap or defiled.
With grace so generous and so free,
You have won my heart forever.

2707. You were despised

(Highly exalted)

Is 53:3, 5, 7, 9; Mt 27:39; Phil 2:9

Reflectively

Paul Baloche
& Robin Mark

B
A
Bsus4
va-tion has come; yet by Your suf-f'ring our free-dom is won.
B
Chorus
E
For God has high-ly ex-alt-ed Your
G♯m
A
name; He has en-throned You on high,
1° & 3° D.S.
2° D.C.(v.2)
B
Bsus4
B
Je-sus, the name a-bove all names.
To end
Bsus4
E

2708. You were God from the outset

(Run)

Jn 1:1; Eph 1:4; Rev 4:8

Capo 4 (C)

Joel Houston

With energy and passion

Verse

C♯m(Am) A(F) E(C) B(G)

1. You were God from the out - set, pow - er - ful

C♯m(Am) A(F) E(C) B(G) A(F)

and cre - a - tive; You who saw us here be - fore You

(v.2)

C♯m(Am) B(G) **1.** A(F)

called all the stars and the earth to ex - is - tence.

D.C.(v.2) **2.,3.** A(F) *Chorus*

2. You are God for Your glo - ry. So we will run,

𝄋 E(C) B(G)

all to - ge - ther with hearts a - flame,

(D.S.) our sur - ren - der to bring You

C♯m(Am)
A(F)
E(C)
with a fi - re that can't be tamed.
fame, our de-si - re that You be praised.
Our God,
F♯m(Dm)
C♯m(Am)
1.
A(F)
C♯m (Am)
A(F)
all glo - ry to Your name, Je - sus.
D.C.(v.3)
E(C)
B(G)
C♯m (Am)
A(F)
E(C)
B(G)
3. You are God
Last time to Coda
(Play 4 times)
2.,4.
D.S.
3.,5.
A(F)
A(F)
C♯m(Am)
A(F)
E(C)
B(G)
We will run, Je - sus.
A(F)
C♯m(Am)
A(F)
(Play 3 times)

2. You are God, You are holy,
History is Your story;
You who was and is
And who forever will be.
God, we live for Your glory.

3. You are God, You are freedom,
You're alive now within us;
You who saw us here
Before You conquered the grave,
And delivered on the promise.

In the beginning was the Word, and the Word was with God, and the Word was God.

JOHN 1:1

2709. You will keep the fires burning
(Fires)
Ps 23:4; Ezek 37:4; Mt 17:20; Lk 3:16; 2 Tim 1:6
Matt Redman & Jonas Myrin
With energy
Intro
G Gsus4 G Gsus4
You will keep the fires burn - ing.
1.,3.,4.
Last time to Coda 2
G Gsus4 G Gsus4
You will keep the fires burn - ing.
2.
Verse
C G
We're stand-ing in the de-sert of dry bones, but still
D Em
we see Your life, walk - ing through the
C G D Em
val-ley of sha - dows but hold - ing on to light.

C
And we're wait - ing, wait - ing on You, God.
Em
C
And our hearts will trust, trust
Em
D
in who You are.
Chorus
G
Gsus4
God, who keeps our fires burn - ing,
G
Gsus4
burn - ing through the dark - est night, see the
Em
C
hope in our hearts, the faith in our eyes.

G
Gsus4
You can move the high - est moun - tain,
G
Gsus4
You can keep our dreams a - live. You're the
Em
C
joy of our hearts and You're the
G
Gsus4
Last time to Coda
fire in our eyes.
G
Gsus4
1.
D.S.
2.
We're stand - ing in the
Mid section
G
Gsus4
G
Gsus4
Light up our lives with ho - ly flame, all for the ho - nour of

Em
Your name. Give us the strength to face the day,
1.
C
Je - sus.
2.
C
You're the fire in our eyes.
G
Gsus4
G
Gsus4
D.S.S. al Coda
Coda
G
Gsus4
Em
You're the fire in our eyes.
C
D.C. al Coda 2 (inc. rpts)
Coda 2
G

2710. You won't back down

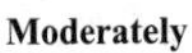

(Still saving me)

Ps 89:35; 121:2; 123:1; 139:4, 7; Rom 2:4; Phil 1:6; Heb 7:25

Chris McClarney, Dave Fitzgerald & John Loux

Moderately

D
G
Chorus
call me beau - ti - ful.
On - ly You can
When I lose my
Em7
o - pen my eyes.
way in the night,
Through ev - 'ry fail - ure,
all my fears are
Am7
through ev - 'ry lie, it's Your kind - ness, Lord, that leads
lost in Your light. It's Your kind - ness, Lord, that brings
C
1.
me to the truth: oh, You're still sav - ing me.
me back to You: oh, You're
2.
i.
G
Em7
still sav - ing me.

D.C.
Am7
C
ii.
Am7
Em7
D
Am7
Em7
D
Am7
And I lift my eyes to You, my help,
Em7
D
Am7
it comes from You.
In You, in You,
Em7
D
Rpt. ad. lib
I de-light in You.

Thematic Index

The following index is designed to help church leaders, worship leaders and musicians find songs and hymns appropriate for various themes, settings or occasions. It should be noted that this is by no means an exhaustive listing, and many of these inevitably overlap. If looking for a particular theme, therefore, it is recommended that one looks at several associated categories, rather than just one.

The "seasonal" section has deliberately been kept short. Apart from Easter and Harvest (Christmas songs and carols can be found under the "Jesus: Nativity" section), most other occasions in the church calender will be covered by themes already listed below.

A. GOD THE FATHER

1. General

2. Creation

3. God's love and faithfulness

4. Salvation and protection

5. God's grace and mercy

Song no.

6. Forgiveness

7. Thirst for God

8. His presence

B. JESUS

1. Kingship

2. Nativity

3. The cross and redemption

Song no.

4. Sacrifice (the Lamb), the blood of Jesus

5. Second Coming

6. His name

7. Resurrection

C. HOLY SPIRIT

1. Love

2. Joy

3. Peace

4. Holiness, passion and the fire of God

5. Faith

6. Hope

7. Power and anointing

8. Guidance

9. Refreshing and the river

D. CHURCH

1. General

2. Call to worship

3. Praise and thanksgiving

4. Proclamation and evangelism

5. Worship, love and adoration

6. Confession and repentance

7. Communion

8. Commission and revival

9. Commitment

10. Unity

11. Healing and personal renewal

12. Spiritual warfare and deliverance

13. Justice

14. Prayer

15. Church Eternal

16. The Bible

17. The worldwide Church

E. CHILDREN

Song no.

F. SEASONAL

1. Easter

2. Harvest

Index of Tunes

A more extensive selection of tunes is available in the first Songs of Fellowship Music Edition (Songs 1-640)

GUITAR CHORD CHART

The following chord diagrams show the fingering for many of the guitar chords in this songbook.

Key

o = *play open string*
x = *don't play string*
1 = *thumb*
2 = *index finger*
3 = *middle finger*
4 = *ring finger*
5 = *little finger*
▨ = *index finger bar*
3 = *fret number*

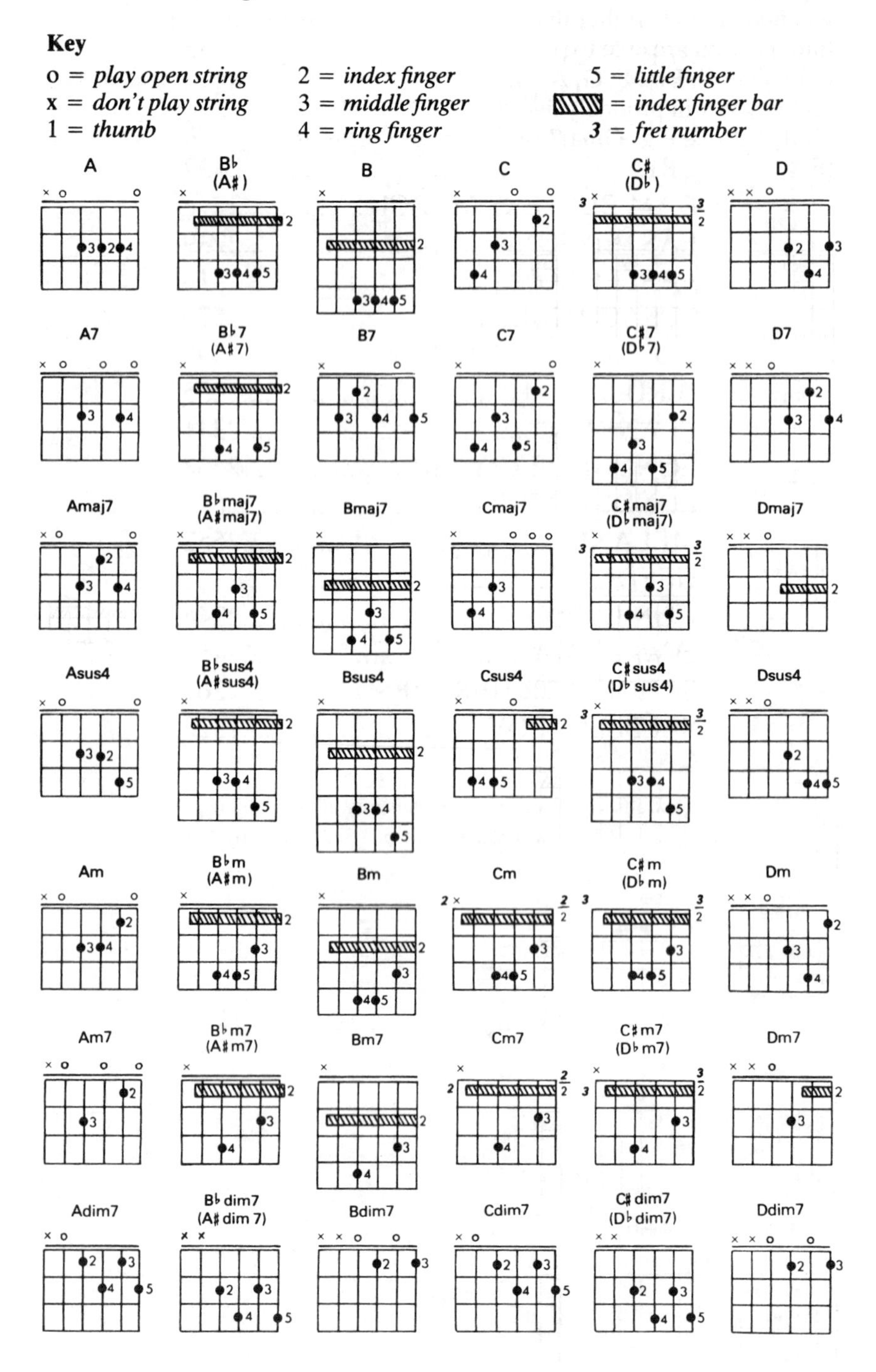

The chords which have been used throughout the book have been carefully chosen with the elementary guitarist in mind. Capo markings, in the left hand corner of many of the songs, allow simple chord shapes to be played with a capo in position. *Capo 3 (C)*, for example, means place the capo at the third fret and play the simple chords in brackets, which you will find are in C rather than E♭. If you use these capo markings you will find that you are able to play almost all of the songs using just ten chords: C,D, Dm, E, Em, F, G, A, Am, B7. If you do see a chord which you don't know, you will probably find that it is playable by mentally stripping it of all its 'extras' e.g. Gmaj7, just play G; Dm9, just play Dm; Csus4, just play C.

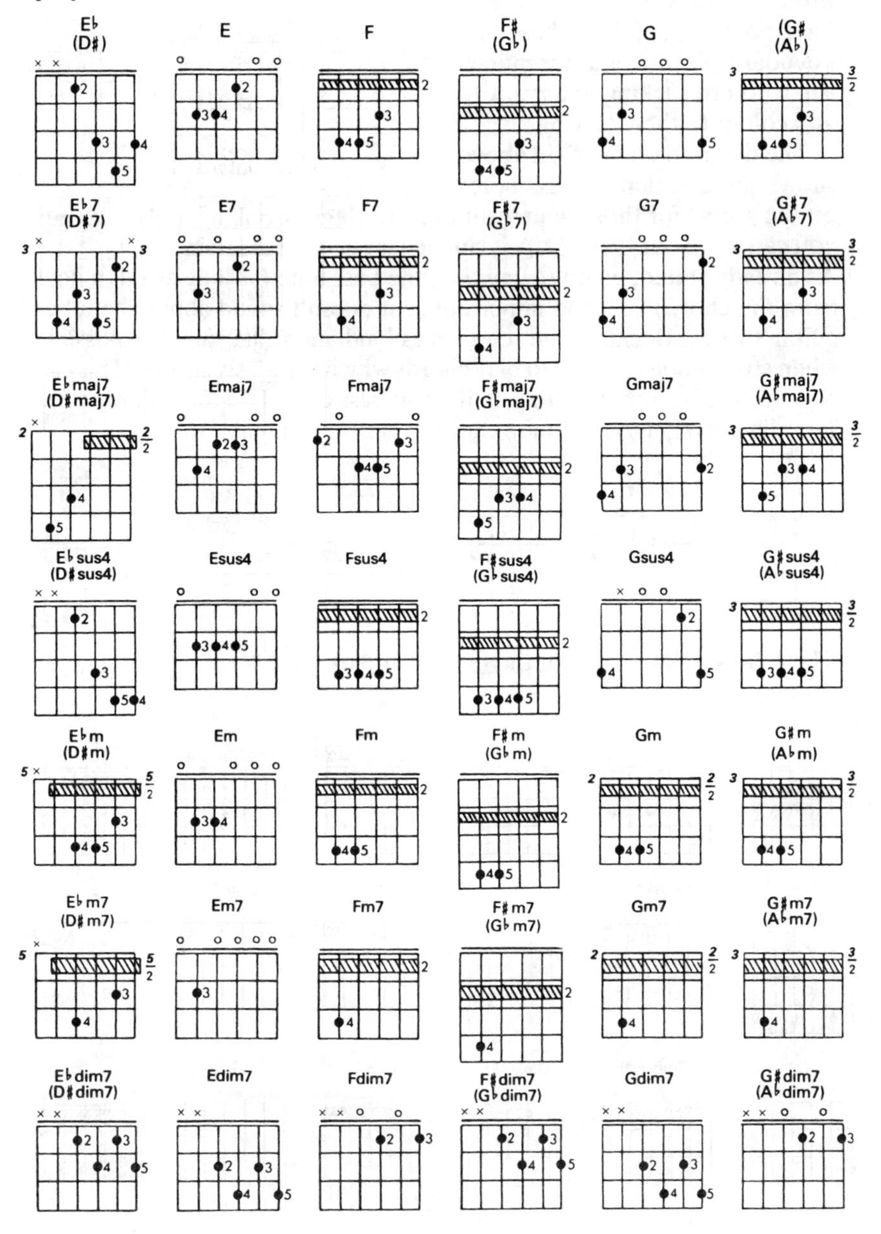

More unusual chords

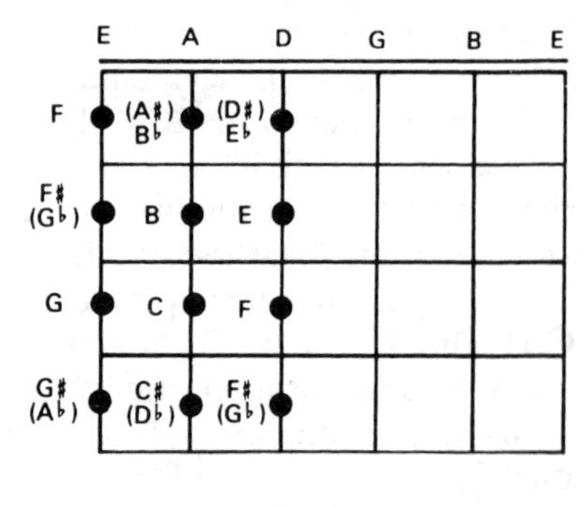

In this songbook you will come across some more unusual chords—mainly chords with different bass notes. If you see D/A, for example, this means play the chord of D with the note A in the bass. For a guitarist who is strumming, this bass note isn't too important and he can just play an ordinary chord of D, but the A bass note is useful for bass and keyboard players, and for guitarists who are picking and want to add colour to their playing.

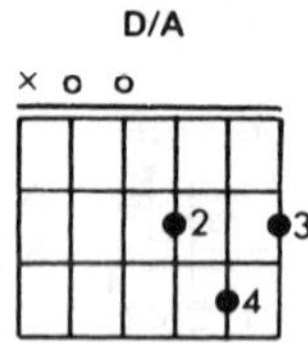

The diagram on the right above shows the position of bass notes on the guitar for those who want to learn them. Looking at the diagram you can work out that a D/A is simple (see second diagram).
As already stated, when *strumming,* the bass note (as long as it is a note from the chord) isn't too important as it doesn't sound above the other guitar strings. Because one requires as loud and full a sound as possible when strumming it is best to play chords which use all six strings. This can be achieved by incorporating a different bass note. Use the following full sounding versions of common chords when strumming. For—

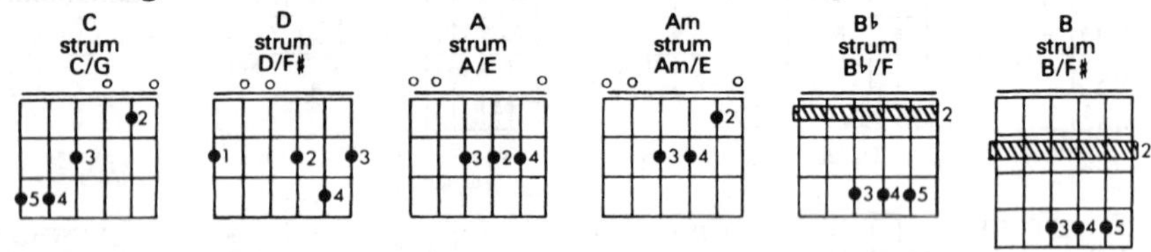

The following are some of the more complex chords you will find in the songbook:

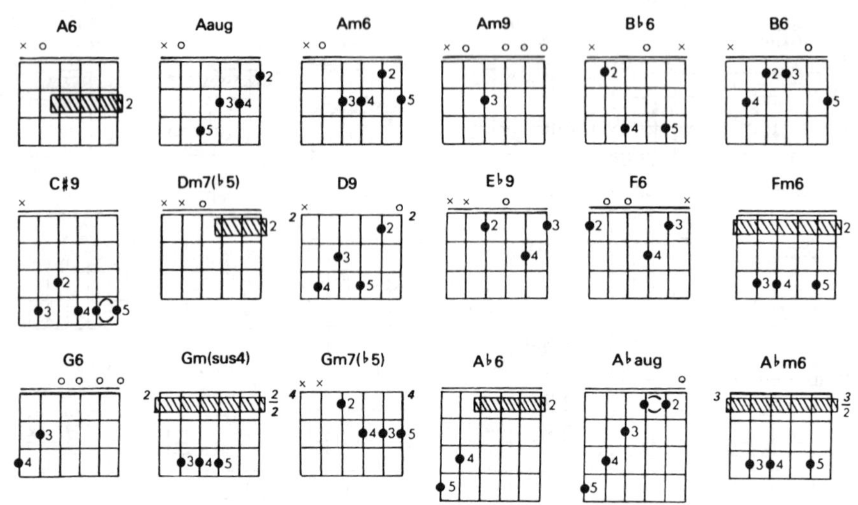

Scripture Index

This index lists Bible verses quoted or echoed in the songs. While not exhaustive, it provides a biblical backgound for many of the ideas expressed.

John *(cont.)*

Acts

Acts *(cont.)*

Romans

Romans *(cont.)*

Song no. *Song no.* *Song no.*

Index of Titles and First Lines

Authors' titles, where different from first lines, are shown in *italics*.

DISK USERS - PLEASE READ NOW!

Enclosed is your Songs of Fellowship 5 words CD. This contains the words to all the songs in this book. They are laid out simply and clearly, one to a page, and are ideal for 1) use with song projection software or printing on to OHP acetates; 2) making your own customised church songbook; or 3) incorporating in service sheets.

Please note, files have been scanned for all current known viruses.

IMPORTANT NOTE: Purchasing this songbook does not grant the purchaser the right to reproduce the words from the CD. Any church or individual wishing to reproduce a song for church use must hold a current CCL licence for the territory in which the words are to be used. Permission to reproduce a song (or any part of it) must be gained from the individual song copyright holder (addresses given at the bottom of each song in the songbook). Any unauthorised usage is illegal.

To find out more about obtaining a licence, please contact CCLI at info@ccli.co.uk or by using the details shown on the Bibliography page at the front of the book.

REQUIREMENTS AND USAGE

The CD should auto-run on inserting it into your CD Rom drive. If the CD does not load up automatically, then you can start the program in the following way:
1) Click on the 'start' button on your task bar. (bottom left of the screen)
2) Click on 'run...'
3) Type in 'd:\menu.html' (assuming that <d:> is your CD Rom drive letter)
4) The menu should now run allowing you to open the text files as required.

If this menu will still not load, the files are stored on the root of the CD which you can see by selecting your CD drive in 'My Computer'

PC Users

The words are saved as Rich Text Format (.rtf) files. You will be able to open or import the files if you have Microsoft Word™ or almost any other word processor.

Macintosh™ Users

Please double-click on the text files in the 'Mac' folder. Alternatively, you should be able to import the rtf files into your word processor.

IN CASE OF DIFFICULTY

If you encounter problems using the disk, please email us at support@kingsway.co.uk Problems with using your word processing package should be referred to your software provider's technical support line.

ALSO AVAILABLE

SONGS OF FELLOWSHIP 5 BOX SET
VARIOUS ARTISTS // KWCD3284

Songs of Fellowship has been a cornerstone of church worship over recent decades, and this - the fifth release in the series - continues to invest in songs of substance that strengthen the local church.

Songwriters and worship leaders like *Tim Hughes*, *Stuart Townend*, *Ben Cantelon*, *Delirious?*, *Miriam Webster*, *Vicky Beeching* and *Cathy Burton* are all represented. '*God Of Our Yesterdays*', '*Desert Song*', '*Love Come Down*', '*Cannons*', '*How He Loves Us*' and '*Saviour of the World*' are all included too, making this a uniquely strong, contemporary compilation of modern worship classics.

TRACK LISTING

All For Christ
Love Each Other
At Your Name
Glory To God Forever
Blessed Assurance
By Faith
A New Hallelujah
Christ For Me
Come People Of The Risen King
Creation Sings
Praise Him
God Only Wise
Saviour Of The World
Jesus Messiah
How He Loves
Holy
Jesus Saves
Give Us Your Courage

This Is My Worship
Our God Saves
Not Guilty Anymore
Cannons
Christ In Me
Rain Down
Salvation's Song
Counting On Your Name
Your Love Never Fails
Love Come Down
Desert Song
The Saviour's Song
Adoration
King Of Wonders
Not Ashamed
I Am Redeemed
God Of Our Yesterdays
Cling To The Cross

Healing Streams
Friend Of God
The Way That You Father Me
Mercy From The Throne
Find Me In The River
Have You Heard?
God Be In Everything
You're The Light
My Refuge
The Cross Speaks
It Is Jesus (Fresh Mercy)
The Kingdom Is Coming
Exalt
Far Greater